SUBMARINE CANYONS
and Other Sea Valleys

SUBMARINE

CANYONS
and Other
Sea Valleys

by FRANCIS P. SHEPARD and ROBERT F. DILL

Rand McNally & Company • Chicago

RAND M^CNALLY GEOLOGY SERIES
L. L. SLOSS, ADVISORY EDITOR

Flawn, MINERAL RESOURCES: Geology, Engineering, Economics, Politics, Law
Shepard and Dill, SUBMARINE CANYONS AND OTHER SEA VALLEYS
Whitten, STRUCTURAL GEOLOGY OF FOLDED ROCKS

FOR
ELIZABETH
AND
SONIA

PREFACE

OUR CLOSE ASSOCIATION in the study of submarine canyons has led to this book, which includes both our published and unpublished results of extensive exploration from surface ships and from diving operations. These studies have been made possible largely through the enlightened attitude shown by the U.S. Navy towards broad fields of research. Contracts received by Scripps Institution of Oceanography from the Office of Naval Research (Nonr 2216(23)) and from the Bureau of Ships have permitted the expensive ship operations and the employment of assistants to help process the data from many expeditions. The National Science Foundation has given several grants to the senior author for canyon research, and the U.S. Navy Electronics Laboratory has supported the work of the junior author and his assistants.

In recent years, both of us have devoted almost full time to the study of the valleys of the sea floor. Trips to many parts of the world have been made to obtain information which we are presenting in this book.

We are grateful to many of our colleagues. Field assistance has been given with enthusiasm by Arnold Bouma, James Stewart, Neil Marshall, Erk Reimnitz, John Beagles, John Houchen, William Bunton, and many others. The sediment laboratory analyses are the work of Neil Marshall and the late Ruth Y. Manar. Foraminifera identification and interpretation has been made principally by F. L. Parker. Frans Emmel has been particularly helpful in plotting soundings and in contouring charts, work in which he has had the voluntary assistance of G. C. Hazenbush. The latter has converted many of the charts originally contoured in fathoms to the metric scale used in most of our illustrations. D. G. Gorsline and E. L. Hamilton have read the entire book and given us many helpful suggestions. Chapters have been read critically by J. R. Curray, B. C. Heezen, E. C. LaFond, D. G. Moore, and E. L. Winterer. Margaret Miller has typed the manuscript several times, and her literary background has been a great help in choosing words and clarifying style. Special appreciation is expressed to J. R. Moriarty for the final illustrations and extensive help with the cartography. Finally, we wish to acknowledge with gratitude the help given us by our wives, both in the manuscript revision and in field work. The enlightened policy of Scripps Institution in allowing wives who are useful at sea to accompany expeditions has been given a rewarding test.

Francis P. Shepard
Robert F. Dill

La Jolla, California
July, 1965

CONTENTS

SUBMARINE CANYONS
and Other Sea Valleys

CHAPTER I

INTRODUCTIONS AND DEFINITIONS

T HE AMAZING VIEW from the rim of the Grand Canyon has been a great stimulus to geologists. Barring some as yet untold miracle, we can never get the same broad vistas of the large sea-floor canyons. Nevertheless, knowing that such features exist and that their shallow heads can be visited by scuba diving provides considerable appeal for their investigation. Exploration of canyons from deep-diving submarines adds further impetus.

The present writers have long been interested in these sea-floor valleys but have investigated them with quite different methods. The senior writer has made what could be called an indirect approach, that is, studying the sea-floor valleys largely from surface ships; whereas the junior author has made the direct approach by diving extensively into the canyons with an aqualung. Recently, both have been observing the canyons from the bathyscaph *Trieste II* and Cousteau's *Diving Saucer*. We have both spent many years in the investigation of a large number of marine valleys in different parts of the world, and are therefore collaborating to bring together some of the information from these studies. The text was prepared largely by the senior author; the junior author has contributed Chapter XV and much of the information for Chapters II, III, and V.

In this book the distinction between various types of marine valleys is emphasized. The valleys that resemble land canyons are given special attention. However, we do not expect that this book will solve many of the problems raised by the existence of the great chasms which resemble the river-cut gorges of the land. Rather, we hope that setting forth some factual information will provide geologists with more background for the discussion of hypotheses of the origin of canyons, and may stimulate others to further investigations.

HISTORY OF SUBMARINE VALLEY STUDIES

So far as the present writers know, valleys of the sea floor were first discussed about 100 years ago by Dana (1863, p. 441), who called attention to the valley off the Hudson estuary. This was further considered by Lindenkohl (1885, 1891), as a result of more extensive soundings taken by the U.S. Coast and Geodetic Survey in the gorge 60 miles seaward of New York City. However, the first descriptions of sea-floor canyons that included any well-contoured maps were published by Davidson (1887). His work was based on fairly extensive soundings taken in canyons near the coast, where the soundings could be far more accurately located than those of the outer Hudson gorge.

Shortly after the contour maps of the submarine valleys appeared, speculation began as to the origin of the valleys. Noting that they resembled land canyons, they were first explained as submerged river valleys (Davidson, 1887; Dana, 1890; Le Conte, 1891). This idea was followed shortly by several articles challenging the river origin. Lawson (1893, pp. 57-59) attributed the central California canyons to diastrophism, and Smith (1902) was the first to suggest that ocean-floor currents had produced the valleys. Milne (1897) was the first to note that displacement of materials along the axes of the valleys was a cause of cable breaking.

Rather widespread attention by geologists to submarine canyons developed around the turn of the century. At that time a series of articles was presented before the Geological Society of America by A. C. Spencer (1898, 1903), who proposed the hypothesis that the canyons were cut as a result of great continental uplifts which also caused the Pleistocene glaciation. This same idea was presented by Hull (1912), who published maps of various submarine valleys found off Europe and eastern America. However, geologists soon became very skeptical of this idea and their doubts extended even to the actual existence of submarine canyons. When an observation offends one's preconceived ideas, it is easy to dismiss it.

For about 25 years after Spencer's articles, submarine canyons were given little attention. They were called 'figments of the imagination,' or considered as inconsequential and not to be taken seriously. Not until the adoption of echo sounding by the U.S. Coast and Geodetic Survey about 1928 and the making of a series of profiles along the continental slopes off the east coast of the United States, was confirmation provided for the existence of a whole series of canyons extending to depths of a mile or more. The canyons again were brought to the attention of geologists. The spectacular contour maps made by Veatch and Smith (1939) and the relief model made from these maps of the east coast continental slope did a great deal to arouse interest in the canyons.

The senior writer participated in some of the early surveys of the east-coast canyons (Shepard, 1934), and shortly afterwards began studies of California canyons with active help from Scripps Institution of Oceanography. This work led to another publication, accompanied by relief maps of the sea floor off California (Shepard and Emery, 1941). The authors of these treatises on both East- and West-coast canyons supported the hypothesis of sub-aerial origin.

During this period, a series of prominent geologists had begun to attack this hypothesis, suggesting in its place that processes operating on the sea floor were the cause. Thus, Davis (1934) considered outflowing of bottom currents caused by build-up of waves along the coasts as the origin of canyons. Daly (1936) first suggested turbidity currents as the cause of most of the canyons. He was strongly supported one year later by Kuenen (1937). Johnson (1939) attributed the canyons to artesian sapping, and Bucher (1940) suggested that tsunamis were the cause. Wegener (1924, p. 177) and De Andrade (1938) followed Lawson in proposing diastrophism as the origin. In this free-for-all hypothesizing the various authors had at least one thing in common; none of them had studied the canyons other than by examination of published charts. One can scarcely blame them for this neglect. In those days, canyon studies were not easy to make, and the spectre of world-wide drowned river canyons thousands of feet deep was devastating to those with a firm belief in the orderly processes of geology. It smacked of the outmoded ideas of catastrophism.

A second stage in canyon investigations began about the time when the outbursts of theoretical hypotheses were appearing. This phase, consisting of the field study of the canyons, has suffered from lack of investigators and still can be considered as only in its early stages. In the mid 1930s, Henry Stetson (1936) began the investigation of the Georges Bank canyons off the northeastern coast of the United States, and at the same time the senior writer started studying California canyons. These studies were followed some years later by Jacques Bourcart's (1938) work on the French canyons of the Mediterranean. However, all work was interrupted by World War II, and in Stetson's case by his untimely death shortly after the war.

A third stage of canyon studies has consisted of determining the nature of the canyons' seaward terminations. Of those canyons investigated to date, most have been found to end in great fans that lie at the base of the steep rock slopes into which the canyons are cut. Crossing those fans for many miles are valleys with bifurcations and natural levees, like the channels of rivers that cross deltas.

The field work included sampling of the canyon floors by cores (Revelle and Shepard, 1939), dredging of canyon walls (Stetson, 1936; Shepard and Emery, 1941; Bourcart, 1950), and measurement of currents along the canyon floor (Stetson, 1937; Shepard et al., 1939). Also, accurately located profiles in the canyon heads were repeated to look for depth changes (Shepard, 1937). Submarine photography of the canyons at shallow depths was added somewhat later (Shepard and Emery, 1946) and soon was adapted to deep-water canyons.

A fourth phase of canyon investigation has been the actual observation of canyon heads by diving. It is with this field that the junior author has been especially concerned. So far as we know, the first dives into canyons for scientific purpose were made in 1947 by Frank Haymaker (Shepard, 1949), although he lacked geological training and was handicapped by the use of the old 'hard hat' diving equipment, which involved cumbersome air hose connections to the surface. Free diving in the canyons began about 1949, when Jacques Cousteau's aqualung was introduced by Conrad Limbaugh in the work at Scripps Institution (Limbaugh and Shepard, 1957). Many people have now made scuba dives into Scripps and La Jolla submarine canyons. The junior author has been making such dives since 1951; he has made a total of about 900 dives into 15 different canyons. The majority of these dives have been made in the two canyons off La Jolla. In addition, he has made dives in five canyons off Baja California, several in the canyons off Monterey and Carmel, and a few in the canyon heads of the Mediterranean. His underwater observations, along with those of other investigators, have now yielded a large mass of visual information that is documented by photography.

A fifth phase of canyon studies has just begun. This is based on observations from the portholes of deep-diving submersibles. Dives of this sort have been made in bathyscaphs—the U.S. Navy Electronics Laboratory's (N.E.L.) *Trieste I* and *II*, the French *F.N.R.S. III* and *Archimede*. A number of dives by geologists of the U.S. Navy Electronics Laboratory have been made in La Jolla and Coronado canyons off the San Diego area. Also, Cousteau and Pérès have made dives in the canyons of the French Mediterranean and off the Portuguese coast Pérès, 1957). Most recently, Cousteau's Diving Saucer (*Soucoupe*) has been used by Scripps and N.E.L. scientists for dives off La Jolla (Shepard *et al.*, 1964) and Baja California (Shepard, 1965). The authors have participated both in bathyscaph and Diving Saucer descents. Probably the future will see a good many improvements in deep-diving submersibles with a far greater range of observations.

TYPES OF VALLEYS

Many scientific articles have discussed the origin of submarine valleys (usually called submarine canyons) as though only one type existed. As investigations have proceeded, however, it has become evident that the valleys of the sea floor are as diverse in type as the valleys of the land. No reputable geologist would attempt to explain all land valleys as having the same origin. Many land valleys are primarily stream-cut, although their wall slopes and their tributaries are often the result of soil creep and spring sapping; other valleys are clearly shaped by glaciation, whereas faulting has been the primary cause of still others. With this diversity in mind, it becomes important to consider marine valleys and their origin according to the particular character that each may possess.

The most investigated type of marine valley clearly resembles the land canyons found cutting unglaciated mountain ranges and the steep margins of plateaus. These valleys, both on land and under the sea, usually have V-shaped profiles, high steep walls with rock outcrops, a winding course, and numerous tributaries entering from both sides. It is proposed here to use the name *submarine canyon* in reference to sea valleys that are of this type. As examples, we have Monterey Canyon (Fig. 1) and Hudson Canyon along the American coasts, Nazare and Cap Breton canyons off the west coast of Europe, Trincomalee Canyon off northwest Ceylon, and Tokyo Canyon off Japan.

A second type of valley is found cutting the large submarine fans beyond the submarine canyons. This type may be V-shaped or trough-shaped, and its walls (so far as is known) do not have rock

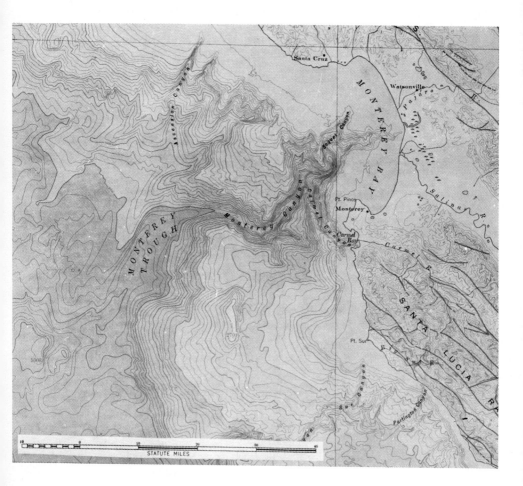

Fig. 1. Monterey Canyon and other rock gorges off the central California coast. Contour interval 300 ft; shade changes for every 3,000 ft. Reproduced from Shepard and Emery (1941). For larger scale map contoured in meters see Fig. 39.

outcrops, although they may be precipitous and not infrequently have heights of as much as 600 ft (183 m)[1]. Low ridges comparable to natural levees are found along the sides of many. These valleys, like land canyons, have winding courses but virtually lack tributaries and frequently have distributaries. They will be referred to here as *fan-valleys*, although *channels* has also been used for them in the past (Buffington, 1952, 1964; Dietz, 1953; Dill *et al.*, 1954; Shepard, 1963, p. 312). An example is located off the Congo (Fig. 2).

A third distinctive type of valley is observed in a few places extending across continental shelves. These valleys are never deep and their floor depths do not ordinarily exceed 600 ft (180 m). They are rather discontinuous and have small basins along their length. These will be referred to as *shelf-channels*. The best-known lies off New York Harbor where a valley crosses almost to the shelf edge (Fig. 3). In no place do these shelf-channels actually connect with submarine canyons.

A fourth type, also a continental shelf-channel, occurs in many places off glaciated coasts. These are trough-shaped and usually have depths greater than 600 ft (183 m) with rather large basins along their lengths. They may have both tributaries and distributaries. An exam-

[1]Feet and meters are used in this text because of ease in comparison with land valleys.

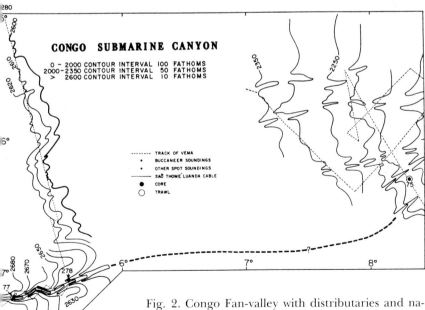

Fig. 2. Congo Fan-valley with distributaries and natural levees well indicated. From Heezen *et al.* (1964).

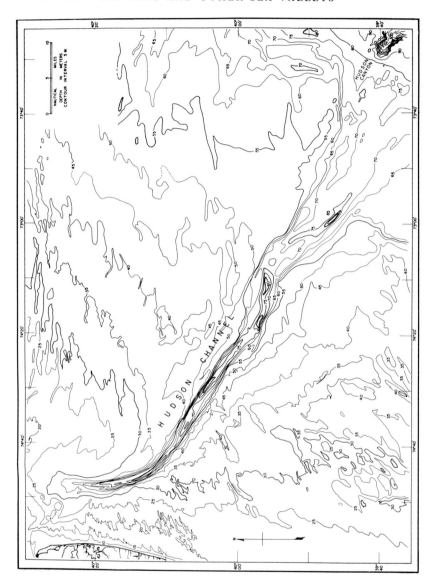

Fig. 3. The Hudson shelf-channel off New York Harbor. Note the basin depressions and the inner channel on the right, winding between straight outer slopes. Based on unpublished U.S. Coast and Geodetic Survey soundings.

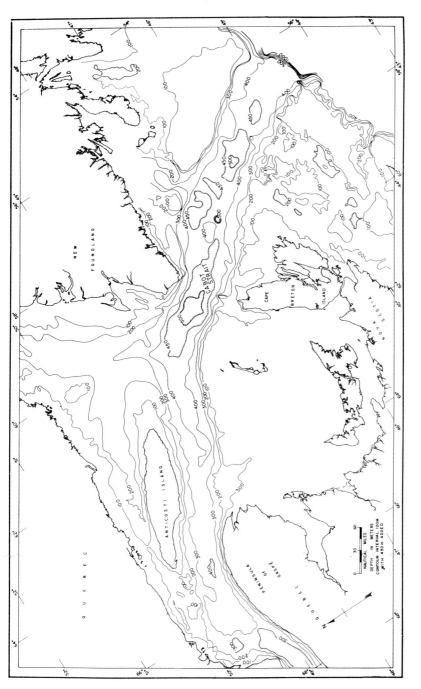

Fig. 4. The Laurentian Trough that extends deep into the Gulf of St. Lawrence and across the continental shelf. From U.S. Oceanographic Office charts.

ple is the trough coming out of the Gulf of St. Lawrence which extends across the shelf (Fig. 4); a similar valley comes out of Oslo Fiord and curves around the southern end of Norway. These will be referred to as *glacial troughs,* although their glacial origin is not universally accepted.

A fifth type is found off a few deltas. These valleys are trough-shaped but, unlike those off glaciated coasts, the floor slopes continuously seaward across the shelf and down the continental slope beyond. There are few if any tributaries and the walls, so far as known, do not have hard rock. As an example, there is the Swatch of no Ground off

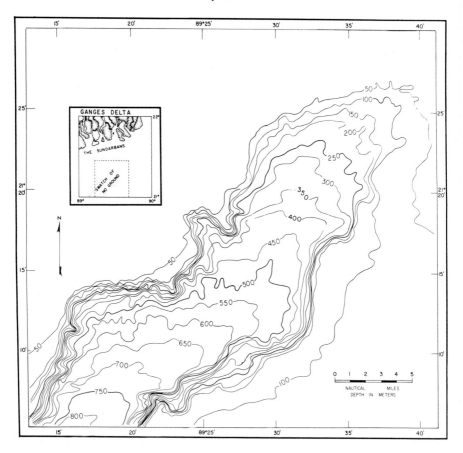

Fig. 5. The delta-front trough that extends diagonally across the shelf off the Ganges Delta. From Pakistani Navy soundings.

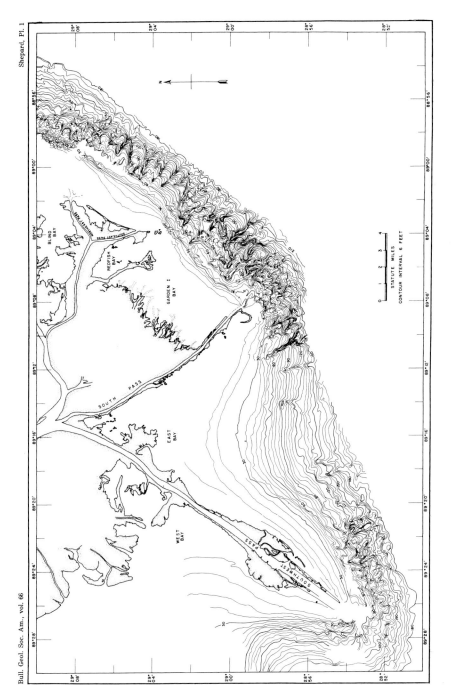

Fig. 6. Slope gullies on the front of the advancing Mississippi Delta. Contour interval 6 ft (2 m). From Shepard (1955).

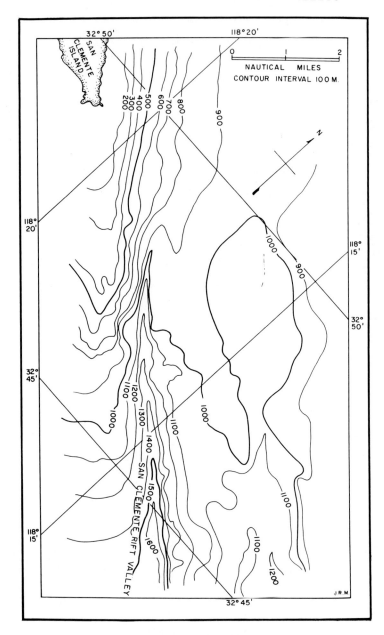

Fig. 7. The straight V-shaped valley extending south-east along fault scarp that forms the inside slope of San Clemente Island. Unpublished soundings of U.S. Coast and Geodetic Survey.

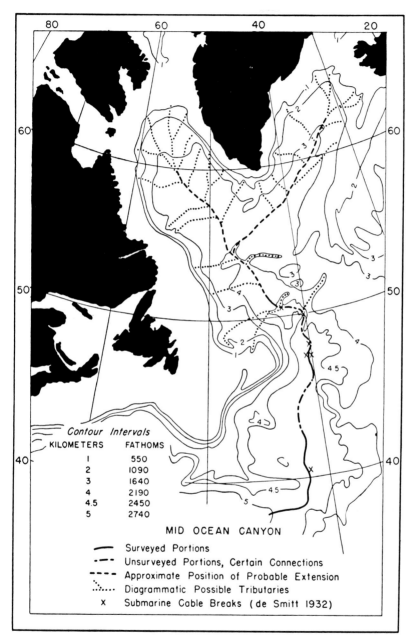

Fig. 8. Mid-Ocean Channel in the northeast Atlantic.
Note contours are in kilometers. From Heezen *et al.*
(1959, Fig. 29).

the Ganges Delta (Fig. 5) and similar valleys off the Indus, Niger, and Mississippi deltas. These will be called *delta-front troughs*.

A sixth type is found on many otherwise rather straight slopes. These valleys, usually of rather small relief, are discontinuous. Often the head of one is adjacent to the foot of another, and they commonly lack tributaries. They are located on submarine fault scarps and on the fronts of deltas (Fig. 6). These will be referred to as *slope gullies*.

A seventh type of valley occurs in areas where diastrophism is active. The valleys are straight, seldom have tributaries, and their trends are related to structural features on land. They may be either V-shaped or trough-shaped in cross-section. As an example, San Clemente Rift Valley, off southern California, is shown in Figure 7. In order to avoid using generic names when origin is not clear, these will be referred to as *valleys resembling grabens or rifts*.

An eighth type of valley is found in the deep sea. It has a trough shape, rather low relief, and few tributaries. Some of these valleys run parallel to continental margins, and others at large angles to the margins. These will be referred to as *deep-sea channels*. In some cases these channels may be outward continuations of fan-valleys, but others do not appear to be connected with land canyons. An example is shown in Figure 8.

Although the preceding eight classes or types of submarine valleys appear to be relatively distinct one from the other, there is, of course, no assurance that they were all formed by different processes. Nor is there any assurance that all of the same type have the same origin. Just as we are faced with the fact that among land valleys those that are U-shaped with cirque heads are ordinarily of glacial origin, but similarly shaped valleys are found in the typical mountain valleys of many tropical islands, where we can be sure there has been no glaciation. These tropical land valleys are generally considered to be due to slope wash and stream erosion. The same confusion may apply to a sea-floor valley type.

Another difficulty confronting the classification is that some marine valleys appear to be intermediate in type between two or more of the classifications. Still others are hard to classify. Despite these problems, we feel that it is far easier to seek the origin of marine valleys by dividing them into these classes. Special attention will be paid to some of the difficult cases, such as the valley off the Congo.

SCALES EMPLOYED IN THE BOOK

One of the most troublesome problems encountered by marine geologists is the choice of scales for use in contour charts and text discussions. Feet, fathoms, and meters often have been used with the maps and text in different systems. There is no doubt that the majority of English-speaking geologists are more familiar with feet, whereas most European geologists, as well as those from the other non-English parts of the world, use meters almost exclusively. In an attempt to conform with the trend toward use of the metric system in the United States, the contouring in this book is almost entirely in meters. Exceptions are made where contour charts in fathoms have been made by other scientists and the soundings were not available for conversion. In the text, both feet and meters are given, with feet mentioned first if the soundings were in feet or fathoms. Meters are given first if the soundings used for the contours were in meters. Approximate depths of heads of canyons, etc., are given with numbers rounded to nearest 10 for both feet and meter equivalents, except with small numbers.

For scales of miles in both charts and text, it was decided to use nautical miles because this is always available on all charts and apparently is a scale that is familiar to marine geologists and most other marine scientists the world over. For slopes of valley floors, meters per kilometer are given, whereas slope angles for valley walls are indicated in degrees.

CHAPTER II

METHODS OF
EXPLORATION

F OR GEOLOGISTS, the purpose of investigating submarine valleys is
to determine their origin and to discover the processes that are going
on within them. Such knowledge may contribute to the understanding of marine erosion and sedimentation in the geological column.
Definite applications to petroleum geology are indicated. Therefore,
as stated previously, a combined attack has been conducted involving
soundings, sampling, current measurement, and, most recently, diving—both with scuba equipment and in deep-diving submersibles.
Scuba investigations include a study of mass physical properties. Use
of acoustic probes and profilers, here called *continuous reflection profilers*, to determine the thickness of bottom and wall sediment in the
canyons has been initiated recently.

Canyon Soundings

Soundings within the canyons have included both wire soundings
(commonly referred to as vertical casts) and echo soundings. Obviously, the only practical way to explore any large submarine canyon is
by echo sounding. Surveys by this method are just as fast in deep

water as shallow, since the echo profile is registered regardless of depth of water or speed of vessel. However, for best results a slow speed is recommended as it shows less telescoping of topography and shows certain details that are not distinguishable at high speed. The great trouble with echo soundings is that the echo in ordinary instruments comes from a sound cone with a width of 30°. Therefore, in steep-walled canyons the echogram gives a deceptive picture, as illustrated in Figure 9. The result is not necessarily as bad as indicated, because a canyon with a moderately flat floor produces a sharp echo that may give a fairly accurate depth to the canyon bottom. Narrow, flat floors often reflect the edge of the sound cone, producing an inverted cone that crosses under a V-shaped profile made by the wall echoes (Fig. 10). In the interpretation of echo-sounding surveys it is important to measure the tops of these inverted cones in order to determine the approximate depth of the canyon crossing. The authors have found that this method checks well with depths

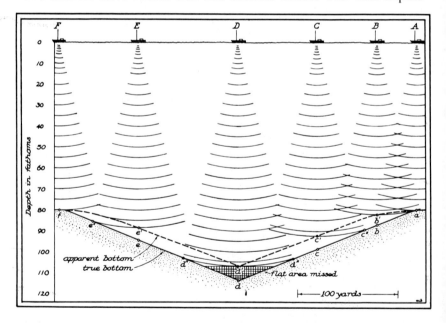

Fig. 9. Illustrating the slope error in echo sounding across a valley. Here, because of the 30° sound cone, the bottom of a V-shaped valley is missed. Also, the true bottom depth is greater than the apparent bottom. Courtesy of E. C. Buffington, U.S. Navy Electronics Laboratory.

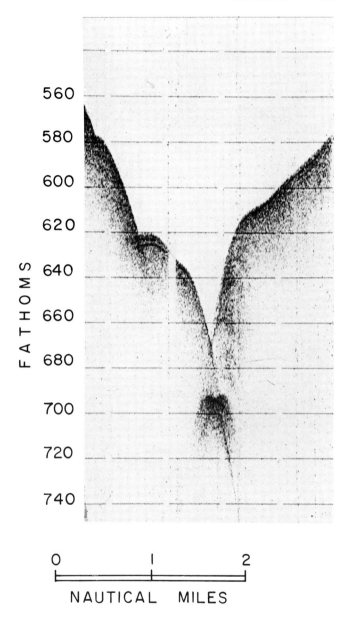

Fig. 10. The inverted V that often appears on a fathogram below the crossing of the canyon profile may indicate the true depth of the canyon floor, in this case 693 fms.

obtained while taking samples of the canyon floors and during bathy-scaph dives.

To obtain a reasonably accurate profile of a steep-sided canyon in relatively shallow water, there is as yet no generally available substi-tute for wire soundings. Narrow beam projectors are being tested that give a trace with a much closer approximation of the true profile than that of the standard echogram. Wire soundings are practical in some localities; such a survey was made in 1934 by the senior author in Scripps and Carmel canyons. The project took about four months of sounding from a skiff, using a hand reel and positioning by horizontal sextant angles along ranges. The results showed for the first time the surprising steepness of the walls of these two submarine canyons. During the surveying of Scripps Canyon, it was a regular occurrence to feel the lead weight touch bottom and then keep on sliding for as much as 100 ft (30 m) before it encountered a surface with a slope gentle enough to stop the weight. With such steep slopes, it was vital to have good ranges and to maintain vertical wire. Also, because the canyon center was approached from each side, allowance had to be made for the few feet that separated the wire from the sextant reader. On the other hand, for a good sextant reader near land there is no difficulty in getting an accurate fix, provided the range is sharp. A good range should have the object in the foreground near the surveyor and the object in the background at a considerable distance from that in the foreground (Fig. 11). Objects must, of course, be sharp rather than indefinite, such as rounded hilltops. Buoys are generally unsatisfactory because, unless taut-wired, they can move, according to the extent of their scope. A more accurate method utilizes measurements by surveyors with alidade telescopes on land.

Echo soundings for canyon surveys produce variable results, de-pending on accuracy of location as well as clarity of the sounding traces. At present, methods are available for highly accurate location maps, even hundreds of miles at sea. The expense of such electronic equipment has been prohibitive for oceanographic institutions, ex-cept for projects with military support. Only recently have we made use of the precise positioning instrument known as *Moran* (Buffing-ton, 1964).

Almost all of the surveys that will be discussed in the present book are based on a combination of horizontal sextant angles, pelorus bearings, and radar (bearings and ranges) (see Shepard, 1963, pp. 7-13). Ordinarily two or three of these methods have been used simul-taneously, fixes being based on the fit of the combined methods together with dead reckoning to offset particularly weak fixes. Lines are usually run across the canyon, but a few longitudinal lines are also included, to look for tributary valleys.

Echo soundings have been particularly useful in showing depth changes in canyon heads. In looking for the latter, it is vital to use good ranges so that lines can be repeated along exactly the same range at successive intervals. In addition, it is helpful to make use of the same sequence of sextant angles for marks on the echogram, so that these marks will coincide with the same position in each survey. In running lines off La Jolla (Fig. 11), we have been fortunate because the Scripps Institution pier extends seaward between the heads of Scripps and La Jolla canyons. Various pier pilings can be ranged on a relatively permanent but distant object. This method has provided a means for determining appreciable depth changes, which have subsequently been verified by scuba divers.

Bottom Samples

Common methods used in sampling submarine valleys have been dredging and coring. These have been supplemented recently with box-core samples. Dredging has been important in establishing the

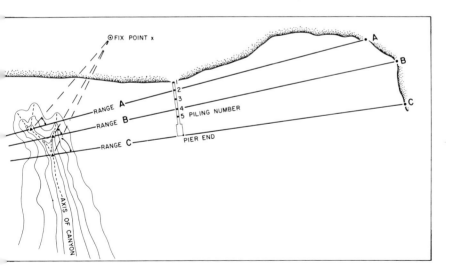

Fig. 11. Illustrating method of repeating exact ranges for sounding lines to determine changes in depth along the canyon heads.

character of the valley walls. The most successful dredging has come from the use of pipe dredges, which are pulled slowly up the walls until they encounter rock. If the rock is hard, it may anchor the ship, but the pipe dredge can almost always be broken loose by slowly reeling in the wire until the ship is pulled back on top of the dredge. Then the lift of the ship by waves will almost always break off the projecting outcrop. In most places, rock is broken easily and the ship will not become anchored, but the presence of rock is indicated by more or less violent jerking of the wire. In dredging, it is important not to let out a wire length of more than about twice the greatest depth, and the last part should be let out only after going ahead so that the wire is dragging behind the ship at an angle approximately of 45° to the surface.

Coring is used to determine the nature of fill on the canyon floor; either gravity or, preferably, piston cores may be used. However, coring is often unsuccessful along a canyon axis, because of the rather common finding of densely packed, coarse sediments or rocks that resist penetration and bend the core tubes, resulting in little, if any, core recovery. The method used by Reineck (1963) for taking box cores has been adapted by Bouma (1964), after somewhat modifying the instrument for deep-sea use. To orient the box cores, Bouma and H. de Klerk added a compass. X-ray studies of large oriented samples of bottom sediments have been made (Bouma and Shepard, 1964). This box corer (Fig. 12) has penetrated the bottom in many places where piston cores had been quite unsatisfactory, and has brought up many rock fragments and has shown the sedimentary structures in the canyon fill.

Remote Photography Within Canyons

Canyon walls and floors in water depths too great for diving have been investigated by lowering specially developed automatic under-water cameras. The most successful method has been to attach an acoustic *pinger* to the camera, allowing the positioning of the camera at a more or less definite height above the bottom. Remote photography is difficult while drifting over a canyon because of the danger of hitting cliffs with abrupt changes in depth. By far the safest procedure is to determine the direction of drift and then lower the camera on the wall relatively near, but up-current from, the axis. Then the camera can be successively lowered as the ship approaches the axis, keeping

Fig. 12. Large box corer, designed by H. E. Reineck. Used to take undisturbed and oriented samples on canyon floors. Orientation is by compass (designed by A. H. Bouma) shown at top on right side. The corer is coming up closed with the 'shovel' holding in the sample. When descending, the corer is open and the shovel is pivoted to the side.

the camera near the bottom and in focus without danger of encountering a cliff that requires sudden raising of the instrument. After crossing the axis, the camera should be brought back to the surface, and thus the dangerous climb up the opposite side can be avoided.

Measurements of Water Currents Along the Bottom

A series of current measurements were made in 1936 in canyons outside Georges Bank (Stetson, 1937), and in 1938 in the California submarine canyons (Shepard *et al.,* 1939). In both cases, small boats (or ships) were anchored directly over the canyon axes, and Ekman current meters were lowered to the bottom for short periods. Records and measurements were repeated at as close an interval as possible over periods of 24 or 48 hours. This, unfortunately, is almost all that has been done in measuring canyon floor currents, except for short-period observations made in relatively shallow water by scuba divers. However, on dives in the fan-valley off La Jolla in the bathyscaphs *Trieste I* and *II,* the junior writer has observed and estimated the speed of currents when the vehicle was resting on the bottom. During explorations in the Diving Saucer off La Jolla and off Cape San Lucas, currents were measured by several observers. Some questionable estimates also have been made of the velocities of turbidity currents in the Grand Banks earthquake cable breaks (Heezen and Ewing, 1952), although these are not known to be related to submarine canyons. Clearly, the field is wide open for future investigation.

Scuba Methods

One of the important ways of obtaining information about the heads of submarine canyons has been by scuba diving. Between 1951 and 1964, more than 1,000 dives have been made by marine scientists in the heads of at least 15 different submarine canyons throughout the world (Limbaugh and Shepard, 1957; Nesteroff, 1958; North, 1960; Buffington, 1961; Dill, 1961, 1964-a, 1964-b; Inman and Murray, 1961; Kaplin, 1961; Chamberlain, 1964). The data gathered during these dives has documented the following: (1) the changes in depth of the top of the sediment fill that accumulates in the canyon heads, (2) the physical properties of the fill, (3) the occurrence of submarine erosion, and (4) the nature of the processes actively moving sediment out of heads of nearshore canyons into deeper water. Relatively undisturbed samples were also obtained for laboratory determinations of density, shear strength, porosity, water content, packing, and grain size. *In situ* measurements of shear strength, sediment movement, relative changes in the thickness of the fill, and local sediment distribution patterns were also determined.

In situ density of sediment fill was determined using a method developed by Hamilton and Menard (1956). Thin-walled brass tubes were carefully inserted into the sediment by a diver, then plastic discs were used to cap the ends of the tubes after the surrounding sediment had been removed by hand. This encapsulated a known volume of sediment which was then returned to the laboratory still covered with sea water. These samples were used to compute the *in situ* density, water content, porosity, and packing of the sediment (Richards and Keller, 1962). These properties are particularly useful in canyon studies, for they can be used as indicators of a metastable state of grain packing, and show whether a sediment is subject to structural failure by liquefaction when stressed by overloading or earthquake shocks.

The shear strength of submarine sediments has been measured under water by carefully inserting a small vane-shear instrument into the sediment fill. The technique for obtaining shear-strength measurements in this study was devised by Dill and Moore (1965), employing a modified torque screwdriver as the testing instrument. The values obtained from *in situ* shear strength are useful in predicting the stability of slopes and the bearing capacity of sediments. In addition, zones of weakness, associated with areas of gravity creep and slumping, can be delineated by their low shear-strength values.

Diving observations show a slow, almost continuous movement of sediment down the heads of many nearshore canyons. Measurements of the mass movement of this sediment fill were made using glaciological techniques to measure the slow creep of ice bodies. Steel stakes having a diameter of 0.25 inches (0.63 cm) and lengths of about a meter were inserted vertically in the sedimentary fill of several canyons. At each test site a straight line of evenly spaced stakes was established, usually at right angles to the axis. The rate of movement for the stakes, and presumably of the sediment fill of the canyon, as well as the direction and amount of each rod's deviation from the vertical, was then observed over a long period of time. Measurement of displacement of individual stakes relative to their starting points was made by stretching a line across the canyon between reference stakes driven into the rock walls on opposite sides of the canyon. Areas of instability, amount of gravity creep, and active slumping of the sediment fill over a given period, were thus delineated by the moving stakes.

Underwater photography has been another important method used by divers for recording data in the heads of submarine canyons. The comparison of sequential photographs and motion pictures taken at specific locations over a period of time allows recognition of the variations of bottom conditions; many of the relatively subtle, slowly occurring changes which take place in the sedimentary fill of the canyons become apparent.

Bottom-slope measurements were made by a clinometer on a 6 by 4 inch (15 by 10 cm) plastic plate (Dill and Shumway, 1954). Slope was measured directly to within 1 degree by placing the flat edge of the plastic plate on the sediment surface and reading the slope angle from a protractor mounted on the instrument (Fig. 13). The average slope of a sediment surface was also measured by comparing changes in depth between two locations over a given horizontal distance.

Fig. 13. Technique and instrument used to measure bottom sediment slopes. In Sumner Branch of Scripps Canyon, depth 50 ft (15 m). U.S. Navy Electronics Laboratory (N.E.L.) photo by W. J. Bunton.

To determine whether or not the sedimentary fill of the canyon was slowly moving downslope en masse, large easily recognized objects (such as concrete blocks and an old automobile body) were placed on the bottom of Scripps Canyon at a time when it was relatively empty of sediment. The large objects became incorporated in the sediment as the canyon filled. Any subsequent movement downcanyon by these large man-made bodies demonstrated the type of movement of the sediment mass, and gave a rough estimate of its strength and transporting capabilities. In one such test in Scripps Canyon (Dill, 1964b, p. 165), two large blocks of concrete, each weighing 690 pounds in sea water (1200 pounds in air), were placed on the rims of the gorge at a depth of 70 ft (21 m), on opposite sides of Sumner Branch of Scripps Canyon (Fig. 14). The two blocks were then connected by a heavy chain, which draped over the canyon walls and crossed the main channel on top of a thin layer of sediment fill resting on the rock bottom. As the sediment gradually accumulated, the chain became incorporated in the fill. The plant material that forms most of the fill was sufficiently cohesive so that it transmitted any movement or strain to the chain. The high stresses involved in the slow gravity creep of the canyon were demonstrated by the pulling of one of the concrete blocks into the canyon.

In addition to objects purposely placed in the canyon, measurements have been made of the movement of small concrete blocks, automobile tires, lobster traps, and other man-made devices, all of which slowly made their way down into the head of the canyon by natural processes. These objects, when partially buried in the fill, made good reference markers for a given mass of sediment, and permitted the measurement of movements when compared to reference points on the canyon wall.

One of the important discoveries made by scuba diving was the variability of the nature of the sediment fill. The true surface of the fill is often difficult to determine, because of the algal and sea-grass debris continually moving along the sea floor into the canyon heads. As a result, variation in each echo-sounder profile or lead-line soundings along a given profile may be somewhat deceptive, if the depth differences are used to calculate the amount of sediment loss from a canyon head over a given period of time. After intense storms, the heads of canyons are often filled with a deposit of loosely packed kelp and sea grass torn from its footings in nearby rock areas. Such a deposit has the general consistency of a haystack and is extremely unstable (Fig. 15). When the canyon is full of such material, echo-sounding profiles falsely record a considerable increase in sediment filling, which is deceptive because of the good acoustic reflectivity of the gas-charged decaying grass and algal material. Successive profiles made after the loosely packed material has compacted or moved down the canyon indicate large depth changes. If it were assumed that these depth changes were attributable to loss of sand or matted sediment fill, as has been the case in the past, gross errors could result in predicting the amount of sediment annually lost down a particular canyon. This type of error can best be eliminated by correcting indirect soundings through diver observations of the true nature of the bottom sediments.

Overburden thickness above bedrock has been determined by divers using high pressure water to jet long pipes through the sedi-

Fig. 14. One of the large concrete blocks resting on the north edge of Sumner Branch. Chain is connected to a similar block on the south side of the branch. N.E.L. photo by Dill.

Fig. 15. Diver examining the loosely packed interwoven mat of algae and sea grass initially deposited in
the canyon bottom after a major slump. Depth, 75 ft
(23 m) in Sumner Branch. N.E.L. photo by Dill.

ment. This technique, when used by an experienced investigator, can
also be a rough indicator of sediment type through notation of
changes in the rate of penetration and the 'feel' of the pipe as it passes
through different layers of sediment. Probe surveys in areas of fine
sand, have delineated irregularities in bedrock surfaces covered by up
to 20 ft (6 m) of overburden. This method is especially useful in
shallow water where sonic profile techniques are ineffective due to
reverberation and wave action.

CHAPTER III

SUBMARINE CANYONS OF THE LA JOLLA, CALIFORNIA AREA

T HE FORTUITOUS LOCATION of Scripps Institution of Oceanography between the heads of La Jolla and Scripps submarine canyons (Fig. 16) has made available an excellent natural laboratory for the study of processes active in canyons. La Jolla Canyon is located approximately 4,000 ft (1,220 m) south of Scripps pier and comes to within 700 ft (210 m) of the shoreline. Scripps Canyon, shoreward of the juncture with La Jolla Canyon, crosses the shelf diagonally and loses its identity just outside the breaker zone about 3,000 ft (910 m) north of Scripps pier. The close proximity of these canyons to the pier permits use of easily maintained and inexpensive small boats. Consequently, more has been learned here about the shallow heads of canyons than in any other place in the world.

The study of the outer part of La Jolla Canyon (Fig. 17) required the use of larger ships belonging to the Scripps Institution, the University of Southern California, and the Navy Electronics Laboratory.

Not only have the La Jolla canyons been studied from surface craft, but emphasis on direct observations by the scientists has resulted in far more study by scuba and deep-diving submersibles than in any other canyons. The bathyscaphs, *Trieste I* and *Trieste II,* and Cousteau's Diving Saucer have been used to explore visually the deeper parts of La Jolla Canyon and its adjacent fan-valley (Table 1).

The first underwater observations were made in La Jolla and Scripps canyons by Frank Haymaker, using standard 'hard hat' diving equipment (Shepard, 1949). By 1950, many scientists, both at Scripps and the Navy Electronics Laboratory, were using scuba for canyon sedimentological studies. The junior author, with numerous companions, has been studying the canyons with scuba since 1951, observing their walls and the nature of their sediment fill down to depths of 250 ft (75 m). Earl Murray and T. K. Chamberlain, working closely with Douglas Inman and several graduate students at Scripps, made extensive measurements and observations in these canyons for geological and related oceanographic data for many years (Chamberlain, 1960; Inman and Murray, 1961).

Starting in October, 1961, a new phase of canyon studies began with the use of deep-diving research submersibles in the exploration of the La Jolla canyons. The bathyscaphs *Trieste I* and *II* have made a total of nine descents into the fan-valley outside La Jolla Canyon (Dill, 1961; Buffington, 1964; Moore, 1965). The large size of the bathyscaphs restricted their use to the fan-valley, and even there it was sometimes difficult to work in the narrow channels or on the steep slopes found unexpectedly during the first dives.

In February of 1964, Cousteau's Diving Saucer was chartered and flown to the United States for a joint U.S. Navy-Scripps Institution evaluation study. During a six-week period, over 20 dives were made to obtain biological and geological data in Scripps and La Jolla canyons (Shepard *et al.,* 1964). The axis of much of Scripps Canyon was explored, along with La Jolla Canyon down to the juncture of the two (Fig. 16). The success of this initial program resulted in a renewal of the lease and the instigation of a more extensive program of Saucer dives between November, 1964 and April, 1965 (Shepard, 1965).

SCRIPPS CANYON

Scripps Canyon runs in a relatively straight line in a west-southwestern direction, diagonal to the trend of the coast. It joins La Jolla Canyon 1.3 miles from its head, at a depth of 920 ft (280 m). The existence of Scripps Canyon was first discovered in 1928 as a result of a lead-line survey made jointly by the late E. G. Moberg of Scripps Institution and C. M. Durgin of the U.S. Coast and Geodetic Survey. Their chart was improved by the senior author with additional soundings from a more detailed lead-line survey in 1934, using the help of staff and students of Scripps Institution. Soundings were so closely spaced that the precipitous walls could be detected, and the lead weight was felt to slide down the walls for a hundred feet or more in many places.

After World War II, the head of Scripps Canyon was more completely surveyed by echo soundings from small craft and with additional wire soundings. This work showed that there were three

Fig. 16. The two canyons located off La Jolla, California. For outer continuation of La Jolla Canyon see Fig. 17; and for details of head of Scripps Canyon see Fig. 18. Dashed lines indicate paths of Saucer dives. Mostly from surveys by the authors.

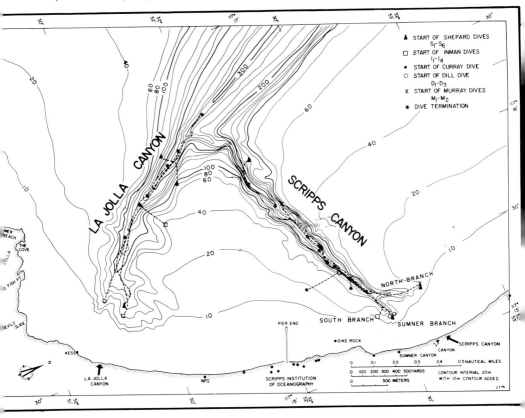

Table 1. NEL Dive Number, Depth, Location and General observations on dives made in the Bathyscaph *Trieste I* & *Trieste II*.

Dive No.	Depth	Location	Scientific Observer	General Observations and Results
83	1920 ft. (580 m)	La Jolla Fan-Valley	Dill	Observations restricted to terrace-like features in canyon. Sediment type, silty clay. Bottom, flat with no ripple marks or evidence of scour; sand and mica not observed. Slump scars observed at sharp drop-off into main axis of canyon. Bottom slope of 33° measured at drop-off between terrace and inner-channel.
91	1920 ft. (580 m)	La Jolla Fan-Valley	Dill	Descended to terrace with a bottom slope of 5°. The bottom sediment is a silty clay with a high mica content. No ripple marks or scour. Hummocky topography indicating slumping at inner edge of terrace. Measurements of 47° 43°, and 46° made on steep inner slope (Fig. 29). Axial slope of canyon at the base of steep slope, 12°.
93	1980 ft. (605 m)	La Jolla Fan-Valley	Dill	Descended to the axis of the inner-channel. Bottom sediments have an extremely high organic content and exhibit much churning due to organisms. Sand and silt sediments are bedded. Bottom slope, 8°-10° at down position decreases to an almost flat-lying bottom at the center of the erosion channel. Bathyscaph crossed the erosion channel at right angles to its axial trend. Large slump scars in axis with fresh surfaces indicate recent movement. No ripple marks or scour scars in sediment. Matted eel-grass and brown algae exposed in one slump scar. The steep 35° slope leading from terrace to the channel consists of silty clay and does not have sand layers as do inner-channel sediments. On the face of slump scars, sand flows from beneath a 1/2-inch layer of overlying consolidated clay, when disturbed by bathyscaph.
102	1970 ft. (600 m)	La Jolla Fan-Valley	Dill	Descended to terrace on north side of canyon. Bottom sediment, fine-grained silty clay. Hummocky topography sloping gently to the south. No ripple marks. Traversed to south into canyon axis where bottom steepens to 25°. Bottom axial slope of inner-channel abruptly flattens. Large block of concrete observed resting on the bottom, no scour scars, indicating low velocity currents. Sighted large scattered 3 ft. diameter semi-rounded boulders on inner edge of one of the channel meanders (Fig. 32). Sandy silt bottom with some pebbles in area of boulders. No evidence of scour or ripple marks. Moved along axis; no boulders deeper in canyon. Bottom flat. Encountered south wall of channel, slope 30°. Slump scar at base of slope. Channel meandering (Fig.).
104	2250 ft. (686 m)	La Jolla Fan-Valley	Dill	Descended to south side of canyon. Bottom slope at contact point, 70°. Landed on small ledge of bedded sediments. Bathyscaph slowly slid to base of the steep slope which decreased to 15-20°. Moving out into the axis of the inner-channel, the slope decreased abruptly to an almost flat bottom. Bottom material a mixture of algae, sand, mica, and silt. Very loosely compacted. Axial slope of inner-channel varies between 5-10°. However, it is interrupted by occasional slump scars with much steeper front slopes. Channel meanders.

No.	Fan-Valley	Position	Depth	Observer	Description
105	Coronado Fan-Valley	117°22'W 32°27.5'N	3480 ft. (1060 m)	Dill	Descent to axis of Coronado Canyon. Bottom flat and gently sloping to the south. Bottom sediment fine grained cohesive clay. Many organisms churning the bottom. No evidence of high velocity currents or scour marks. Large amounts of man-made detritus—milk cartons, cans, paper, etc. Slopes leading down to flat-bottomed inner-channel up to 25°.
101 & 114	La Jolla Fan-Valley	117°24.5'W 32°54.9'N	2100 ft. (600 m)	Buffington	Descended to a relatively smooth sandy-silt bottom. Traversed on crs. 350°T at a speed of one knot. Crossed an abrupt drop-off with an estimated minimum slope of 75-80°. No suggestion or evidence of other than unconsolidated sediment. The drop-off was approx. 90 ft. and probably the inner-channel of the canyon (fan-valley). (From Buffington 1964).
	La Jolla Fan-Valley	117°26'W 32°55'N	2430 ft. (705 m)	Buffington	Descended to a relatively flat inner-terrace. Traversed across a flat bottom for 40 min. Then encountered the drop-off into the inner-channel in the form of steps with slopes of up to 20°. The floor of the channel near the slope was broken by a series of ridges up to 1 ft. high trending diagonally across the channel. The cohesive clay forming the ridges was full of burrows. Low areas between the ridge contained sand covered with a thin layer of mud. Crossing the channel revealed that the channel had many burrows. The north wall had a slope of about 20°. Sighted hagfish and many sablefish. Large anemonies on stalks up to 2 ft. high seen. Visibility up to 50 ft. (15 m).
Trieste II 7	La Jolla Fan-Valley	117°31'W 32°53.5'N	2640-2700 ft. (804-823 m)	Dill & Shepard	
11	La Jolla Fan-Valley	117°33'W 32°52'N	2900-2925 ft. (890-900 m)	Moore	Descended on northwest side of inner-channel to a 30° slope of cohesive silty clay with a thin layer of loose silt covering the surface. Upon contact, chunks of consolidated clay slide downslope generating turbid clouds which also flow downslope. Crossed an approximately 150 ft. (50 m) wide channel to southwest wall which sloped 40-45°. Outcropping beds of cohesive clay appeared to be nearly horizontal. Walls are erosional in origin. Large grooves up to 2 ft. across and 6 inches deep trend directly downslope. A block of stiff clay 12 inches across was found in the channel bottom at least 150 ft. from its point of origin. (From Moore, 1965).

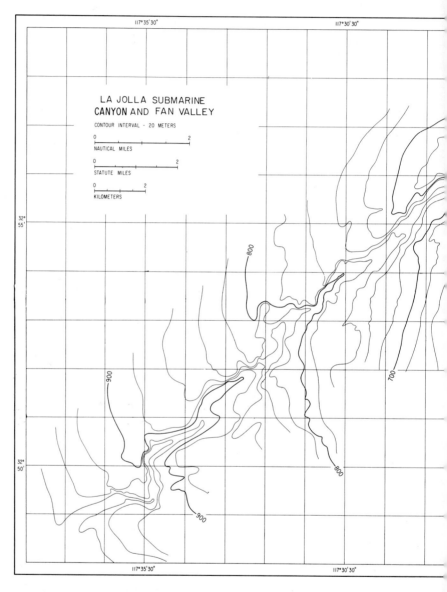

Fig. 17. The La Jolla canyons and the La Jolla Fan-valley. The fan-valley continues a short distance beyond the limits of the chart, but the outer part is not as well sounded. From surveys by the authors and Buffington (1964).

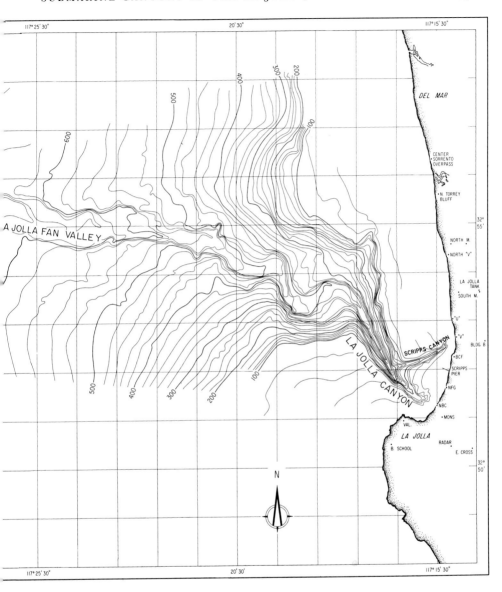

principal tributaries, named respectively North, Sumner, and South branches. A fourth branch was discovered in 1950 following an earthquake and a period of storm swell. (Shepard, 1951). The upper portions of all branches have been thoroughly investigated by scuba-equipped scientists from many institutions. A map of these branches, made from scuba traverses along the upper lip of the canyon, from echo soundings and from wire-line soundings, has been constructed (Fig. 18).

The detailed information, not usually obtainable from other canyons, concerning small-scale topographical features and the geological processes active in the canyon are given in the following paragraphs.

North Branch

is the largest branch of the canyon head with a length of 1,500 ft (450 m) and an average width of 175 ft (53 m). It extends in towards shore to a depth of about 40 ft (12 m). Here, at its shallowest depth, the head consists of a sand-filled bowl-shaped depression. To the south, bedrock appears on the sides of the bowl at a depth of about 70 ft (21 m), and the rock walls increase in height from this depth to the juncture with the other tributaries at an axial depth of 328 ft (100 m). There the walls form a relatively narrow-bottomed gorge with progressively steepening walls. Minor tributaries enter this gorge from both sides as sand chutes and rock-floored hanging valleys. The tributaries are better developed on the shoreward side where there is a source of sand from longshore transport of sediment. On both sides there is evidence of undercutting at the base of the rock walls, and numerous large boulders of wall rock are found on the sediment-covered floor. However, undercutting is only seen in areas where sand does not presently spill over the upper lip into the canyon.

In areas where sediment is set into motion by swell-induced bottom currents, the rock walls of the canyon are rounded and cut by narrow chutes with polished and smoothed sides and bottoms (Fig. 19). The effect of this type of submarine erosion is most evident halfway along the landward wall of North Branch. At this location, the rounding of the upper lip stops where a tributary diverts sand moving across the shelf. Deeper in the branch where there is a minimum amount of sand transport, due to this type of piracy, the overhang of the rock walls is as much as 20 ft (6 m), and they are covered with a lush growth of sessile organisms.

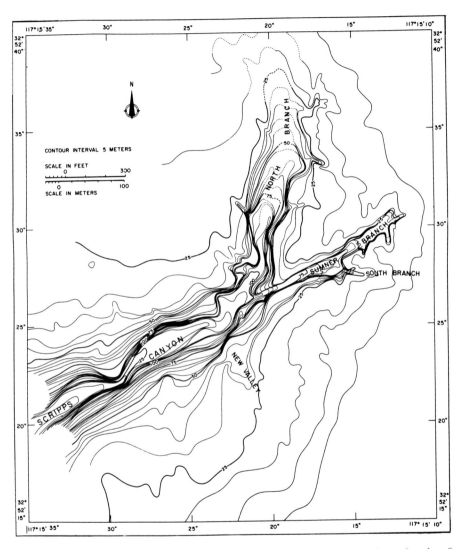

Fig. 18. Detailed topography of the three heads of Scripps Canyon. The surveys by the authors include wire soundings and scuba diving with tracking of bubbles from a surface skiff. Dotted contours denote sediment surfaces.

The head of North Branch is partially filled with a thick mat of interbedded sand and intertwined algae and sea grass. Rubbish is also commonly found in the sediment fill at the head of this and other branches. Small U-shaped slump channels cutting to a depth of 2 ft (0.6 m) run parallel to the trend of the branch near the walls where the fill is structurally weak (Dill, 1964b). These channels were observed all along the base of the west wall in Saucer dives. Slump scars form a hummocky surface in many places on the sediment-covered floor. Such scars often expose planks (Fig. 20) that have been incorporated in the fill, and are now as much as 4 feet below its upper surface. This indicates a recent origin for both the fill and the slump.

Sumner Branch

heading just seaward of the surf zone, extends first south and then southwest to join North Branch at a depth of about 330 ft (100 m) as a

Fig. 19. Deep grooves, partly filled with plant debris incised in the rounded upper lip of North Branch. N.E.L. photo by Dill.

hanging valley. It is the second largest of the tributaries, with a length of 750 ft (230 m) and an average width of 125 ft (38 m) between its upper lips. The trend of the longitudinal axis of Sumner Branch lines up with Callan Canyon. This is a small land canyon that cuts through a 300 ft (90 m) sea cliff, but interestingly enough does not have an extensive drainage pattern. The subaerially exposed extension of this branch ends abruptly in a well-developed uplifted terrace.

Fig. 20. A small plank of processed lumber found incorporated in one of the sediment layers 4 ft (1.2 m) below the sediment surface in North Branch. Depth approximately 100 ft (30 m). N.E.L. photo by Dill, May 7, 1963.

Bedrock profiles made by jetting through the sediment overburden with high pressure water has shown that a rock-walled channel extends shoreward from the main part of Sumner Branch to a depth of 10 ft (3 m) below mean sea level, and only 330 ft (100 m) seaward of the base of Callan Canyon (Chamberlain, 1964, Figs. 2, 4). However, the main arm of Sumner Branch swings northward at a depth of about 50 ft (15 m), ending as a shallow, elongate depression in the sand bottom approximately 900 ft (275 m) out beyond the cliff. This sand-filled channel has a southerly trend down to an axial depth of about 70 ft (20 m), below which it gradually turns to its dominantly southwesterly direction. During times when the sediment level is low, a nick point is found in the rock floor, forming an 8-ft (2.6 m) cliff between the rock bottom and the rock terrace into which the head of the canyon is cut. Usually this sharp break in the rock floor is covered by a 5 to 10-ft (1.5 to 3 m) deposit of interbedded sand and plant detritus resting at an angle of repose between 20° and 30°. Below the nick point, rock walls of the branch form a relatively narrow gorge with precipitous walls, which in places overhang the channel bottom.

An almost complete cover of organisms is found in areas where the rock walls are overhanging and are not subjected to bottom currents or periodic burial. The activity of crabs, fish, lobsters, sea anemones, gorgonian corals, polychete worms, pholads, and sponges is breaking down the rock walls by organic erosion and weathering (Limbaugh and Shepard, 1957; Chamberlain, 1960; Dill, 1964b). The rock wall beneath sessile organisms is deeply bored, giving it a rough surface. However, when the sediment that normally fills the bottom part of the channel is removed, the exposed wall rock is found smoothly polished with undercuts that truncate the organically roughened surface (Fig. 21). Numerous small hanging valleys or tributaries are cut into the upper rim of the canyon wall. These too have undercut, smoothed walls in areas usually covered with sediment.

Below an axial depth of 120 ft (37 m), a conglomerate forms much of the walls of the outer part of this branch. At a depth of 70 ft (21 m), the undercut wall rock of silty shale contains unweathered tests of foraminifera. This same type of sedimentary rock breaks down rapidly when exposed to subaerial weathering. Road cuts exposing such shale for periods of several years contain only a few highly weathered remains of fossils. It thus appears that the shale exposed in walls of the canyon head has not been subjected to subaerial weathering during the Pleistocene lowering of sea level or, more likely, all evidence of subaerial weathering was removed by submarine erosional processes since the most recent rise of sea level (Dill, 1964b).

Four relatively large sub-tributaries cut the upper lip of Sumner Branch, entering as hanging channels. The largest of these, located on the south side and called Intermediate Branch, forms a narrow rock cleft with overhanging walls cut into the rock terrace surrounding the canyon head. During times when the level of the fill is low, Intermediate Branch can be traced across the narrow ridge separating Sumner and South branches.

The floor of Sumner Branch is filled with a matted sediment that varies in thickness and is similar to that found in North Branch. Shallow slump channels cut the fill revealing that it is composed of interbedded sand and intertwined mats of plant debris. The sediment filling Sumner Branch is relatively unstable, and often moves en masse into deeper water and exposes much of the rock floor (Dill,

Fig. 21. The rock wall of a tributary to Sumner Branch showing polished surfaces, undercut and truncated animal burrows, gouge marks, and erosion scars (black arrow). The upper part of the wall is roughened by the large number of living pholads burrowing into its surface. Depth 73 ft (22 m). N.E.L. photo by Dill.

1964b). However, the entire fill is rarely involved in these slumps. Even after the largest deepening by slumps, large clumps of sediment fill are found as remnants forming irregular discontinuous terraces along the side of the channel. Under conditions of maximum fill, the head between axial depths of 40 and 70 ft (12 and 21 m) has a sediment slope of about 17°; the surface is hummocky and has many minor slump scars 3 to 6 ft (1 to 2 m) across. Below 70 ft (21 m), there are short-lived steep slump scars with slopes up to 90° in inclination. The average sediment slope is between 25° and 30°, depending on the plant content and its state of decay. Below axial depths of 100 ft (30 m), the average sediment slope decreases until below the juncture with South Branch, at 225 ft (68 m), it is around 15°. Near the juncture with North Branch, observations from the Diving Saucer show that the bottom greatly steepens. Large angular boulders of bedrock up to 12 ft (4 m) across have fallen from the upper walls, forming a jumbled pile of rock blocks where Sumner enters North Branch as a hanging valley at a depth of about 330 ft (100 m). The cliff-like drop-off at the junction is about 50 ft (15 m) high. Here, the bottom slope is not dependent on the physical properties of the fill, but on the occurrence of bedrock and large rock blocks in the axis of the channel.

Chamberlain (1960) observed that the surface of the sediment fill in the shallow head of Sumner Branch often exhibits textural and compositional variation in a downcanyon direction of: (1) quartz sand, (2) micaceous sand, and (3) plant debris. This sequence is only surficial and does not persist in depth (Dill, 1964b, p. 93).

The decay of the plant debris incorporated in the fill generates gas that usually can be seen bubbling up to the surface from the floor of Sumner Branch in depths shallower than about 120 ft (35 m). The state of decay of plant material greatly affects the strength characteristics and stability of the fill. Slight pushes by a diver's hand on the surface of the fill increase the amount of bubbling and show that the mat is capable of storing gas.

South Branch

extends directly shoreward from where it enters Sumner Branch midway along its east wall as a hanging valley. The trend of South Branch lines up directly with a land canyon cut into the high cliffs just north of Scripps pier. This branch has a length of about 325 ft (100 m) and a width that varies between 6 ft (2 m) at the narrowest point near its junction with Sumner Branch to 75 ft (23 m) in its upper bowl-shaped head. According to the jet probes made by Chamberlain (1964), the rock head of the canyon is a broad shallow depression in the bedrock shelf and comes to within 200 ft (60 m) of the rock cliffs at the mouth of the adjacent land canyon. The latter, like Callan Canyon, lacks an extensive drainage pattern.

South Branch, except at its head, has precipitous to overhanging rock walls along almost all of its entire length. In places it is so narrow that a scuba diver can simultaneously touch both walls with his hands. The extremely smooth rock walls are mostly mudstone, fluted and scarred by drag marks from hard objects contained in the moving fill, which have gouged material from the walls. Pholad burrows are found truncated and, along with the larger gouge marks, are smoothed and polished by submarine erosion. Only a few sand chutes cut the upper lip of this gorge.

The floor of South Branch is usually filled with a sediment mat; plant debris gives this considerable internal strength. When the sediment moves out of this branch, it moves as large blocks of cohesive sediment in a series of slumps. Headward slumping of the fill often leaves masses of the mat with steep or even overhanging walls (Fig. 22). Gravity creep was common in this branch until, in 1964, TNT explosions were set off by D. L. Inman below the bottom. This increased the density and strength of the sand part of the fill, creating a plug or dam of densely packed sediment with sufficient strength to prevent further creep temporarily.

South Branch ends with a precipitous descent from 140 ft (43 m) into Sumner Branch, which has a bottom depth of about 225 ft (70 m). The cliff face below the drop-off has been cut back, forming a re-entrant of at least 20 ft (6 m) into the wall of Sumner Branch. Near the juncture, the rock wall of Sumner Branch is also undercut and overhangs the channel about 20 ft (6 m) (Fig. 23). Large, narrow joint-controlled sand chutes cut back into the overhanging cliff up to 20 ft (6 m). The rock surfaces in the area of the overhang are covered with sessile and burrowing organisms, and many fish of numerous species congregate in this region.

New Valley

Prior to February, 1950, a considerable number of echo-sounding lines had been run along ranges south of South Branch. These lines showed irregularities but no appreciable valley-like branches. In

February, 1950, following an earthquake and a period of storm waves, a repeat run showed a valley where sediment had been removed since a survey made in November, 1949. This valley extends in toward Dike Rock, a basalt ridge just awash at mean tide, that lies approxmately 350 ft (105 m) seaward of the cliff forming the shoreline. Dives made into this branch reveal that its walls are not as high as in the other branches, but it does resemble them in having steep walls

Fig. 22. Cliff of fill material in South Branch. Objects such as lobster traps, broom handles, swim fins, and beer cans are found incorporated in this material, attesting to its recent nature. Depth 100 ft (30 m). N.E.L. photo by Dill.

and indications of sediment moving along its axis. This instability is shown by slump scars and hummocks. The sediment on the floor is very cohesive, has a high clay content, and many interweaving worm tubes penetrating to a depth of at least 2 ft. In places, the worms are attached to the bedrock below, but this apparently has not stabilized the sediment—at least since 1950.

Processes Operating in the Head of Scripps Canyon

Beginning in 1934, sounding profiles were made along well-established range lines based on prominent landmarks so as to provide a constant location for crossing the canyon at different points. Retaking of these profiles soon showed that the bottom depths change. After World War II, when echo-sounding equipment became available, the senior author started resurveying the Scripps Canyon head at frequent intervals. The sounding runs were conducted regularly until

Fig. 23. Overhanging wall at the mouth of South Branch where it enters the main channel of the canyon. Note the lush organic growth in areas not subjected to sediment flow. Depth 110 ft (34 m). N.E.L. photo by Dill.

1951. Occasional profiles have been run since that time by D. L. Inman, E. A. Murray, and T. K. Chamberlain. All of this work indicated that there are periodic deepenings, at least along the axes of Sumner and South branches. Since 1950, similar changes have been occurring in New Valley (Shepard, 1951). Variations up to a maximum of 21 ft (6.4 m) were detected by repeated echo soundings. Records show that the greatest deepenings were related to periods of large storm swell. Two of the deepenings occurred after unusually severe earthquake shocks. However, there is no proof that the shocks caused the deepening because there was always a time interval between earthquake and resurvey, during which time the canyon was subjected also to storms and associated large waves. The only documented case wherein an earthquake might have triggered a loss of sediment fill took place on Christmas Day in 1951. A survey two weeks before revealed considerable fill in South and Sumner branches, but the day after the earthquake a resurvey showed a deepening of up to 10 ft (3 m). Water directly above the canyon had much mud in suspension, as if there had been a recent disturbance. However, it must be pointed out that even in this case a large storm had passed through the area prior to resurveying and before the strong shock. Subsequently, other earthquakes of relatively high intensity, and two reportedly as strong as the 1951 quake, have failed to produce a change. *In situ* density samples and the physical properties of the sediment fill (p. 307) with its high plant content may explain its resistance to failure under earthquake-induced stresses.

The sands found in the canyon have *in situ* physical properties that, when compared to those analyzed and tested in the laboratory, were found to be near their critical density. In such a state of packing, the sands would neither collapse nor expand when subjected to shear stress during earthquakes (Dill, 1964b).

Statistically, Chamberlain used both his and Shepard's data to show that most of the deepenings, obtained by repeated sounding lines, are not significantly related to earthquakes, but have occurred after periods of large waves during storm seasons.

The first visual evidence of the depth changes was obtained when scuba permitted the direct observation of the canyon heads. *In situ* measurements of the physical properties of the fill, long-term observations, and measurements of the displacement of marker stakes downcanyon, and the close correlation with overloading by sediment rapidly carried into the canyon heads during storms, showed that the deepenings were caused by large slumps. Further, although the movement of sediment downslope is more pronounced during periods of storms, it is not restricted to these periods. The canyon head is an extremely active submarine environment (Dill, 1964b), as indicated by the loss of marker stakes within a period of a few months. These studies pointed out the difficulty of interpreting data obtained from samples and soundings solely from surface vessels. The extensive diver studies for Scripps Canyon are presented because they are the only data of this type available on canyon sediments.

Type of sediment

Recent shelf sediments surrounding Scripps Canyon are entirely different in composition and structure from those found within the canyon head. The shelf sediments are relatively clean, homogeneous, fine-grained quartz sand (Inman, 1953; Wimberly, 1955), whereas the canyon fill is composed of a heterogeneous mixture of interbedded layers of micaceous silty sands and matted organic debris of marine plant origin (Chamberlain, 1960; Dill, 1964).

The main sources of sand-sized sediment that eventually enters the head of the canyon are the intermittent rivers of the region and the reworked nearshore and beach deposits. Material reaching the beach is transported by longshore drift in the outer surf zone and along the beach as a narrow wedge of sand until it is intercepted by the head of a submarine canyon (Inman and Chamberlain, 1960; Shepard, 1963, p. 184).

Motion-picture studies by Dill of dye-marked bottom water and studies by Vernon (Gorsline *et al.,* 1965) of dyed sand grains show that during storms, swell-induced bottom currents set the surficial nearshore sands into motion as a thin, loosely packed layer of grains. This layer, although moved shoreward and seaward during the passage of a wave, has a slow net movement along shore and downslope. The depressions formed by the canyon head are a natural trap for the mobile sands, and are slowly filled by a prograding sandy deposit with a bottom slope near the angle of repose.

During the passage of a wave, the micaceous grains, which are an important constituent of the nearshore sands, remain suspended longer and are thus transported farther downslope than the rounded quartz grains. The net result of this differential suspension is the separation of the nearshore sands into two distinct zones: (1) a highly micaceous sand primarily confined within the canyon head, and (2) a shallower sand dominantly composed of quartz grains. This separation is important as it permits the recognition of possible source areas for sand found in deep-sea sediments. All of the sediment which the authors have found filling the canyon heads have been typified by their high mica content.

Analysis of 12 sand samples from the heads of Sumner and South branches (Fig. 24) shows that the micaceous sands are quite uniform in size but, probably due to bridging between platy grains, have porosities that range between 48.8 and 62.9 (average 50.1) per cent, and have wet densities between 1.63 and 1.87 (average 1.85) gm/cm³. This widespread difference in structural packing, as is pointed out in Chapter XV, greatly affects the strength characteristic of the sediment.

The canyon head is also a natural trap for marine plant detritus that is broken from its growth areas during periods of storm. The same currents that transport the micaceous sands also carry large amounts of plant detritus into the canyon heads. Here, it becomes intermixed with the sand and builds up in large haystack-like layers. Broken pieces of the giant brown algae *Macrocystis pyrifera*, *Egregia laevigala*, and the surf grass *Phyllospadix torreyi* are the main constituents of the organic part of the canyon fill. When compacted, successive layers of this organic material form a springy interwoven mat that binds together the individual layers of sand and silt, giving the entire sediment fill physical properties that are very different from those of its individual components. The intertwining of long strands of plant material, from one bed to another, develops structures that give the sedimentary body considerable internal strength. Because of this composite structure, the fill of any one tributary or branch, upon failure, tends to act as a single sediment body.

Recognition that plant detritus is an important part of the structure of the fill has led to a better understanding of the processes which bring about the periodic movement of sediment from canyon heads.

Scripps Canyon Beyond Scuba Diving Depths

As a result of the 1934 wire-line survey, it was strongly suspected that the outer portion of Scripps Canyon had cliffs with vertical walls, but this could not be established until we made our descents in the Diving Saucer. Now we know that vertical or overhanging walls exist all along the length of the canyon, with sheer cliffs up to at least 300 ft (90 m) in

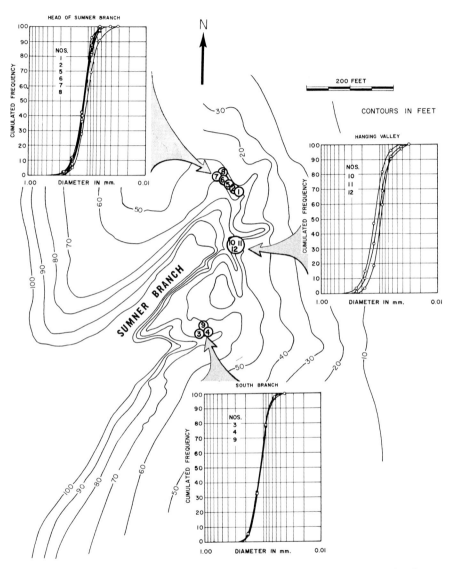

Fig. 24. Station locations and cumulative grain-size curves of micaceous fine-grained sands taken by divers from the head of Scripps Canyon between May 9 and 13, 1962. Station numbers also apply to other mass physical properties recorded in Table I.

height. Three descents down the axis of Sumner Branch showed that the floor has an alternation of rather gentle slopes and steep drop-offs. The steps are partly controlled by hard rock layers and partly by large boulders that have fallen from the walls, damming sediment behind them. Despite the evidence of active erosion described above, the marine processes have not brought the canyon floor to grade. Particularly steep descents were found at the lower end of Sumner Canyon where it joins North Branch as a hanging valley, similar to the hanging valley at the mouth of South Branch.

North Branch was found to have a more even slope but may steepen slightly near the juncture with Sumner Branch. A large number of boulders are incorporated in the floor sediment below the juncture with Sumner Branch.

In the main canyon, below the juncture of the heads, the gradient is considerably reduced, changing from an average of about 270 m/km in the tributaries to 80 m/km for the deeper part. The mouth of Scripps Canyon enters La Jolla Canyon with a constant slope rather than as a hanging valley. The walls of the outer part of Scripps Canyon are similar to those at its head, having many overhanging ledges. Organic growth virtually covers all such surfaces except near the contact with the fill. During the February 1964 Saucer dives, the sediment appeared to have been removed, leaving bare rock up to 3 ft (1 m) above the fill surface (Shepard *et al.*, 1964). In the areas devoid of sessile organisms, the walls are very smooth and show truncated pholad holes like those found in the canyon heads (Fig. 25). Thus, it appears that a similar type of erosion to that occurring in the steep heads (Dill, 1964b) is also taking place in the deeper areas where axial slopes are greatly reduced.

The floor of the outer Scripps Canyon has steps similar to those in its shoaler parts. Some of these are definitely due to rock outcrops, and the gentle parts between steps have a thick fill, much of it interbedded with large mats of balled-up surf grass. In several places, longitudinal trough-like depressions were observed within the grass mat, and in these a sand floor was seen to underlie the grass. The width of the floor varies from about 10 ft (3 m) to 60 ft (18 m), but at several places, the walls are so close that the 10 ft- (3 m-) wide Saucer could not get to the bottom. Although the axis runs in a fairly consistent direction, there are some rather marked bends. These are shown partly by the sounding lines and by the compass course followed by the Diving Saucer. The walls were found to be mostly conglomerate containing unsorted boulders up to about one foot in diameter. Sandstone and mudstone were also seen, and some of the

Fig. 25. Showing similarity between erosion features in the steep head and the gentler sloping intermediate part of Scripps Canyon.

a. Undercut and polished wall of a hanging tributary to Sumner Branch at a depth of 72 ft (22 m). Note that striations below truncated pholad holes are parallel with angle of repose of the sandy sediment. N.E.L. photo by Dill.

b. Floor and vertical wall of Scripps Canyon at a depth of 460 ft (140 m). Note smoothness of rock and truncated pholad borings. Photo from Diving Saucer by D. L. Inman.

undercut portions have developed where the softer sandstones and mudstones underlie the conglomerate.

LA JOLLA CANYON (Figs. 16 and 17)

The presence of a submarine valley just north of Pt. La Jolla was known to the founders of Scripps Institution in 1907 and called Soledad Drowned Valley, but later known as La Jolla Canyon. It differs considerably from Scripps Canyon in shape and the type of rocks outcropping on its walls. Inland, the coast is low and separated from the sea by a barrier beach. Until modified by man, a shallow lagoon extended along the coast for about one-half mile (Fig. 26). Farther inland, fans border the mesa approximately 300 ft (90 m) high along the back side of the lagoon, and several land valleys cut through the hills and fans. One of these, Hidden Valley, is essentially in line with La Jolla Canyon and runs along the north side of Mount Soledad, the highest point of land in the region, 822 ft (250 m). The mesa is part of a Pleistocene terrace that extends at least 12 miles inland and is topped by low beach or dune ridges. The north side of Mt. Soledad is fractured by a large fault that can be traced offshore, in places trending along the south wall of the canyon.

Thick peat deposits are found immediately behind the sand beach in the former lagoon (white areas in Fig. 26). These peat deposits continue offshore and are buried by only a thin layer of Recent sand and gravels (Robert Thompson, personal communication). Seaward of the beach, the bottom has a relatively flat slope out to a depth of approximately 40 ft (12 m). Here, the sharp drop-off into the canyon forms an almost vertical cliff up to 80 ft (24 m) high and forms the inner boundary between the wide bowl-like head and the sand-covered terrace surrounding the canyon. Several wide re-entrants in the head of the canyon form broad branches that extend to within 700 ft (214 m) of the beach. The branches are filled with fine-grained quartz sand which, during some periods of storm, is carried over the sharp edge of the canyon lip as sand falls.

Approximately 2,000 Indian mortars have been recovered from the terrace surrounding the canyon head. These and associated artifacts are believed to represent a submerged Indian camp site (Moriarty, 1964) and to be representative of a culture about 5,000 to 6,000 years old. The greatest deposit of artifact material has been recovered from deposits averaging 10 to 40 ft (3 to 12 m) below present sea level. Outcroppings of peat directly offshore and about 150 ft (45 m) from the beach have been dated by radiocarbon methods and found to have an age of $4,230 \pm 100$ years B.P. at a depth of 6.5 ft (2 m) below present sea level.

Similar lagoonal deposits outcrop in the walls of the canyon and are cut by its innermost branches. The stratigraphy of these exposed deposits shows the following depositional sequence (Fig. 27): (1) a fanglomerate was deposited, now exposed at depths of 50 to 150 ft (15 to 45 m) below present sea level; (2) as sea level rose, a sand beach formed and created an offshore bar on top of the submerged alluvium; (3) this zone moved shoreward as a transgressive deposit; (4) inside the bar in the still-water lagoon, a fine-grained silty clay deposit with abundant reeds and large pieces of driftwood was laid down; and

Fig. 26. The unmodified lagoon shoreward of La Jolla Submarine Canyon as it appeared in 1930.

Fig. 27. The stratigraphy exposed in the wall of La Jolla Submarine Canyon at the site of a Carbon-14 date (C). A and B represent possible environments during rise of sea level, and C present-day conditions.

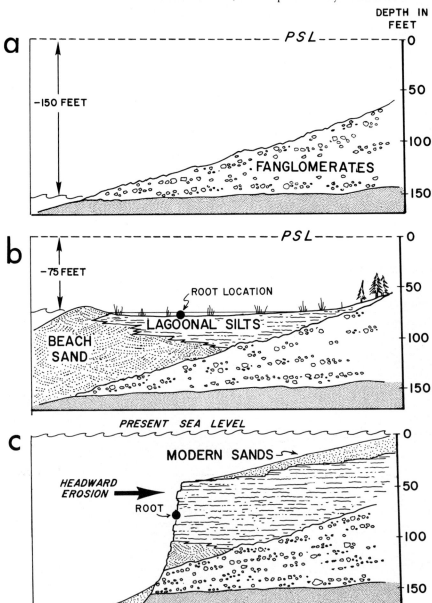

(5) continued rise in sea level covered the lagoonal deposits with the prograding deposit of marine offshore sands. This entire sequence is now cut by the headward erosion of La Jolla Canyon.

The junior author found a root of a small tree in place at a depth of 75 ft (23 m) (Fig. 28). The root was completely enclosed in a 4-inch thick clay layer belonging to the lagoonal sequence (see Fig. 27). Dated by radiocarbon methods, it was found to have an age of 8,270 ± 500 years B.P. The canyon head extends locally for 780 ft (238 m) shoreward of the root site. The canyon head must have been eroded at least this amount in the period since deposition of the clay surrounding the root. Erosion by submarine processes is necessary because there is a continuous sequence of lagoonal sediments above the location of the root and no evidence of a lowering of sea level since the deposition of the clay surrounding the root (Dill, in press, a). Therefore, evidence exists that the headward erosion of La Jolla Canyon has been at a minimum rate of one inch per year. The root

Fig. 28. A root (arrow), exposed by erosion, having a Carbon-14 dated age of 8,250±500 years B.P. Depth is 75 ft (23 m) in La Jolla Canyon head. N.E.L. photo by Dill.

site is on a steep cliff that extends down to 120 ft (37 m). It thus appears that there has been considerable downward as well as head-ward submarine erosion of the canyon head. Soundings made in 1965 compared to those of 1950 indicate that locally there is an even faster retreat of the submarine cliff at the canyon head (over 2 ft per year).

Beyond the alluvial head wall of La Jolla Canyon, there is a decrease in the gradient and the valley floor widens to almost 1,000 ft (300 m). Three Saucer dives were made within three months down the inner canyon in this area. In November, 1964, the junior author observed bedrock on the canyon floor. This resembled the Cretaceous sand-stones and shales of Point La Jolla. In December, 1964, D. L. Inman found the same floor covered with a thick deposit of surf grass and kelp. This organic mat had a wavy surface and completely covered any canyon floor sediment. The senior author, diving in February, 1965, found no rock and very little organic cover; the floor consisted of relatively smooth sand with some fine material intermixed. In addition, the February dive, at depths between 200 and 425 ft (60 to 130 m), showed a series of small terraces with intervening drops of a meter or less. The slopes between drops were all covered with sedi-ment, with no rock structure exposed. These terraces were not reported from the earlier dives. They are interpreted as slump scars.

At a depth of approximately 330 ft (100 m), some 2,000 ft (610 m) from the canyon head, the channel narrows considerably and steep rock walls are encountered on both sides. From here down to 1060 ft (323 m), the outer limit of the Saucer observations, there is a continu-ous rock gorge. In most places the rock was found to be covered with organisms right down to the contact with the sediment-covered floor. Commonly, the sediment slopes away from the rock contact, and small fans were found at the entrance to gullies that cut the walls. During the February, 1965, dive, the floor slopes were quite even between depths of 425 ft (130 m) and 850 ft (260 m), but a dive made in February, 1964, beginning at 660 ft (200 m), a number of steps were seen in the floor with drops of about 10 ft (3 m). Some of these showed boulders at the lip but others had slopes entirely covered with sediment.

Many places were observed where large boulders had fallen from the walls onto the floor. These apparently are concentrated in certain zones, as at about 720 ft (220 m) on the south side, and on both sides beyond the 920 ft (280 m) juncture with Scripps Canyon. The rocks have rolled well out onto the floor in many places and locally form barriers across the floor with sediment piled up behind them. In many places, small depressions could be seen around the boulders.

The currents in La Jolla Canyon, observed during the Saucer dives, were quite variable. During one dive they changed several times from up- to downcanyon in direction. In another dive the bottom velocity increased within one minute from no current to 0.45 knots at a depth of 460 ft (140 m). Maximum velocities were sufficient to move the fine sand on the bottom and on two occasions formed ripple marks of low relief. Where bottom slopes exceeded 5°, these same ripples were later destroyed as the current slowed and planed off the crests.

A sample obtained from the Saucer dive in February, 1965, at a depth of 755 ft (230 m), showed coarse sand in contrast to the fine sand upcanyon. Beyond the limits of Saucer dives, the rock walls are known to continue to depths of approximately 1,800 ft (550 m). Along this part of the axis, box cores retrieved sand covered with a thin layer of mud. The bottom of one core had gravel and small angular rock fragments.

Tributaries are scarce in the canyon walls, although one small one comes in on the north with a trend that points roughly to the Sorrento Valley, 4 miles north of La Jolla. The course of the canyon becomes more winding at a depth of 1,260 ft (380 m) and changes from northwest to approximately west. Buffington (1964) attributes the bends in the outer canyon and fan-valley to displacement along faults, showing that the bends could fit a pattern of faults extended from the nearby land.

LA JOLLA FAN-VALLEY (Fig. 17)

The La Jolla Fan-valley is far better known than any other in the world. The electronic positioning used by Buffington (1964) in the surveys of most of the valley provides an unusually good base map. Cores from this valley were described by Ludwick (1950), Shepard and Einsele (1962), and box cores by Bouma and Shepard (1964). In 1965, another series of box cores was obtained by the authors that gives a much better coverage of the channel and the levees of the fan-valley (von Rad et al., 1965). Additionally, the La Jolla Fan-valley has been the locus of 8 dives in the bathyscaphs *Trieste I* and *II*. (see Table 1 for details and Fig. 17).

At longitude 117°23' the character of the fan-valley changes rather abruptly. For the next three miles to the west there is quite clearly a

relatively straight large valley about 0.6 miles across with an intrenched smaller channel that winds from side to side of the larger.
This is better shown on the 5-fathom contour intervals used in
Buffington's (1964) map. The valley changes in two other respects.
First, the walls, judging from dredgings and observations from the
bathyscaph, are made of a semi-consolidated clay, rather than hard
rock that forms the canyon walls shoreward. Second, we see above the
walls of the valley the first appearance of what are usually referred to
as natural levees, that is, marginal embankments rising slightly above
the average level of the sea floor bordering the canyon. These levees
are almost continuous on the north wall but rather intermittent on the
south wall. The depth of the valley floor below its surroundings
decreases from more than 1,000 ft (300 m) to about 250 ft (75 m).
Accordingly, we are calling this outer portion a fan-valley, indicating
that it is cut through a fan of sediment that has formed outside the
submarine canyon and outside the rocky slope off La Jolla. Beyond
the three miles of the westerly trending wide outer valley, the fan-
valley changes character again. The main trend changes to southwest
and continues for about 11 miles to where the incised inner valley
disappears. The valley has a moderately winding course with one very
twisting section near the axial depth of 2,650 ft (810 m), and then
again a twisting section in the outer part from axial depths of 3,000 ft
(910 m) to 3,300 ft (1,000 m). Beyond this point, the sounding lines
are not well located or closely spaced. Present data show that the
valley decreases in depth below its surroundings to negligible
amounts, and finally merges with the floor of San Diego Trough at a
depth of about 3,600 ft (1,100 m).

The Channel

A typical profile of the La Jolla Fan-valley (Fig. 29) shows four
features: levees, walls, one or more terraces, and the channel at the
bottom. Since the channel has been the most investigated, it will be
discussed first. Some echo-sounding profiles indicate that the inner
channel may be very narrow, but the bathyscaph dives have all shown
that the floor is wider than found in the rock-walled inner canyon,
perhaps averaging 100 ft (30 m). The floor is generally flat with a
downvalley slope ranging from almost zero to about 10°, and averaging 14 m/km for the 18 miles between axial depths of 1,800 ft and
3,300 ft (550 and 1,000 m). Locally, the smooth mud-covered floor is
broken by a series of steps that range in size from small cracks (Fig.

30) up to 4 to 6 ft (1.2 to 1.9 m) in height. These steps are evidently due to slumping and are like those found higher up in the canyon. This was shown by occasional slump scars with vertical faces and by the curving trend of the scarps. Some of the slump scars did not extend across the channel.

The sediment on the channel floor is usually a thin layer of soft mud at the surface, but this is underlain almost everywhere by a relatively clean sand of varying texture. The sand has been found in numerous cores and especially in the box cores. On several occasions,

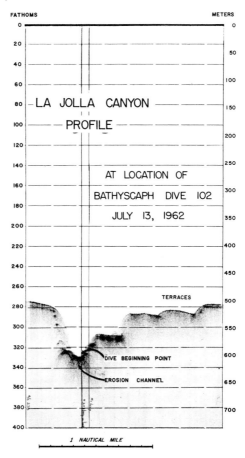

Fig. 29. A typical echo-sounder profile across the La Jolla Fan-valley. (Scale is 400 fathoms from top of chart to bottom.)

Fig. 30. Small slump scars in the fill of La Jolla Fan-
valley at a depth of about 2,200 ft (670 m). Taken
during dive no. 7 in *Trieste II*. N.E.L. photo by authors.

Fig. 31. X-ray photo by A. H. Bouma of slice from
box core taken in axis of La Jolla Fan-valley in 3,370 ft
(1,027 m). Note cross-bedding and ripple marks (22),
laminations (23), clay lumps (27), and cracks in slice
(2). Arrow shows downcanyon direction.

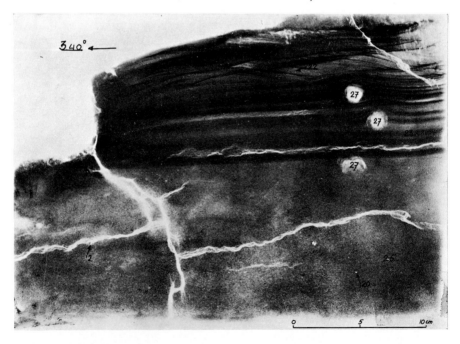

the bathyscaph scraped through the thin mud cover, exposing the underlying sand. The cores show that the sands may be thin layers alternating with silty clays, or may have a thickness of up to 25 cm of continuous sand. Rarely, the sand contains pieces of gravel. X-ray photographs of slices of the box cores (Fig. 31) show local cross-bedding with the foreset beds sloping downvalley (Bouma and Shepard, 1964). In some places, the box cores indicate that there is no mud or sand cover. An apparently undisturbed sand with evidences of organism tracks was seen in a core from a depth of 3,140 ft (960 m). In two localities at depths of 2,592 and 3,258 ft (790 and 993 m) a thin mud covering was found to overlie a hard clay with no intervening sand layer.

During one dive, the bathyscaph hit bottom while traveling at a speed of 0.5 kn, creating a shock wave that could be seen advancing along the surface of the sediment for at least 10 ft (3 m). The underlying sandy sediment must have been in a quasi-plastic state to propagate such a wave, a condition probably resulting from loose packing.

At a depth of 2,000 ft (610 m) in the channel, the junior author observed several rounded boulders up to 3 ft (0.9 m) in diameter (Fig. 32). These boulders were located on the north side of the channel away from the steep slope on the south side. They were associated with pieces of small gravel and mats of decomposing kelp fronds and other organic debris. When the bathyscaph hit one of these boulders it proved to be hard enough to scratch off the paint, as could be seen upon surfacing. Probably the boulders were of hard rock, in contrast to the clayey nodules and blocks of semi-consolidated clay which are known to fall into the channel from the valley walls (Moore, 1965). Some boulders were resting on the sediments and the others partly buried in the fill.

Currents were measured from the bathyscaph on a number of occasions (Table 2). The direction of flow is not constant and pulsates either up or down the valley with a maximum recorded velocity of 0.2 kn. The general appearance of the channel floor indicated that currents were not strong enough to produce scour marks around man-made objects, such as oil drums, which were seen on the bottom. However, the places where the bottom has no mud cover probably have been recently subjected to appreciable bottom currents. Of course, the sand layers and the cross-bedding found in box cores are also an indication that relatively strong currents (up to 0.5 kn) must operate here from time to time. Since the boulders are resting on or in

Table 2. Average velocity of bottom current in La Jolla and Coronado[1] Fan-Valleys (from visual measurements from the bathyscaph).

Dive No.	Date	Time	Depth (ft)	Trend of Canyon Axis (from Buffington 1964) (sloping towards)	Current Direction (flowing towards)	Velocity (kts)	Velocity (cm/sec)
La Jolla Fan-Valley							
83	10/13/61	1047	1920	270°	280°	0.03	1.5
		1314					
91	3/21/62	0856	1920	270°	260°	0.19	9.8
		1252					
93	4/4/62	1107	1920	270°	090°	0.07	3.6
		1523				0.05	2.6
						0.20	10.3
						0.04	2.1
						0.07	3.6
102	7/13/62	0930	1970	270°	no bottom current		
		1000		270°	070°	0.06	3.1
		1008		270°	070°	0.07	3.6
		1044		270°	045°	0.10	5.1
104	7/27/62	0830	2250	295°	050°	0.20	10.3
		1201					
Coronado Fan-Valley*							
105	8/3/62	0852	3552	220°	310°	0.07	3.6
		1237	3552	220°	200°	0.07	3.6

[1]See Chapter IV

mud sediments that contain matted sea grass, they clearly were not transported into the channel by strong currents, and their origin remains somewhat of an enigma.

Valley Walls

The most surprising thing about the walls along the La Jolla Fan-valley is their steepness. Dill (1961) and Buffington (1964) observed slopes of 75° to 80°, and other investigators have found inclinations almost as great. The very steep slopes are usually on the outside of a bend and the inside of bends have far gentler inclines, generally interrupted by terraces. Slopes observed on several occasions by the junior author and one of the steep slopes encountered by Moore (1965) had horizontal outcropping layers of compact cohesive clay alternating with cohesionless silt. The organisms, such as crabs, on the slope were undermining the hard clay layers, and a block was seen which had rolled down the slope and slid out over the channel floor. There can be little doubt but what these steep slopes represent recent erosion, despite the evidence that no strong currents are now operating on most of the floor.

Dredging of the walls has failed to find any thoroughly consolidated rocks. Most of the dredge hauls consisted of blocks of relatively hard clay. In some cases, the edges of the blocks had orange-brown colors indicative of weathering, and calcareous worm tubes were attached to them, suggesting that they had been exposed on the slope for a long time.

The foraminifera from some of the blocks of clay were examined. Frances L. Parker reports that the benthic foraminifera are similar to those in Recent sediments of the same depth, but they may contain a fauna of planktonic organisms which represent a cooler climate than now exists. Thus, these deposits may have been formed during the glacial stages of the Pleistocene.

Terraces

The transverse profiles in this, as in other fan-valleys, show terraces. Virtually all of these, and certainly all of the wider terraces, are found

Fig. 32. Rounded rock boulders found at a depth of 1,920 ft (585 m) during a bathyscaph dive in La Jolla Fan-valley. N.E.L. photo by Dill.

on the inside of curves. At first it was thought that the terraces represented partial fill of the fan-valley, followed by rejuvenation. If this were the case, there should be some sections showing matching terraces on the two sides, but this has never been found despite numerous close-spaced profiles. Furthermore, the profiles show that the terraces change radically in short distances downvalley (Fig. 33). Some of the terraces quite clearly slope in toward the valley walls. Also, the terraces occur at all levels, from near the upper rim to near the channel floor. Therefore, there is no indication from the available data that the terraces are the result of rejuvenation of erosion and entrenchment of an old valley fill. Terraces could also be the result of slump, similar to the terraces found on the sides of many land valleys.

Only a few cores have been taken on the terraces. With one exception, these consist of mud without any sand layers. The exception, at a depth of 3,060 ft (933 m) on the northwest wall opposite an axial depth of 3,200 ft (975 m) was the only relatively long core from the terrace. It had two clean sand layers in its 6 ft (1.83 m) length. Both layers extended across the 6 inch (15 cm) diameter of this long box core. It appears that mud forms a thick layer over the floor of most terraces. The observations from the bathyscaph show this mud is being churned up by organisms to a depth of at least 6 inches (15 cm) and numerous mounds were seen on the terrace surface.

The margins of the terraces were seen to have slump scars, and on one dive made by the authors, small down-dropped blocks were seen on the bordering channel floor, which might suggest pressure ridges. Clearly, the margins of the terraces are unstable.

Natural Levees

The rim of the fan-valley has well-developed levees (first referred to by Buffington, 1952) at the top of the northwest wall and discontinuous levees on the southeast wall. The levees vary in shape from broad, gentle slopes to very narrow ridges. The top of the levees apparently slopes quite continuously in a downvalley direction. In some places, there appear to be at least two levees on the same side roughly parallel to each other.

Cores were taken in many places on the crest of the levees. These cores are largely mud from top to bottom, but four of them contain thin sand layers. All of the sand is fine-grained and most of it is relatively clean; several layers of sand were found in one core. The

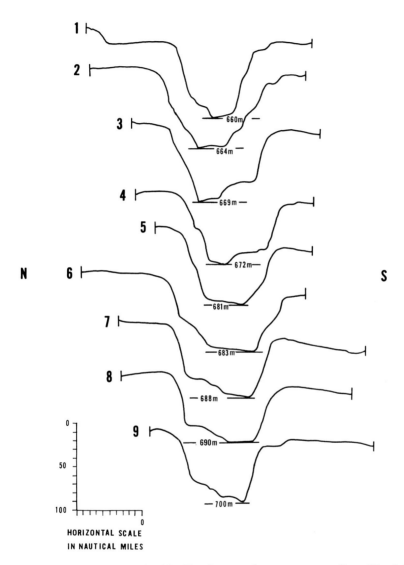

Fig. 33. Closely spaced transverse profiles of La Jolla Fan-valley showing changes in terraces. Terraces are usually on gentle slope on inside of a bend. Taken from fathograms on *Horizon*.

examination of the sand showed that it is largely terrigeneous like that of the channel floor.

Summary Concerning La Jolla Fan-valley

The extensive studies of the fan-valley, which extends seaward of La Jolla Canyon, show that it is a locus of important present-day erosion and deposition. The channel at the bottom of the valley has fill that is predominantly sand interlayered with mud. The precipitous walls on the outside of the bends are clearly erosional. Sand of varying degrees of coarseness found just under a thin mud cover, or actually at the surface, indicates appreciable current activity. Because many of the foraminifera in the sand layers have proven to be of shallow water origin (Shepard and Einsele, 1962), it appears that sand has been carried down from the shallow head of the canyon. Whether turbidity currents have introduced this sand or some other transporting agent has been involved, is discussed in Chapter XVI. Whatever the cause, currents appear to be capable of rising above the valley floor and depositing sand on the high levees. However, the usual thick mud blanketing the terraces and most of the levees suggests that the occasions when sand is carried well above the channel are rare and at least have not taken place between 1934 and 1965, a period when sands are actually known to have moved downslope repeatedly from the canyon head. The terraces have characteristics that are much more indicative of slump origin than of either rejuvenation of old valley fills or of lateral cutting during a stage of excavation of the valleys.

CHAPTER IV

OTHER UNITED STATES WEST COAST CANYONS

I N ADDITION TO the detailed investigations of canyons lying off La Jolla, there have been many investigations of other canyons along the West Coast of the United States. Because of its proximity to San Diego, Coronado Canyon has been given much attention by Scripps Institution and the Navy Electronics Laboratory. Scientists from the University of Southern California are studying canyons offshore from the Los Angeles area, and Monterey and associated canyons have been sampled and surveyed by all of these institutions. Other canyons are known largely from the soundings made by the U.S. Coast and Geodetic Survey, but a description of many of them seems warranted as they show topographic features that may give insight into the investigations of canyons in general. A few of the sea valleys that have been called canyons are not discussed in this chapter, because they do not fit the definition as used in this book.

CORONADO CANYON AND LOMA SEA VALLEY (Fig. 34)

The southernmost canyon off the West Coast of the United States is located directly off the International boundary, just north of a series

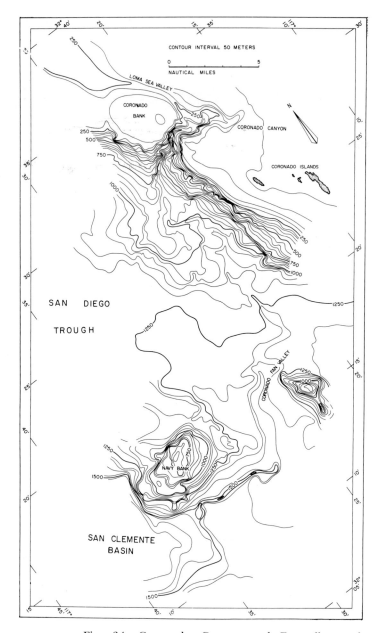

Fig. 34. Coronado Canyon and Fan-valley and Loma Sea Valley. Note the possible extension of Coronado Canyon across a ridge pirating a formerly north-draining Loma Sea Valley. The high ridge west of the inner part of the fan-valley has a rock core but otherwise resembles a natural levee. The basin depressions along the outer fan-valley are not well established. From surveys by Shepard supplemented by Coast and Geodetic Survey soundings.

of small islands. The head of Coronado Canyon is separated from the coast by a broad shelf that is known to be covered by old beach deposits (Emery *et al.,* 1952). The closest land river is the Tijuana River, but there is no assurance that it has been connected with the canyon head in the past. Sono-probe sub-bottom profiles run shoreward of the head were inconclusive, but did not show any well-developed buried channel (D. G. Moore, personal communication). The head of the canyon has a depth of 240 ft (73 m), 7 miles from the coast. Seaward, the main channel has a winding course for the first 3 miles to the point where it is joined by a branch of the Loma Sea Valley entering from the north at a depth of 1,260 ft (384 m). The main part of Loma Sea Valley extends northward along the east side of Coronado Bank and is somewhat unique in that its axis has a drainage divide. Four miles to the north of the juncture, the slope is to the north, a reversal of its southern trend into Coronado Canyon. The northern slope continues down to where the valley turns to the west and enters San Diego Trough. Although continous reflection profiling shows that Loma Sea Valley is filled with a thick deposit of sediment, one dredge haul along the axis and one box core taken in the axis have brought up well-rounded gravel up to an inch in diameter. Bathyscaph dives in this area confirm the coarse nature of bottom sediments, and bottom currents up to 0.5 knots were reported (A. Rechnitzer, personal communication).

Beyond the juncture with Loma Sea Valley, Coronado Canyon continues seaward along the south side of Coronado Bank in a fairly straight line for a distance of about 3 miles. D. G. Moore, in the Diving Saucer, descended the north wall to a depth of 1,000 ft (305 m) and reported that it is predominantly sediment covered and does not have abundant rock outcrops, as do the canyons farther north. However, rock of indeterminate age has been dredged from both walls. The profile of the canyon is narrow and has steep walls. The width of the floor is not known, because no bathyscaph dives have been made to the floor in this part of the canyon. Cores show either an entire length of silty-clay or alternating silty-clay and thin sand layers. The bottom gradient here is approximately 100 m/km.

Some resemblance to the water gaps in land valleys is shown where the rock-walled Coronado gorge cuts through the structural ridge, a continuation of Coronado Bank and the Coronado Islands to the south. It appears that the canyon head had eroded shoreward across the ridge, reversing the slope and pirating sediment that had formerly been filling a continuously sloping Loma Sea Valley.

The large number of hagfish trapped in this area by Scripps Institution scientist Dr. David Jensen is illustrative of the abundance of fish along the canyon. Over 24,000 have been taken for studies of an extract made from this primitive fish with three hearts.

Coronado Fan-valley

Beyond the upper gorge, the valley bends sharply to the south and its character changes completely. The outer part is tentatively included in the fan-valley category, although it is difficult to say for certain where the canyon stops and the fan-valley begins. For the next 10 miles, the valley extends south in a somewhat winding course that lies in part along the base of the escarpment west of the Coronado Islands. The gradient decreases to about 20 m/km, and the west side of the valley consists of a ridge about 400 ft (120 m) high to the north, but decreasing in height to the south until it disappears in San Diego Trough. This ridge, because of its flat curving top, was originally interpreted as an old delta (Emery *et al.,* 1952). Alternatively, it could be interpreted as a natural levee. The top of the ridge is very hummocky, and the sounding profiles suggest that there has been extensive slumping of an unconsolidated mass of sediment. Cores along the top show either alternating sand and silty-clay or entirely mud. The sand, as in the levees of the La Jolla Fan-valley, is terrigenous. Dredging along the base of the ridge on the east side yielded some relatively soft rock. Also, a continuous reflection profile across the ridge showed what appeared to be a rock core within the ridge (J. R. Curray and D. G. Moore, personal communication). Therefore, this may be a rock ridge with some sediment from Coronado Canyon built up on top of it.

The channel of the fan-valley, at a depth of 3,480 ft (1,060 m), has been visited by the bathyscaph *Trieste I* in a dive made by the junior author. A flat floor was seen sloping gently to the south. Many organisms were churning the cohesive clayey sediment on the bottom (Fig. 35). Large amounts of man-made debris lay partly buried, with no indication of scour or other signs of active currents. Side slopes as high as 25° were measured near the comparatively flat-bottomed axis. The channel was approximately 100 ft (30 m) across and had a sinuous trend.

Cores taken on the floor in this section of the valley at a depth of about 3,400 ft (1,040 m) were much sandier than those from the Coronado Canyon. One badly disturbed core 360 cm below the surface had coarse terrigenous sand and fine gravel. Another core had course calcareous sand and gravel that increased in size downward (Shepard and Einsele, 1962). The sand in both cores differs from that found on the shelf off the Coronado Islands and is much coarser than the thin sand layers from the Coronado Canyon floor. Source of this sand is uncertain.

Farther out, the valley winds to the southwest across the relatively flat floor of the southern end of San Diego Trough, with a channel incised about 300 ft (90 m). There are low natural levees along most of this part of the valley, but beyond this the valley is more deeply entrenched, forming another gorge along the south side of Navy Bank.[1]

[1]So named because of the difficulty of working in the area, due to almost continuous U.S. Navy operations. On one trip, an important sounding line was run between a destroyer and the practice target upon which it was firing. The salvos of live shells sailing over the survey ship made one wonder if this part of the channel was really important.

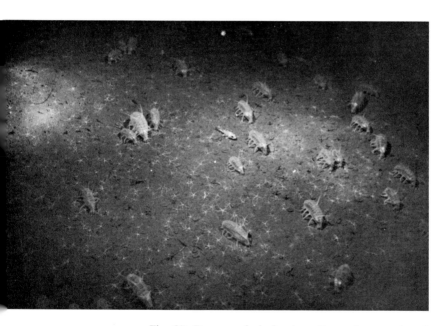

Fig. 35. Deep-sea holothurians (Scotoplanes, sp) and brittle stars (Ophimuseum lymoni) reworking the sediment in Coronado Fan-valley. Photo was taken from the bathyscaph *Trieste I* at a depth of 3,480 ft (1,060 m). N.E.L. photo by Dill.

Echo-sounding profiles across this steep gorge are hard to interpret because of its narrow width and steep sides. Judging from the inverted cone on the echogram, the bottom is about 600 ft (180 m) below the rather flat sea floor on the south side of the channel. John Beagles, in a 4,350-ft (1,325-m) bathyscaph dive, observed nearly vertical slopes cut into what appeared to be a compacted sediment along the southern wall of the channel near a sharp turn from a southerly to a westerly direction.

The outer part of the narrow gorge may continue on into San Clemente Basin, but the soundings do not locate the channel precisely. Small basin depressions may also exist in this part of the channel. Continuous reflection profiling shows that the basin has received sediment channeled down the valley (Moore, 1965b).

REDONDO CANYON (Fig. 36)

Aside from the maps and brief discussion by Davidson (1897), Redondo Canyon, off the southern end of Santa Monica Bay in southern California, was first mentioned by Ritter (1902). He reported the dredging of shallow-water shells, fresh-water species, and driftwood in the bottom of the canyon well out from shore. Many years later, the senior author sampled the canyon (Shepard and Macdonald, 1938), and more recently various studies have been made there by Emery (1960, p. 46), Emery and Hülsemann (1963), and other members of the Hancock Foundation. Poland et al. (1948) showed the relation of the canyon head to the coastal geology. Crowell (1952) discussed this canyon, referring particularly to the apparent absence of any old or modern river valley at its head.[2] He also states that it cuts Pleistocene and Recent formations, and points out the proximity of the canyon to the headland at the Palos Verdes Hills.

In 1935, the city engineer at Redondo Beach surveyed the canyon head prior to the construction of a jetty for a harbor directly to the north. This survey showed a bowl-shaped, sandy-floored trough about 1,500 ft (460 m) across, descending with a 120 m/km grade into a narrower but flat-floored trough some 800 ft (240 m) across. This outer trough has walls apparently composed of soft sediment, sloping up to 17°. Farther out, the floor narrows to a V-shape and the gradient gradually decreases to about 20 m/km. The walls steepen

---

[2]Emery (1960, p. 43), on the other hand, claims that wells show a filled extension on land inside the head of Redondo Canyon.

and rock crops out in some places. Thus, the name *submarine canyon* is applicable.

Redondo Canyon extends in a west-southwesterly direction with a winding course. Two miles from its head, at a depth of about 780 ft (240 m), it is joined from the north by a broad trough-like tributary. This tributary is notable as a locus for oil seepages. Blobs of oil frequently rise to the surface, and when they drift ashore form tar deposits on the beach.

The canyon can be traced for about 8 miles across the narrow continental terrace in a curving line. Beyond this, it bends sharply to

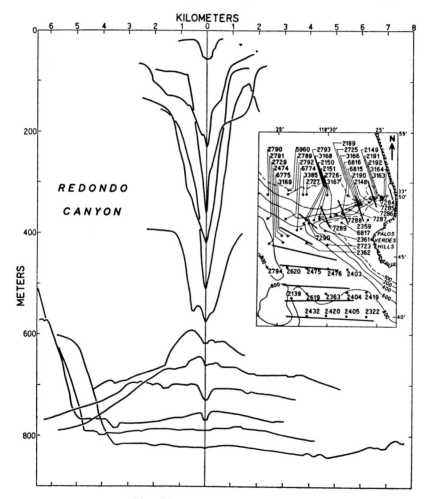

Fig. 36. Submarine canyon off Redondo, southern California, with fan-valley on outside. From Emery and Hülsemann (1963).

the south, like Coronado and La Jolla canyons. At this bend, the V-shaped canyon terminates at a depth of about 1,920 ft (590 m). Beyond this point, a fan-valley can be traced for a few miles down the inshore side of the fan. This fan was first interpreted as a drowned delta (Shepard and Emery, 1941, p. 64), but it is actually intermediate between the large ridge feature of the west side of Coronado Canyon below the gorge and the fan outside La Jolla Canyon.

The walls of Redondo Canyon appear to be less precipitous than those of Coronado, La Jolla, and Scripps canyons. This may be due to rather soft Miocene formations through which it is cut. The canyon is somewhat wider than the previously discussed canyons, but some V-shape sounding profiles have been obtained (Fig. 36). As in many other submarine canyons, cores from the axis have sand layers with a small quantity of gravel.

Depth changes at the head of Redondo Canyon have been known to occur since 1933, when the city engineer at Redondo Beach discovered that the water at the end of the pier, directly inside the canyon, was becoming too shallow for boat launching. Shortly after this, a sudden deepening occurred, increasing the depth by 25 ft (8 m) and almost wrecking the pier. Fill then shoaled the water until in the winter of 1936-1937 when another sudden deepening took place.[3] Beginning in the 1950s, the U.S. Army Engineers have been making profiles of the area because of the excessive erosion next to the newly created small boat harbor at Redondo. Their soundings show small depth changes in Redondo Canyon, like those off La Jolla.

DUME CANYON (Fig. 37)

Following the coast north and west of Redondo, the next canyon to extend in close to the shore is found along the west side of Point Dume. This was first studied by Shepard and Macdonald (Shepard and Emery, 1941), later by Emery (1960, p. 47), and recently by David Drake (unpublished manuscript). It does not penetrate inside the 50-foot (15 m) contour, but where it borders along Point Dume it comes within 1,800 ft (550 m) of the shore. The topographic map of the coast suggests that this canyon is located off Zuma Canyon in the Santa Monica Mountains.

Dume Canyon differs from the others already considered in that it

---

[3]Fishermen at the pier end found they had to keep paying out more line during the deepening, indicating a slow but continuous removal of sedimentary fill.

has, at least on the east side, basic igneous rock like the trachyte at
Point Dume. The canyon wall is almost vertical on this side, but on the
other side where sedimentary rock of Miocene age is found, the slope
is not over 30°. Wall steepness in general is quite comparable to that of
Zuma Canyon.

Dume Canyon extends seaward for only 3 miles, terminating in a
fan at a depth of about 1,860 ft (570 m). Beyond, there is a fan-valley

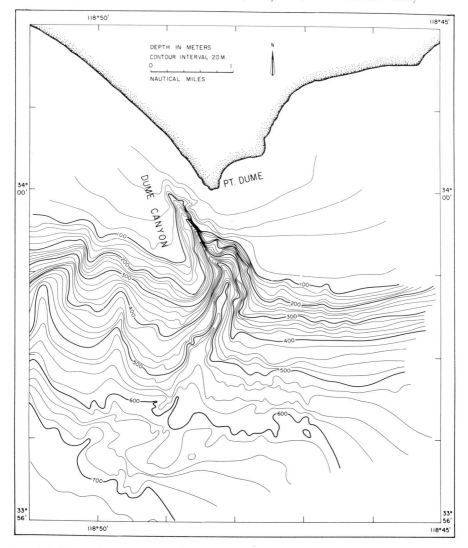

Fig. 37. Dume Canyon, west of Santa Monica, California. Absence of tributaries thought to be due to
lack of longitudinal sounding lines along the walls.
From unpublished soundings, U.S. Coast and Geodetic Survey.

that can be traced out to approximately 2,400 ft (730 m). This fan-valley, like the others, has natural levees. However, unlike La Jolla, Redondo, and Coronado fan-valleys, Dume bends to the right instead of to the left. This is a continuation of the right bend in the inner canyon. So far as known, only very small tributaries enter this short canyon, but many marine valleys exist in the slope farther west. It seems probable that more detailed soundings would show more tributaries on the sides of Dume Canyon.

MUGU CANYON

Just west of Point Mugu, a submarine canyon heads at the coast off the east side of the Santa Clara River Delta (Fig. 38). It was first studied by Shepard and Emery (1941), then by Inman (1950). In 1965, a Saucer dive was made by André Rosfelder in the north branch in depths between 295 and 440 ft (90 and 135 m). Since a somewhat similar valley off nearby Port Hueneme is discussed as a slope valley (see p. 248), reasons will be given for placing the Mugu Valley in the canyon category, although, admittedly, the difference is slight. Mugu Canyon has V-shaped transverse profiles with steep walls (vertical in places). Several tributaries enter the canyon. Dredging and Saucer dives have shown that there are rock outcrops on both sides of the canyon and on the ridges and hill in the canyon center. However, Dill and others, scuba-diving for various oil companies, failed to find rock outcrops in depths down to 150 ft (45 m).

Mugu Canyon has two branches, both extending into the offshore slope of the beach. The steep sandy walls and floor have many slump scars. The two trough-shaped sand bowls at the head have an axial gradient of about 250 m/km. Divers have measured side slopes in the sand up to 30°. These bowls narrow into V-shaped canyons at depths of about 120 ft (35 m), and the gradient of the axis decreases gradually to about 30 m/km at a depth of 1,800 ft (550 m). Beyond the juncture of the two heads, at a depth of 300 ft (90 m), the canyon winds seaward in a truly meandering course, with two more tributaries entering on the east side. The valley terminates in a fan at the margin of Santa Monica Basin in a depth of about 2,400 ft (730 m). No details are available of the outer terminus, but the canyon has a total length of about 8 miles.

Studies by Inman (1950) paid special attention to the sediments of the canyon as related to the adjacent beach sands and shelf sediments. He found that the canyon samples are more poorly sorted and have

Fig. 38. Mugu Canyon, located at the east side of
Santa Clara Delta, California. Note the meandering
course. The canyon extends to slightly greater depth
than shown here, but outer part is not as well
surveyed. From unpublished soundings of Coast and
Geodetic Survey.

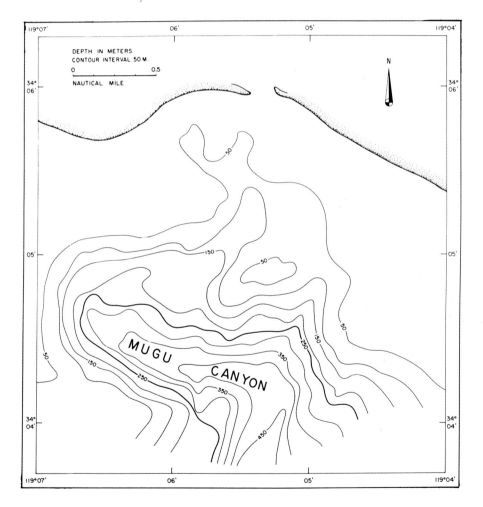

more negative skewness than those of the beach and open shelf. The median diameters, as in other canyons, show no relation to depth of water. Most cores in the canyon showed sediment coarsening with depth below the bottom.

A. Rosfelder (personal communication) states that the north wall has steep to vertical slopes cut in mudstone that overlies steeply dipping hard rock. The canyon floor has a fine silt fill that forms a plastic paste with little evidence of burrowing organisms but with numerous animal tracks. A series of steps, 1 to 5 ft (0.3 to 1.6 m) high and separated by intervals of 15 to 70 ft (5 to 20 m), extend approximately perpendicular to the axis of the canyon. These suggest the slump steps of the La Jolla canyons, described previously. Rounded cobbles of claystone were incorporated in the fill. According to Rosfelder, the entire sedimentary fill appeared to be creeping down-canyon like a glacier.

SUR-PARTINGTON CANYON (Fig. 1)

South of Point Sur, several canyons extend towards the straight California coast. Of these, Sur Canyon is the most interesting, because of its major tributary, Partington Canyon, which has a head running parallel to the mountainous coast for about one mile. At one place, the water is 500 ft (150 m) deep within 0.2 mile from the shore. Farther south, two other heads also come to within about a mile of the shore. Sur Canyon starts 3 miles south of Point Sur at a depth of 300 ft (90 m), and is joined by the large southern tributary 9 miles down the axis at a depth of 4,800 ft (1,460 m). Beyond the juncture, the canyon can be traced seaward for 28 miles to a depth of 10,200 ft (3,120 m) where it enters a fan-valley with natural levees. Including the Partington branch, it has a total length of 49 miles. At least in the inner part, there is a maze of dendritic tributaries, quite like the land canyons in the area. The axis follows a twisting course along its entire length. All tributaries have steeper gradients at the head than farther down. Omitting the portion of the head that follows the coast, the average gradient is 34 m/km. Partington Canyon drops 3,000 ft (915 m) in 8 miles, whereas on land, Partington Creek has the same fall in 2.5 miles.

So far as can be told from the soundings, at no point does the canyon have walls more than about 2,000 ft (610 m) high. No oceanographic exploration of the canyon has been made, but rock bottom is indicated by survey notations on the wall near the canyon head.

MONTEREY CANYON (Fig. 39)

The deepest and largest submarine canyon along the west coast of the United States heads at the center of Monterey Bay. This canyon lies directly off Elkhorn Slough, at the north end of a broad lowland formed at the juncture of the Salinas and Pajaro valleys. This canyon and its fan-valley have been extensively investigated (Shepard and Emery, 1941; Dill *et al.*, 1954; Menard, 1960; Martin, 1964). The most recent investigations were by the senior author in 1964. Data from the canyon has been used as a basis for several hypotheses of canyon origin (see particularly Davis, 1934; Woodford, 1951; Kuenen, 1953).

The head of Monterey Canyon (Fig. 40) was well sounded by both the U.S. Coast and Geodetic Survey and the U.S. Army Engineers. Also, several geologists have made dives into the head with both standard hard hat and scuba. There are three branches at the head. The northern branch heads directly off the jetties that lead into the artificial harbor north of Moss Landing. The southern branch ex- tends shoreward almost to the pier, starting at a depth of 60 ft (18 m) at a distance of 100 ft (30 m) from this structure. The pier end has twice disappeared, apparently sliding into the south branch. On the walls at the canyon head, the divers found only unconsolidated sediment. Cores taken in the floor on two occasions showed alternat- ing layers of mud and coarse sand, the latter similar to the sand found on the adjacent beach. The gradient of the south branch is 125 m/km to the juncture with the center branch, and the north branch has a similarly steep slope. At a depth of 300 ft (91 m), the gradient has decreased to 40 m/km and remains fairly constant from there down to over 4,000 ft (1,220 m). The floor of the canyon develops a winding course at about 300 ft (90 m) and can be described as meandering in some sections, particularly off Monterey Peninsula.

At an axial depth of 6,300 ft (1,920 m), the canyon floor becomes much broader where a trough-like valley enters from the north. Below this point, the V-shaped transverse profiles of the upper canyon give way to a flattened floor having a width of approximately one mile. Just below the juncture with Carmel Canyon, the gradient is reduced to 20 m/km. Despite the relatively flat floor of the lower canyon, steep, high walls continue out to an axial depth of 9,600 ft (2,925 m). At this point the true canyon comes to an end, 51 miles from the canyon head.

The tributaries entering Monterey Canyon are particularly impres- sive. The two largest are Soquel Canyon coming in from the north and Carmel Canyon from the south. Both of these tributaries appear

Fig. 39. Monterey and Carmel canyons off central California. For continuation of Monterey Fan-valley see Fig. 42, and for heads of Monterey and Carmel canyons see Figs. 40 and 44. From soundings of Coast and Geodetic Survey and surveys by Shepard.

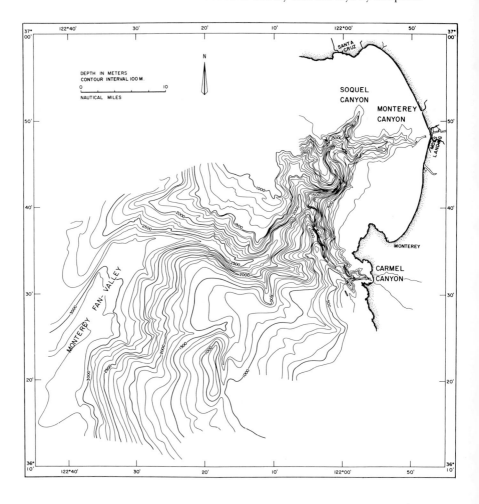

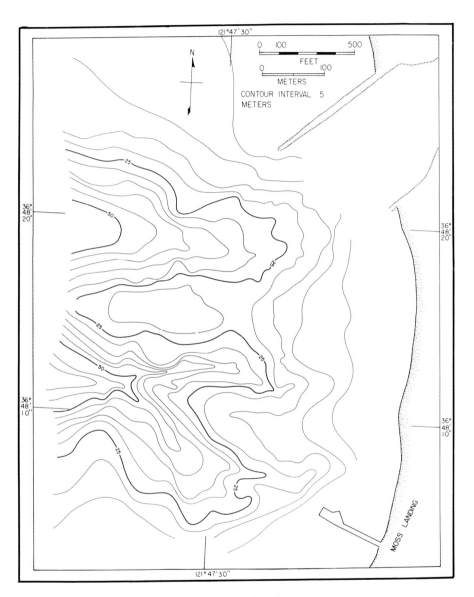

Fig. 40. Head of Monterey Canyon at Moss Landing. Harbor entrance upper right. Survey by Shepard from *M. V. Robert Gray*, U.S. Army Engineers.

to be hanging valleys, or at least steepen in gradient as they approach the main canyon. Out beyond the juncture with Carmel Canyon, only small tributaries enter but they come in from both sides.

The walls of the canyon increase in height outwardly until, at an axial depth of about 6,000 ft (1,830 m), they attain proportions almost comparable with the Grand Canyon (Fig. 41). Because of the limitations of the echo-sounding method we do not know whether there are precipices like those of the Grand Canyon along this rather limited section of high walls. Beyond this point, the wall heights decrease rapidly.

The dredging of the walls of the canyon by Martin (1964) and by the senior author have given quite a complete picture of the wall rock. The inner canyon cuts into unconsolidated sediments and the first rock appears 8 miles from the canyon head at axial depths of 2,100 ft (640 m). Here, Upper Pliocene mudrock was encountered by Martin. Pliocene sedimentary rocks were found farther along on the north side as well as on the west wall of Soquel Canyon. The first granite was encountered on the south wall at the base of the large south bend at longitude 122°01', but the opposite wall on the inside of the bend at this point has only Pliocene sedimentaries. Near the juncture with Monterey Canyon, the east wall of Carmel Canyon has a granite wall, described as weathered by Martin, and Mid-Miocene sedimentaries are found on the west wall. Two dredgings on the north wall beyond the Carmel juncture, revealed sedimentary rocks, including limestone, sandstone, and mudstone. Some of this yielded Lower Miocene foraminifera and coccoliths (F. L. Parker and N. M. Bramlette, personal communication). We dredged only mud on the south wall in this outer part.

Coring along the axis of Monterey Canyon by the senior author has shown that there is sand along much of its length. At a depth of 5,100 ft (1,555 m), a core had mud at the surface grading down into sand, and at 14 to 17 inches (35 to 50 cm), gravel was mixed with sand with one pebble 5 cm across at the bottom of the core. Several layers of sand interbedded with mud were cored at 6,180 ft (1,884 m). In Soquel Canyon, a box core had mud at the surface but rounded pebbles underneath, with shells and a fragment of siltstone. Many attempts to core failed, apparently because of the hard sand bottom.

Monterey Fan-valley

Beyond the rock-walled canyon, the trough-shaped valley, with a broad and somewhat irregular floor, greatly resembles the valley that continues beyond Coronado Canyon (p. 72). This trough runs in a southwesterly direction for about 20 miles. On the northwest, it is bordered by a steep-sided levee with walls as high as 1,200 ft (370 m). Dredging of the walls produced no bedrock, but the dredge contained some sand and two rounded granodiorite cobbles up to 7 cm in diameter, together with many small pieces of gravel. The floor of the trough apparently slopes outward continuously, but in transverse section it is rolling with some terraces on the side, which are suggestive of landslide blocks. Sand overlain by mud was cored from the floor. The southeast wall represents the continental slope and is cut by a number of valleys that head at various depths down to about 5,000 ft (1,520 m).

Where the southeast wall of the trough leaves the continental slope, at longitude 122°40', there is a decided change in the nature of the

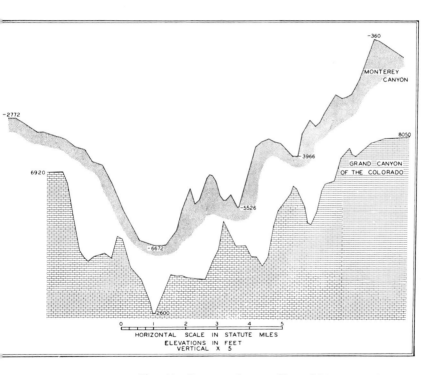

Fig. 41. Comparative profiles of Monterey Canyon and the Grand Canyon using the same number of points and same scales. The resemblance is, of course, coincidental.

valley (Fig. 42). The high northwest levee gradually loses its relief but continues as a low ridge, and a levee appears on the other side. The most marked change is in the trend of the channel. First, it loses its fairly straight course and becomes winding. Then there is a meandering bend and, after a course of 13 miles, a return to the general course less than 2 miles downstream from the divergence. This feature was interpreted by Dill *et al.* (1954) and by Martin (1964) as a trifurcation, but detailed soundings made from the *Horizon* in 1964 combined with a few lines from Martin showed the ox-bow feature of Figure 42. The

Fig. 42. A section of Monterey Fan-valley, a westerly continuation of Fig. 39. Note large meander. Based on detailed surveys by Shepard combined with sounding lines by Bruce Martin on *Velero IV*, and old Coast and Geodetic Survey soundings.

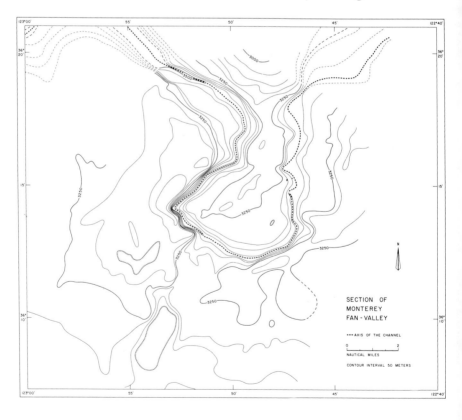

SECTION OF
MONTEREY
FAN - VALLEY

••• AXIS OF THE CHANNEL

0   2
NAUTICAL MILES

CONTOUR INTERVAL 50 METERS

channel along this bend apparently has one basin depression, although this is based only on one line so it is not well established. Sampling the floor along the bend showed that there is sand in the channel. Sand was also found on the levee east of the eastern arm of the bend at a height of 500 ft (152 m) above the channel floor. This sand (Fig. 43) has scarcely any mud cover, suggesting that appreciable currents have swept over the levee in relatively recent time.

The main channel was traced about 20 miles to the south beyond

Fig. 43. Sand layers found in a core at the top of the levee along Monterey Fan-valley at a depth of 10,140 ft (3,090 m).

the wide bend shown in Figure 42. This channel becomes less deeply incised into the fan but is still distinctly seen in the traverses. At a depth of 11,288 ft (3,440 m), Dill *et al.* (1954) obtained a core consisting of alternating micaceous mud and very fine-grained, well-sorted sand. Also, Menard (1964) obtained a core from 13,500 ft (4,115 m) with flat pebbles and shells in a muddy matrix. In both cases, the coarse fraction is terrigenous and its probable source is the mainland, as determined by Wilde (1964).

CARMEL CANYON

The large submarine canyon that comes out of Carmel Bay is the only west-coast canyon heading into a bay which might be described as a drowned river valley, although partly filled by the delta of the Carmel River. The axial trend along most of the canyon is essentially parallel to the coast, rather than directly towards the deep-sea bottom as in most other canyons. The direction follows the structural pattern of the area (Jennings and Strand, 1965; Martin, 1964).

In 1934, the senior author made vertical cast soundings along 50 closely spaced ranges, establishing the configuration of the inner canyon that extends into the south arm of the bay (Fig. 44). This shows that the canyon heads directly off the beach with no intervening shelf. Except for a sand fill at the mouth of San Jose Creek, the submarine canyon appears to be a seaward continuation of the land canyon. The former closely resembles the land valley in the large number of entering tributaries and in the steepness of the walls; both land and sea canyons are cut in granite. The floor of the sea canyon has a channel about 250 ft (75 m) across, slightly wider than that of the land canyon. The gradient of the land canyon from the 1,200-ft (369 m) contour to the coast is one-fifth that of its seaward continuation to the 1,200-ft (369 m) depth. A decided nickpoint is found at the actual shore where the stream has a very low gradient and the sea canyon has a slope of 300 m/km. The average gradient of the marine canyon is 73 m/km. As in the other well-surveyed canyons, the axial slope was found to be continuous in a seaward direction. Even the closely spaced wire-sounding profiles failed to show any closed basins.

Many dives into the head of Carmel Canyon have been made (Peckham and McLean, 1961). The divers found steep granite walls with local sand cover held in place by burrowing worm tubes. Dives by the junior author have also shown the existence of precipitous granite

Fig. 44. The head of Carmel Canyon. Note relation of
canyon heads to shore valleys and coastal indentations. The canyon walls have outcropping granite.
From detailed wire soundings by Shepard.

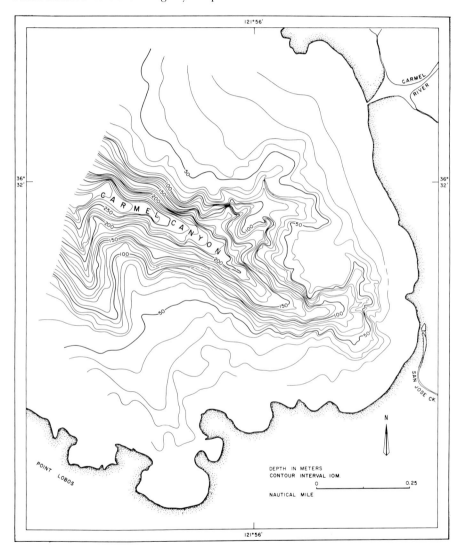

walls with several tributaries entering as hanging valleys. Locally, these are smoothed at the base, apparently by recent erosion.

The tributary system of Carmel Canyon is quite typically dendritic with several arms extending into bays along the shore. However, one tributary heads in 360 ft (110 m) of water, a mile southwest of Pt. Lobos. This tributary runs parallel to the shore and is a prolongation of the outer part of the canyon. Another valley head is found a mile farther offshore and heads in water about 480 ft (150 m) deep. This extends in the same direction for one mile but is blocked by a sill, according to our soundings. A canyon of small proportions is found on the lower slope, west of the Carmel Canyon head. As Martin (1964) has suggested, this may have been connected with the head of Carmel Canyon prior to the uplift of a fault block that diverted Carmel Canyon to the north. Alternatively, the slope valley may be cutting headward toward Carmel Canyon so that it will pirate it, as seems to have happened in the case of Coronado Canyon which apparently captured Loma Sea Valley.

Reruns of lines in the head of Carmel Canyon have shown that the depths are not stable. Differences of 10 ft (3 m) have been found between successive surveys, although these surveys are few compared to those of the La Jolla canyons. Sport divers report considerable changes in the nature and thickness of the fill, especially after large storms (D. R. Ferrin, personal communication).

Coring operations in 1964 yielded coarse sand and gravel in the floor of Carmel Canyon at 1,640 ft (500 m) depth and sand was also obtained at 2,960 ft (902 m).

DELGADA CANYON

North of Monterey Bay there are a number of canyons cutting the continental slope, but none cross the shelf for 250 miles, until Delgada Canyon which heads near shore (Fig. 45). This is in many ways the most unusual of the submarine canyons. Instead of being located off a river valley, it comes in to a precipitous coast halfway between two land canyons (Fig. 46). Almost directly off the beach there is a straight slope of about 45° extending down to about 210 ft (65 m). Farther out, the slope is deeply dissected and there is a V-shaped canyon with 3 heads trending in a south-southwesterly direction. This canyon is similar to the land canyons cut into mountain slopes, to both north and south of the head of Delgada Canyon. The natural inference is that there has been a strike-slip fault, displacing Delgada Canyon from its

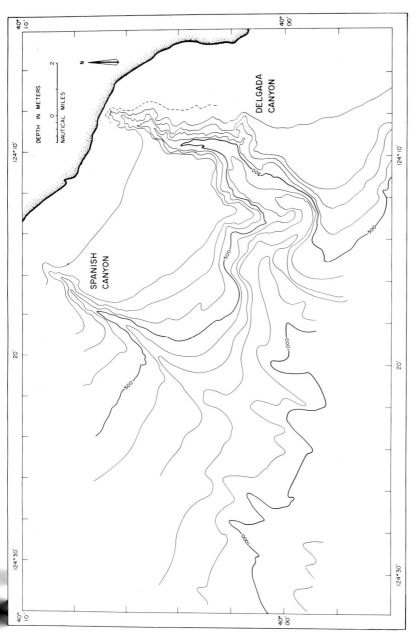

Fig. 45. Spanish Canyon and inner Delgada Canyon along the northern California coast. The juncture of the two canyons is not well determined. From unpublished soundings of Coast and Geodetic Survey.

former land connection. There is some evidence that this fault is connected with the San Andreas fault zone, which may run along the coast in this vicinity (Matthes, 1907; Shepard and Emery, 1941; Shepard, 1957).[4] This canyon head is decidedly different from all of the others for which detailed soundings are available.

[4]Data from J. R. Curray (personal communication) supports this contention.

Fig. 46. Soundings at the head of Delgada Canyon showing the apparent offset in relation to the land canyons and the straight escarpment near the shore. Movement is thought to be related to the San Andreas fault. From Shepard and Emery (1941).

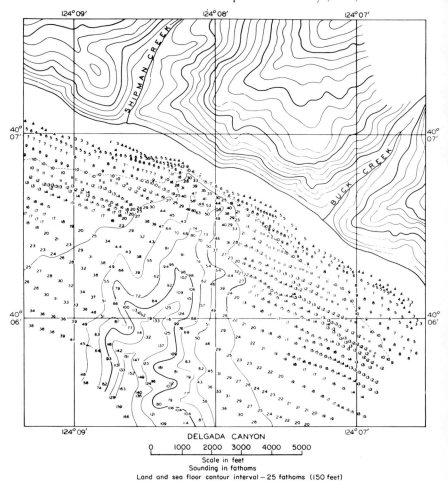

DELGADA CANYON

0   1000   2000   3000   4000   5000

Scale in feet
Sounding in fathoms
Land and sea floor contour interval — 25 fathoms (150 feet)

Delgada Canyon traced seaward (Fig. 12; Shepard and Emery, 1941, Chart IV), winds out to the southwest with a meandering course like Monterey Canyon and terminates at a depth of about 8,400 ft (2,560 m) with a total length of 55 miles.[5] Several tributaries enter along its course. Spanish Canyon apparently comes in from the north but the nature of the juncture is not very clear. A fan may be present at the contact. At no place are the walls of Delgada Canyon more than 2,000 ft (610 m) high. Seaward of the canyon, there is evidence of a large fan, called Delgada deep-sea fan by Menard (1960). He found a fan-valley as a continuation of Delgada Canyon and extending 240 miles across the fan. This fan-valley, like most of the others along the west coast of the United States, bends (hooks) to the left.

MATTOLE AND MENDOCINO CANYONS (Fig. 47)

Just north of Punta Gorda, with its offlying escarpment, Mattole Canyon comes to within less than 0.5 mile of the coast. This valley winds seaward for 16 miles, where it is joined by Mendocino Canyon at a depth of 5,700 ft (1,740 m). It is notable that Mendocino Canyon heads 2 miles off shore near the edge of the narrow shelf. This relationship is similar to that of Delgada and Spanish canyons on the south side of Punta Gorda (Fig. 45), except that Mattole Canyon is not cut off by a faulted head. It lies off, or nearly off, the relatively large Mattole River. Other pairs of canyons that show the same relationship are Sur and Partington near Pt. Sur, and Redondo and Santa Monica in Santa Monica Bay. The pair in Santa Monica Bay does not come together—they both terminate in Santa Monica Basin. Except for Sur and Partington, the canyon that comes closest to shore in each pair is the one upcurrent from a rather prominent point of land. However, in each case the point is so far from the canyon head that it should not now have much effect in diverting longshore currents down the canyon axis. On the other hand, during times of glacially lowered sea levels the points may have been nearer the canyon axis.

Beyond the juncture of Mattole and Mendocino canyons there is a straight valley extending west along the base of the Gorda fault scarp, and hence presumably its trend is controlled by faulting.

In axial depths of 3,300 ft (1,006 m), Mattole Canyon has walls

[5]The outer part is called *Vizcaino Canyon* by the U.S. Coast and Geodetic Survey.

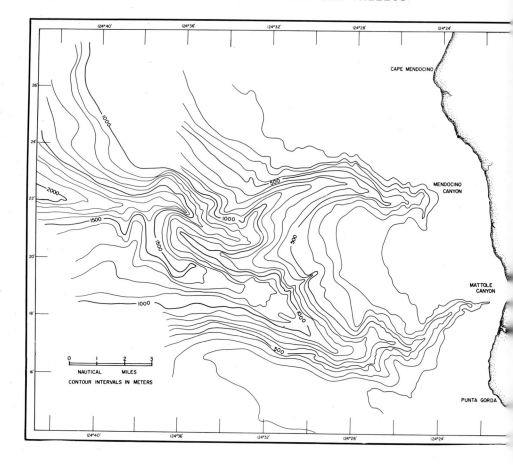

Fig. 47. Mattole and Mendocino canyons along the northern California coast. The outer continuation of these canyons may be a fault trough that extends along the Gorda escarpment. From unpublished soundings of Coast and Geodetic Survey.

almost 2,600 ft (790 m) high. It has a gradient of 59 m/km. So far as can be told from the Coast and Geodetic Survey soundings, the canyons are V-shaped. Survey notations suggest that Mattole Canyon has rocky walls, and sand is also reported in 3,905 ft (1,191 m), well out from shore. Notations of gravel are shown in Mendocino Canyon at 3,170 ft (966 m).

EEL CANYON

The main part of Eel Canyon is located approximately off the Eel River in northern California (Fig. 48). The most surprising thing about Eel Canyon is that it appears to have a high ridge or hill across its axis, and, to the best of our knowledge, bends around this ridge until the outer course moves back into line with the inner section. The gradient of Eel Canyon is unusual in that it shows several large changes. A steep portion lies near the outer end of the horseshoe bend where the gradient is 120 m/km, compared to an average of 51 m/km. Also, the gradient is very low in the inshore section of the bend. This suggests that diastrophism may have played a part during the erosion of the canyon.

Eel Canyon is initiated 5 miles from the shore in 250 ft (75 m) of water. There are several small tributaries at the head, but no evidence of any appreciable branch valleys in the outer portion. The canyon can be traced for 27 miles, terminating in a depth of about 8,500 ft (2,590 m). Near the outer terminus, it has a gorge with walls about 4,000 ft (1,200 m) high. No known oceanographic work has been conducted in the canyon, and "mud" is the only bottom notation on the charts.

CANYONS — COLUMBIA RIVER TO JUAN DE FUCA STRAIT

North of Eel Canyon, the very gentle continental slope is virtually free of valleys up to the entrance of the Columbia River. From there north, at least to the Canadian border, there is a continuous series of canyons, most of them connected with coastal indentations and river valleys. There is no certainty about whether the canyons continue farther north, because the slope surveys are not yet sufficiently detailed.

Columbia Canyon[6]

Off the mouth of the Columbia River, Columbia Canyon extends to within about 10 miles of the estuary and crosses approximately half of the continental shelf (Fig. 49). The head has a minimum depth of

---

[6]Called Astoria Canyon on Coast and Geodetic Survey charts, but the name Columbia is retained here as it has priority (see Shepard and Beard, 1938) and was originally accepted by the Coast and Geodetic Survey.

close to 360 ft (110 m), and there are several short branches entering farther downslope, which join at a depth of a little over 1,000 ft (300 m). After a fairly straight westerly trend for 15 miles, the canyon develops a sinuous course and it may be blocked at a depth of about 4,960 ft (1,510 m) in a northerly trending structural valley. Alternatively, at a depth of 4,800 ft (1,460 m), it may possibly extend south to enter a fan-valley, called Astoria Channel by Hurley (1960, Fig. 5). This channel follows the southeast side of one of the fans described by Menard (1955). Assuming the former interpretation (shown in Fig. 49), Columbia Canyon has a total length of 35 miles and an average gradient of 19.6 m/km.

Columbia Canyon has walls about 2,500 ft (760 m) high at the outer edge of the shelf and is 5.5 miles across. No samples are known to have been taken in the canyon. A bank on the south side has a survey notation of "shale," so it seems likely that the canyon is cut through a rock shelf.

WILLAPA CANYON

The next canyon is found 16 miles to the north and is located directly off Willapa Bay, for which it is named (Fig. 49). This canyon and its large tributary have been investigated by scientists of the University of Washington (Royse, 1964). The heads lie near the outer edge of the shelf about 16 miles from the coast. Guide Canyon enters Willapa from the north at a depth of about 6,000 ft (1,830 m). According to Royse, Willapa Canyon extends seaward for 60 miles, with an outer depth of about 9,000 ft (2,740 m). Beyond, there is a fan-valley (called a seachannel by Royse) that extends out into Cascadia Basin. The inner canyon, including Guide Canyon, has considerable relief with walls up to 3,600 ft (1,100 m) high and wall slopes up to 30° or 40°. The lower canyon is wider and has more gently sloping walls. At about 8,000 ft (2,440 m) the canyon apparently cuts across some northwest trending ridges.

According to Royse, (1964), the sediments of the canyon are predominantly green pelagic muds with some sandy layers along the floor. The sandy layers, however, are much thinner than those found in cores from Cascadia Basin outside, suggesting to Royse that turbidity currents have by-passed much of the sand beyond the canyon. Displaced foraminifera are found in the canyon floor sediments but not as commonly as in sediments from Cascadia Basin, and hence reinforcing the conclusion of by-passing. The data from Royse's tables

Fig. 48. Eel Canyon off the Eel River in northern
California. Note the curious bend along the course
of the canyon. From unpublished soundings of Coast
and Geodetic Survey.

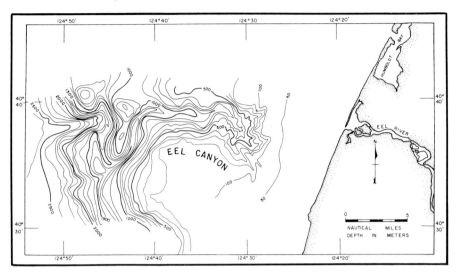

and on his chart indicate that not many samples are available from the
canyon floor, and, in view of the rough sea encountered during the
work, one cannot help but wonder if it was possible to distinguish wall
and floor samples.

Rock dredged from the north wall of the canyon consisted of
siltstone and contained fossils of Pliocene age.

Grays Canyon

The next canyon to the north is directly off Grays Harbor, from which
its name is derived (Fig. 49). Its head lies in about 500 ft (150 m) of
water, 25 miles offshore. The canyon is cut about 14 miles into the
edge of the rather deep shelf, one of the rare unglaciated shelves as
deep as 600 ft (180 m). Here, also shale bottom is reported on the
chart on the south side, so it is likely that this canyon, too, is cut into
rock. At about 30 miles from its head, a depth of 6,000 ft (1,830 m) is
reached and no clear continuation of the canyon is shown but it may
join Cascadia Channel. Grays Canyon does not have as high walls as
the other two to the south, probably about 1,000 ft (305 m) high.
Again, the walls are rather gentle in slope.

Quinault Canyon

A very impressive canyon is found 20 miles directly seaward of the relatively large Quinault River (Fig. 49), for which it is named. It is hard to say how far this canyon cuts into the shelf because its numerous heads form a broad bight over a span of 17 miles. There is no definite re-entry into the shelf, such as the single canyon off the

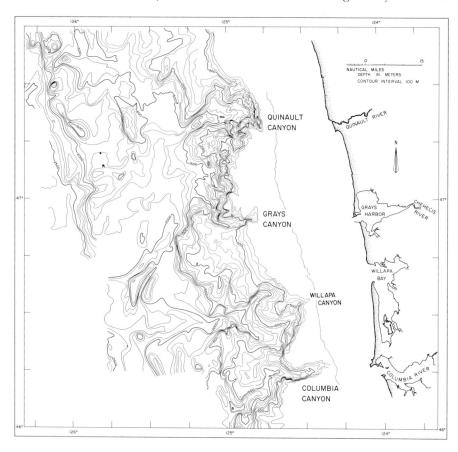

Fig. 49. A group of canyons extending north of the Columbia River along the coast of Oregon and Washington. Note apparent relation to the rivers and bays on land despite intervening shelf. The outer parts of the canyons are open to question but some closed basins seem likely. From unpublished soundings of Coast and Geodetic Survey.

Columbia River. Quinault Canyon, like those to the south, is also a broad valley. It has a north wall rising at least 3,500 ft (1,070 m) above the floor at an axial depth of 6,000 ft (1,830 m), where the valley is 9 miles across. According to the soundings there is a sill beyond this point, but this is an old survey and may have serious errors. Beyond 21 miles, the canyon enters a broad trough and bends to the south.

Juan de Fuca Canyon

Off the Strait of Juan de Fuca, a glacial trough extends virtually to the edge of the shelf (Fig. 133), and in direct continuation with the trough there is a submarine canyon called Juan de Fuca. This appears to resemble the other canyons to the south. It is also wide and has a gently winding axis. At the edge of the shelf it has walls slightly over 2,000 ft (610 m) high, but at greater depth, these decrease in height where many other canyons cut the slope, leaving relatively narrow divides in between. The canyons along this part of the slope do not have axes reaching much deeper than 5,000 ft (1,520 m), where the slope ceases and a broad belt of hills and ridges are found inside Nizinat Fan (Hurley, 1960, Fig. 5).

CHAPTER V

CANYONS
OF BAJA CALIFORNIA

A LONG THE WEST COAST of Baja California, south of the U.S.-Mexican border, there are a few widely spaced canyons and one group of small, closely spaced canyons about halfway down the coast. Farther south, off Magdalena Bay and vicinity, rather gentle slopes predominate and Scripps Institution sounding lines show no signs of valleys.

Near the southern end of the peninsula, a series of large canyons is encountered. They continue around the south tip and up the east coast of the peninsula to Pescadero Point (Chart I). These canyons, with their precipitous rock-walled gorges, are among the most impressive in the world. Almost all of them extend in close to the shore, as do most California canyons to the north.

Baja California canyons were first investigated briefly on a Scripps expedition in 1940, but have been extensively studied since 1957 on 11 expeditions by Scripps Institution ships. During seven of these expeditions, scuba diving into the canyon heads was conducted, in all but one case under the direction of the junior author. In 1965, several Scripps Institution and Navy Electronics Laboratory scientists, including the authors, used the Cousteau Saucer for dives into two of the canyons. The study of the canyons from surface vessels has been under the direction of the senior author in all but one expedition.

Prior to these expeditions to this region, only scattered soundings around the lower peninsula had been made by the U.S. Navy. However, the topography is now fairly well-defined by the detailed soundings taken during the Scripps Institution expeditions. Closely spaced sounding lines exist for all of these canyons out to their termini, and in most cases include the fans and fan-valleys where found seaward of the canyons. Several hundred samples have been obtained within the canyons. These serve to characterize the rocks forming the canyon walls and the sediment of the canyon floor. Photographs of some of the deep parts of the canyons have been taken by lowering cameras to the bottom, and many photographs of the canyon heads have been made by scuba-equipped divers. The Diving Saucer was used for extensive investigation of San Lucas and Los Frailes canyons in February, 1965, down to depths of 1,035 ft (315 m). Continuous reflection profile surveys have been run showing the subsurface structure of bedrock and the deep-sea fans associated with the canyons.

LAND AND SHELF CONDITIONS IN THE CANYON AREAS

The lower end of Baja California is a desert with extensive subaerial coastal fans leading down from a central mountainous region. Geologic maps of the area show the backbone range as granite. However, reconnaissance flights and trips into the region show it to be a complex, highly faulted range of metavolcanics, gneiss, metamorphic, and granite intrusives.[1] Preliminary investigations indicate that the central granitic massif is associated with an older metamorphic sequence.

The central mountain range extends in a north-south direction. It lies somewhat west of the center of the peninsula and includes a row of granitic peaks ranging in height from 3,000 to 6,490 ft (915 to 1,980 m). Along the west coast, a lower range of rounded hills parallels the high central peaks. Rocks of this region are mostly metamorphics and contain slates, marble, gneiss, and schist. Large dikes cut the area in a northwest-southeasterly direction. The coastal

[1]The granites from the tip of San Lucas have been dated by J. G. Gastil, San Diego State College, and are tentatively reported to be of pre-Cambrian age (personal communication).

mountains or hills are not more than 1,000 ft (300 m) high, and are in many cases partly buried by younger fan deposits spreading out from intermittent rivers originating in the high central range. The river channels are commonly incised into the fans, indicating that there has been a change in base level since the formation of the extensive fan system.

Most of the submarine canyons line up with a major land valley, although in some instances, this connection is obscured by a flat sand-covered terrace extending shoreward from the break in slope at the canyon heads. Some of the submarine canyons have heads that extend almost to the surf zone.

On the eastern side of the peninsula, the predominant topographic feature is a large structural trough that cuts across the lower end of the cape from San Jose del Cabo to the small village of La Rivera, at Palmas Bay on the gulf side of the peninsula. The northwest side of the trough is marked by an abrupt change in topography at a well-developed fault scarp at the boundary between sedimentary rock and granite intrusives. This change is also reflected in the heads of the canyons. Those canyons that cut through sedimentary rocks have broad heads with wide reentrants. Those cut in harder granite have narrow gorges with steep V-shaped profiles.

The continental shelf is very narrow or nonexistent around the lower end of the peninsula. It widens to 7 miles east of San Jose del Cabo and to 3 miles to the west of the same town. The relatively broad shelf east of San Jose del Cabo has two shallow banks on the outer margin, at least one with outcropping granite. Two other shelf bulges are found on both sides of Point Arena, each with 3-mile wide shelves. Also, there is a 2- to 3-mile shelf west and northwest of San Lucas.

SAN LUCAS CANYON GROUP (Fig. 50)

The most completely studied and the most impressive canyon off the southern tip of Baja California comes into the bay at Cape San Lucas. The canyon head (Fig. 51) extends almost to the shoreline, forming a protected deep-water cove that has been used since early Spanish occupation as a harbor and watering spot. The low granite hills forming the cape also mark the southern wall of the canyon where it cuts back into the coast. One of several offshore stacks is the upper continuation of the almost vertical canyon wall. This stack is unique, being one of the few locations where a surface swimmer can look down and see the wall of a canyon through a face plate. The bottom

Fig. 50. The canyons off the southern end of Baja California are partly cut in granite. Note their termination in the large fans outside the rocky continental slope. For location of sounding lines see Shepard (1964, Fig. 1). Note that Vigia Canyon may have had its sediment pirated by San Lucas Canyon. The small fan-valley outside San Jose Canyon is shown in detail in Figure 59. From surveys by Shepard.

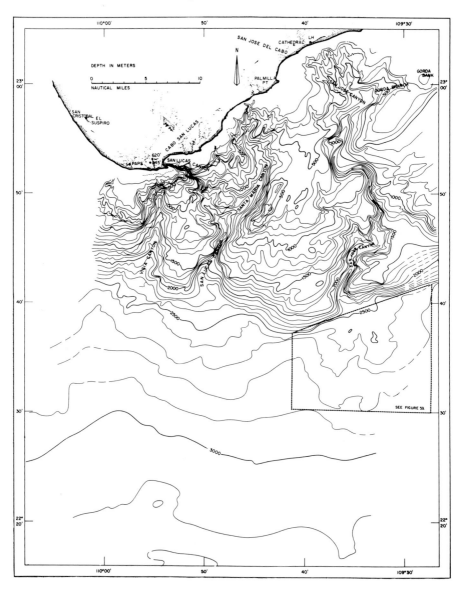

of the canyon below this steep drop-off is over 800 ft (240 m) deep.

The head of San Lucas Canyon has four main branches (Fig. 51), of which three have hanging valleys at their juncture with the largest. The large branch lies directly off the most active channel of the main arroyo draining the region behind the cape. Seaward of the juncture of the heads, several other large tributaries or branches enter the canyon on the northeast side. These canyons are steep-walled gorges and end landward abruptly at a depth of 120 ft (40 m). Apparently they have become inactive since the last rise in sea level and no longer

Fig. 51. The head of San Lucas Canyon. The paths of dives in the Cousteau Diving Saucer are indicated. From surveys by Shepard.

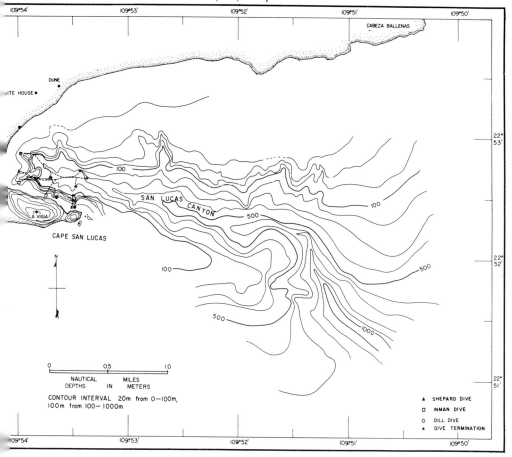

receive sediment, as do the nearshore branches outside the main arroyo.

In the southernmost of the nearshore branches, deep water is found just off the pier of the local fish cannery, permitting ships with considerable draft to enter and tie up at the pier. Water depth of over 100 ft (30 m) occurs about 300 ft (90 m) from the cannery. Anchoring is often complicated in this area because of the deep water and the abrupt, steep, jagged rock slopes down which anchors often slide and are lost.

Dives by the junior author into this head in 1963 revealed the presence of a sandstone cliff 80 ft (25 m) high. The nature of rock samples and the location off a main drainage area with abundant ground water indicate that it is beachrock, formed probably during the rise of sea level at the close of the Pleistocene. The arkosic grains are cemented with carbonate and contain broken shell material. Grains are well-rounded and some of the beds are graded. Burrows of organisms have been truncated by flowing sand on the upper lip of the steep cliff, indicating submarine erosion of the beachrock after submergence. The outcrops of beachrock are covered by sand in depths shallower than 55 ft (20 m). Below this depth, beachrock is in place and forms a vertical cliff down to depths of 135 ft (40 m) (Fig. 52). Outcrops of beachrock not known to be in place, but with beds of similar dips and strike as that found in the cliff, are seen protruding through the sand floor of the canyon down to depths as great as 165 ft (50 m). The outcrops have an east-west strike and dip about 10° to 15° downcanyon, a slope approximately equal to the foreshore slope of the present-day beach. Large blocks of the beachrock, up to 20 ft (6 m) across, have fallen from the steep wall of the canyon. Similar blocks are found downcanyon in depths as great as 300 ft (90 m). Beachrock was not found below 175 ft (53 m), where the walls consist entirely of granitic rock.

The four main branches of the canyon head cut through the beachrock cliff as channels that narrow in a seaward direction. The lower part of the channels are filled with a thin cover of highly organic micaceous medium-grained sand. Marker stakes placed in these channels show that the sediment fill is slowly creeping into deeper water at a rate of approximately 1 foot per year.

Bottom slopes average 20° in depths below 55 ft (17 m). Rock outcrops protruding through the overburden significantly retard creep so that movement is greater in the channels than at the contact with rock walls. The sediment contains large amounts of man-made junk, which is also being displaced downslope with the creeping sediment.

At depths below 180 ft (55 m), the branches have narrowed until the floor in places is less than 10 ft (3 m) across. The branches contain only a thin sediment fill. Slump scars expose highly jointed unweathered granite surfaces along the walls which appear freshly eroded. In areas not associated with slumps, the sediment wall-rock contact is not sharp. The sediment laps up onto the rock (Fig. 53a). Slump scars are associated with sudden steepenings in the bottom slope and are commonly found in areas of overhanging walls or where tributaries enter the channel.

At a depth of 600 ft (183 m), the senior author observed a large hole in the south wall near the floor. Upon closer examination, it was seen to have a sand chute leading down out of sight and to be surrounded by rock with no indication that any of the rock represented a boulder. This might suggest possible ground water erosion along the joint, but it is, of course, possible that this is only a boulder-blocked ravine.

At the extreme tip of the cape, the east-west trending granite ridge forming the south side of San Lucas Bay is bordered by the high stacks on its seaward end (Fig. 54). One of these is ordinarily connected to the mainland by a tombolo of coarse arkosic sand, which is carried diagonally along the coast by the prevailing swell and wind. The tombolo is overwashed by high waves from the south generated during severe tropical storms. Sand cut from the beach pours into the heads of the several tributaries on the south side of the canyon. A spectacular sand flow was first photographed here by Conrad Limbaugh, James Stewart, and Wheeler North during our 1959 expedition. The sand flow was moving at a velocity of about 0.2 knots (North, 1960; Shepard, 1961). At a depth of 130 ft (40 m), the flowing sand reached a sharp dropoff in the rock wall and cascaded down into deep water (Fig. 55). Two years later, while looking for evidence of submarine erosion, the junior author observed other flows which, when followed down to a depth of about 250 ft (75 m), could be seen continuing to still greater depths. Dives made below the area in the Saucer in January and February, 1965, showed that a fan has been built up in the axis of the canyon at a depth of 890 ft (270 m). Large blocks of freshly broken granite, up to 10 ft (3 m) across (Fig. 56), were scattered throughout a coarse arkosic sand fill and appeared to

Fig. 52. Looking up at the cliffed headwall of San Lucas Canyon where it cuts through a thick well-bedded beachrock formation. Divers are entering small gully in the cliff. Depth 135 ft (41 m). N.E.L. photo by Dill.

Fig. 53. Photographs along the axis of San Lucas Canyon, Feb. 4, 1965, showing the abrupt change in current regime with increasing depth. N.E.L. Diving Saucer photos by Dill.

a. Fine-grained sediment lapping up on the granite walls at a depth of 245 m (805 ft).

b. Broken blocks of granite wall rock and sand at a depth of 270 m (885 ft) below an area of sand falls.

c. Ripple-marked sand at a depth of 290 m (951 ft). Current was flowing downcanyon from right to left. Note scour depression on upcanyon side of granite block, showing probable current reversal.

a

b

c

have been carried into the canyon down the steep tributaries. The fresh surfaces of the rocks (Fig. 53b) left little doubt as to their recent origin, and similar blocks were seen resting precariously on small ledges at the edges of the tributaries. Evidently the flowing sand is undercutting the highly jointed granite, forming large unstable blocks that occasionally fall into the tributaries. Bottom currents up to 0.5 knots are associated with sand flows (Dill, in press, b), and rock fragments up to 6 inches (15 cm) across are carried along as a float in the flowing sand. This sudden coarsening of the sediment in the axis below the sand fall areas at depths deeper than 890 ft (270 m) is also associated with a steepening in the bottom slope to about 25° to 30°. The steeper slope appears to be related to slumps or slides triggered by sudden overloading by the sand flows.

In February, 1964, divers working in the area of the sand falls reported hearing rumbling noises, suggestive of an underwater avalanche, rising from deep in the canyon. The sounds of the supposed avalanche came during a period of sand flows and lasted for at least 5 minutes. The evidence for such avalanches was found during Saucer dives in the form of the freshly broken granite blocks of different sizes and the heterogeneous mixture of relatively fine sand, gravel, rock chips, broken shells, and man-made debris. The evidence discovered from the Saucer thus further substantiates the suspected high activity and downslope movement of large amounts of coarse sediment and rock debris to depths of at least 1,000 ft (300 m).

Assymetrical ripple marks, indicators of strong currents, were restricted to the very shallow water above 200 ft (60 m) and to the water deeper than 890 ft (270 m) (Fig. 53c). Most of the area between contained a highly reduced, fine-grained, clayey, micaceous sand covered with a thin brownish mud layer. The fill had been churned by large numbers of manta shrimp, which form small cone-shaped mounds on the sediment. Beer cans with flip-top openers were seen buried at least 2 inches in the sediment in this area at a depth of 820 ft (250 m). It is known that this type of container did not arrive in the cape area until the early part of 1964. Using the can as an indicator of sedimentation, a minimum rate of sedimentation of 2 inches (5 cm) per year can be postulated for the unripple-marked area above 890 ft (270 m). However, the canyon floor below this depth was marked by well-developed ripple marks and scour depressions around blocks of granite in the fill (see Fig. 56). Most of the blocks had depressions on their upcanyon side and elongated tail dunes on their downcanyon side.

The ripples deep in the canyon were restricted to an area below 890 ft (271 m). Here the asymmetrical form of ripple (with steep slopes facing downcanyon and the scour depressions behind rock blocks) indicated that the dominant currents at the time of the dives were flowing downcanyon. There was also some evidence from the interference pattern of crossing ripples that at times strong currents flow upcanyon (see Fig. 53c). Bottom currents up to 0.4 knots were measured during two of the Saucer dives in February, 1965. These currents were not constant and appeared to pulsate. Starting with no current, the velocity would rapidly build up to a peak, which would then gradually dissipate until the currents were no more than a gradual downslope drift of bottom water. The area of bottom currents was not associated with strong changes in temperature nor with any appreciable change of water visibility.

Fig. 54. Tip of Baja California from the air, showing the tombolo beach that connects the mainland to offshore stacks. Sand stored on the beach is carried into the head of San Lucas Canyon during tropical storms. Photo by Shepard.

Tracing San Lucas Canyon seaward of the deepest Saucer dives, it continues as a deeply incised V-shaped gorge with a slightly sinuous course. Its trend undergoes a gradual change from the east-west trend of the canyon head in the vicinity of the cape to a more north-south direction. Several small tributaries join the main channel, forming a dendritic pattern. Finally, at an axial depth of 5,400 ft (1,650 m), it is joined by another major canyon, called Santa Maria. Just below the juncture, the main canyon reaches its greatest depth below surroundings, with 3,240 ft (990 m) the average of the two wall heights. At this point the canyon has a width of about 5 miles. These dimensions make the canyon roughly comparable to V-shaped land canyons in unglaciated portions of Yosemite Park, California.

Fig. 55. Underwater sand fall at a depth of 130 ft (40 m) in a gully leading down into San Lucas Canyon. N.E.L. photo by Dill.

San Lucas Canyon has a total length of 19 miles, or including Santa Maria Canyon, 24 miles, terminating as a canyon at about 8,000 ft (2,440 m). The terminus is approximately at the point where the steep continental slope is overlapped by a gentle, sloping fan to which the name *continental rise* could be applied. Beyond this point, there is a shallow fan-valley that can be traced for 3 or 4 miles down the east side of the large fan bordering the canyon. The average gradient of the canyon is 70 m/km but, except for the steep head above 650 ft

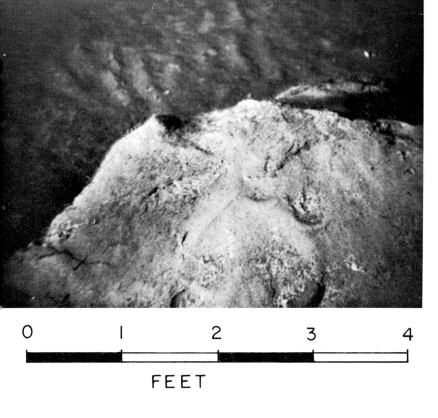

0   1   2   3   4

FEET

Fig. 56. Asymmetrical ripple marks and scour depression around a granite block in the sand fill of San Lucas Canyon. This location, at a depth of 290 m (950 ft), is below the area where sand flows spill into the canyon. Ripples indicate downcanyon flow of bottom currents. N.E.L. photo from Diving Saucer by Dill.

(200 m) and the steep slope at 870 ft (265 m), it has a fairly regular gradient of 130 m/km out to 4,500 ft (1,400 m), decreasing gradually to 40 m/km beyond this point.

The walls of San Lucas Canyon are very rocky in the inner part, and considerable difficulty was encountered in dredging them because of snagging the dredge on the hard granite. Some of the granite dredged from the walls was in the form of recemented breccia. According to R. R. Lankford (personal communication), foraminifera in the groundmass of the breccia are characterisitic of the dredged depths, indicating no depth changes since cementation. In the lower canyon, several dredge hauls yielded only mud despite pulling the dredge over an extensive surface. Also, a group of bottom photographs showed no rock. Probably rock is buried by a sediment mantle in these places. Rock has been dredged out to depths of about 6,000 ft (1,830 m), showing that the partially masked rock walls extend virtually to the fan.

Cores were difficult to obtain in the canyon, because of its narrow width and the hard bottom, which caused bending of core tubes in many localities. Two cores at depths of 5,600 ft (1,707 m) and 7,400 ft (2,255 m) — the latter in the fan-valley — had coarse sand and graded sand. The upper part of the deeper core is graded and overlies ungraded clean sand containing scattered gravel (Fig. 144). The foraminifera, including shallow-water organisms, are so well preserved in this deep core that transportation by slow moving currents is indicated. A high speed current might have crushed or considerably eroded the foraminifera.

Santa Maria Canyon

The large canyon that comes down into San Lucas Canyon from the area east of Cape Santa Maria differs from San Lucas in having less precipitous walls and a wider floor. The head of Santa Maria Canyon has three branches; the easternmost with two minor tributaries extends in very close to the coast directly off a land valley. Numerous parallel gullies run into the shallow heads and appear to divert sand moving along the shore into the canyon. A scuba dive into one of these heads showed nothing but sandy sediment-covered walls and floor. Various other tributaries enter at greater depths, and the canyon makes a broad curve to the right before entering San Lucas Canyon.

Dredging the walls of Santa Maria Canyon yielded mostly claystone and cobbles. Continuous reflection profiling indicates that the walls are mostly sedimentary rock (J. R. Curray, personal communication). However, granite was dredged on the shallow bank above the southeast wall. A fossil bone of a sea lion was brought up from the northwest wall along the deeper part of the canyon.

Ordinary coring has produced largely negative results, but the use of the box corer was very successful in recovering floor sediments from Santa Maria Canyon. Gravel and rock fragments were procured at depths of 2,330 and 3,930 ft (710 and 1,198 m). An X-ray photo by A. H. Bouma of a slice of a box core, taken from 1,090 ft (332 m), shows small erosional unconformities and laminations (Fig. 57). Another core, from 2,200 ft (671 m), showed an ungraded gravel and sand layer sharply truncated and covered by silty sediments with drag folds (Fig. 58).

Vigia Canyon (Fig. 50)

Another deep valley is located just west of San Lucas Canyon. The curious feature relative to Vigia Canyon is that it seems to be located directly south of the land valley that terminates at San Lucas. It heads off a beach that is separated from the valley by a low dune. Here, as at Carmel, it looks as though piracy had taken place with the new head extending up San Lucas Bay and capturing sediment from the large north-south land arroyo.

Vigia Canyon has a straight trend to the south with only minor curves. Aside from several branches at its head, it has only insignificant tributaries. It is cut about 2,400 ft (730 m) below surroundings at axial depths of 4,800 ft (1,460 m). The walls are not nearly as steep as those of San Lucas Canyon, but are similar to those of Santa Maria Canyon. Dredging of the walls has yielded what appears to be decomposed granite. However, according to R. L. Hayes (personal communication), this may be hydrothermal alteration. Elsewhere, rocks consist of laminated shale of Pliocene or Pleistocene age (according to identification of foraminifera by F. L. Parker). Also, rounded boulders of granite were dredged in one place. The canyon terminates at about 7,200 ft (2,200 m), although a fan-valley may continue a short distance down the right-hand side of the fan.

A box core in the center of the canyon at 5,500 ft (1,676 m) showed rock fragments overlain by a thin layer of sand and gravel with rough grading. At 6,000 ft (1,829 m), a piston corer hit a hard bottom, bending the core tube.

Fig. 57. X-ray photo made by A. H. Bouma of slice of
box core obtained in axis of Santa Maria Canyon at a
depth of 1,100 ft (335 m). Arrow upper right indicates downcanyon direction, erosional uncomformity
shown at A and small fault at B.

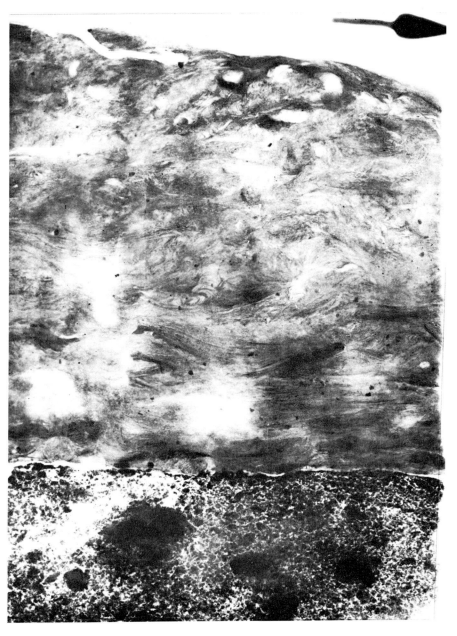

Fig. 58. X-ray photo made by A. H. Bouma of slice of box core taken from the axis of Santa Maria Canyon at a depth of 2,200 ft (670 m). A marked unconformity separates the ungraded gravel and coarse sand from the overlying fine-grained sediments with slump structure. Downcanyon direction shown by arrow.

SAN JOSE CANYON (Fig. 50)

Approximately 15 miles east of the San Lucas Canyon Group, San Jose Canyon extends down the slope in the same southerly direction. This canyon is located a short distance to the east of the coastal termination of the wide San Jose Valley, thought to be a fault trough. At the submarine canyon head there are four branches covering a width of 5 miles. The westernmost of these comes in closest to the shore, about one quarter mile from the beach. This head lies just east of the channel through the sand barrier into the lagoon bordering the town of San Jose del Cabo. The other canyon heads are off a rather hilly coast east of the fault valley. These canyon heads, like several off California, are cut into unconsolidated sediment. A 150 ft (45 m) dive in the western head by the junior author revealed large slump scars with fresh surfaces in a sand that contained rounded cobbles and, in places, large logs.

Traced seaward, the branches of San Jose Canyon join at a depth of about 2,200 ft (670 m). Farther down, a broad tributary comes in from the northeast at axial depths of 2,700 ft (820 m). This tributary heads in the vicinity of the granite-floored Gorda Bank. Below the deeper juncture, the canyon winds seaward as a broad valley to a depth of 4,500 ft (1,400 m), where it becomes a relatively straight narrow gorge. This gorge extends for about 5 miles to the south, but farther out the canyon again becomes sinuous and one tributary enters from the northwest side. The canyon continues out to the head of a fan at axial depths of 8,000 ft (2,440 m). Just inside this outermost canyon depth, the floor lies 3,000 ft (915 m) below the rim, the greatest wall height of any part of the canyon. It is rare that the highest wall is located near the canyon terminus.

Dredging of the canyon walls beyond axial depths of 3,000 ft (915 m) has shown that the dominant rock is either granite or some other type of igneous intrusive rock. Some of these specimens, like those of Vigia Canyon, are deeply weathered. In the middle sections of the canyon, claystone was dredged and continuous reflection profiling by J. R. Curray (personal communication) indicates a thick sequence of sedimentary rock.

Cores along the canyon axis included sand and other coarse sediment, as in the other canyons of the area. Box cores obtained gravel at 800, 2,300 and 4,500 ft (245, 700, and 1,370 m); at the deepest of these gravel localities, the fragments were angular and up to 2 cm in diameter. A core at 6,300 ft (1,920 m) had fine sand interbedded with a silty clay.

There is some indication of a fan-valley extending along the east side of the large fan lying outside San Jose Canyon. A continuous reflection profile shows that this represents a fault-trough depression at the base of the escarpment which extends east of the canyon mouth. However, out beyond the canyon, there is a north-south depression between ridges with a height of 500 ft (150 m) or more above the channel (Fig. 59). The eastern ridge has several hills on top of it and, in fact, somewhat resembles the ridge with a rock core that borders the west side of Coronado Fan-valley, southwest of San Diego (Fig. 34). When attempts were made to dredge the ridge outside San Jose Canyon, no rock was found and the dredge brought up sand in two hauls. A core from the ridge showed that there were sand layers underlying a mud deposit at the surface. In this respect, also, there is a resemblance to the situation off Coronado Islands, in the San Diego area. On the other hand, continuous reflection profiling records indicated that the ridges off San Jose Canyon are indeed part of the fan at the canyon mouth. The valley and ridges extend only for about 9 miles and die out in a rather flat fan slope beyond.

LOS FRAILES CANYON GROUP (Fig. 60)

Northeast of San Jose Canyon, there is a 10-mile gap in the continuous series of canyons extending around the southern end of Baja California. In this area the shelf is appreciably widened. Where it narrows again to the north, another group of canyons appear. It is noteworthy that the three principal canyons, Vinorama, Salado, and Los Frailes, are all located off major valleys on land. Vinorama heads near the outer margin of the 2-mile wide shelf and Salado only slightly indents the shelf, whereas Los Frailes extends directly into the coast south of Frailes Point. This relationship to coastal projections is similar to a number of California canyons, except that the order is reversed. Probably this reversal is due to a change in the dominant current direction from a southerly current off California to a northerly current along the east coast of Baja California.

Vinorama and Salado canyons are roughly V-shaped in transverse section. Detailed soundings at their heads, made by the junior author, show that each has a sharp change to a north-south trend near the shelf margin. Sonoprobe records on the shelf inside these canyon heads indicate a thin sediment cover over what appears to be a wave-cut terrace. No evidence of buried channels was apparent shoreward of either canyon despite their juxtaposition off the land valleys. A box core obtained in the head of Salado Canyon, at a depth of 480 ft (146

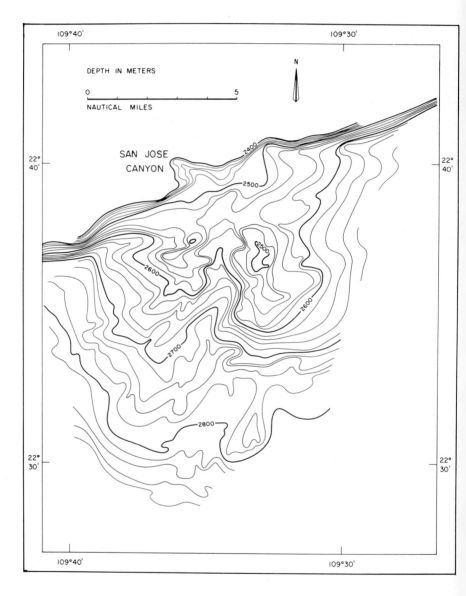

Fig. 59. The fan-valley found outside San Jose Canyon but not clearly connected with it. Note the hills on the levees. Contours above 2,400 m are not indicated.

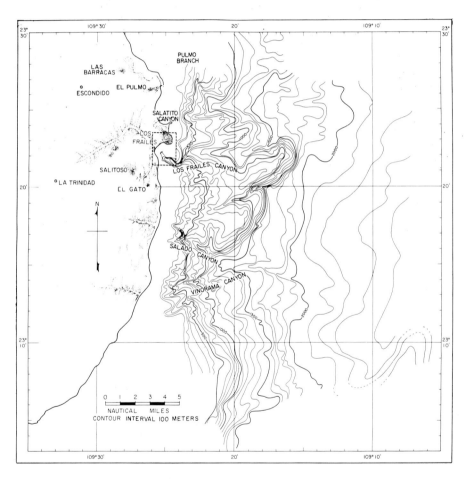

Fig. 60. The canyons in the vicinity of Los Frailes.
Note apparent relation to the land valleys. For inset
see Fig. 61. From surveys by Shepard.

m), had graded sediment with fine sand on the top and coarse shelly sand with fine gravel at the bottom.

Los Frailes (the monks) is a granite promontory 45 miles northeast of Cape San Lucas. Los Frailes Canyon heads in the bay south of the point of land (Fig. 61). The many tributaries that come in close to the shore have been explored extensively by scuba divers.

The largest of these branches is located directly offshore from the main arroyo that drains a large area of the land including La Trinidad, the highest mountain of the region. The studies of the arroyos on land indicate that there has been stream piracy and the branches forming the head of Los Frailes Canyon appear to reflect this piracy. The most active arroyo on land corresponds to the most prominent sea valley branch in the canyon head and less-incised sea valleys off old, abandoned arroyos. The tributaries are mostly asymmetrical in transverse section with the least slope facing the present-day source of land sediment. However, the sea-floor branches are quite different from their counterparts on land. Underwater, there are narrow V-shaped gorges with sharp bends and overhanging cliffs; on land, the arroyos are broad, shallow, relatively straight valleys.

In Los Frailes submarine canyon, beachrock was observed covering the granite at the upper lip of the tributaries. It appears to be found only off old drainage channels, but was not observed below depths of 200 ft (60 m). Both the beachrock and the underlying granite in the tributary heads have been greatly roughened by the activity of organisms. This roughness decreases with depth.

Los Frailes Canyon has a large number of branches, more for the area involved than in any other explored canyon. Starting as sand troughs, the branches become granite gorges in the short distance of a few hundred feet. The smaller tributaries are hanging valleys and spill sand into the larger tributaries.

Examination of the rock in the bottom of the gorges and at the lips of the hanging tributaries shows that the rock has been considerably smoothed in areas of sand movement, in contrast to the rock higher on the walls of the channels. The larger tributaries form narrow gorges, which are remarkable for their hourglass shape and their narrow defiles (Fig. 62). If the sea level at this point should be lowered, a decided contrast in topography of the exposed sea floor would be revealed from that on the present land where no narrow defiles can be seen near the coast.

A sequence of dives in this canyon head have shown that the fill is very unstable. In January, 1963, it was found that there had been extensive deepenings and one new head had been opened up, much like the event in 1950 at Scripps Canyon. Stakes planted in a line across one of the branches of Los Frailes in January, 1962, had moved slightly by April of the same year, with the usual forward bulge in the middle of the fill. In January of 1963, all stakes had disappeared, none being found down to depths of 200 ft (60 m).

Saucer dives made in February, 1965 by the junior author and Earl

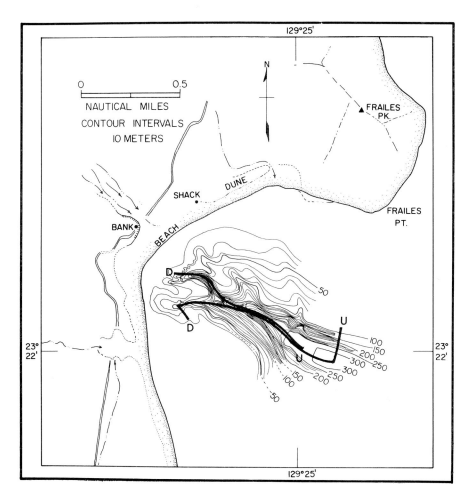

Fig. 61. Head of Los Frailes Canyon showing Saucer dive tracks down the canyon. D denotes down position, U up position. From surveys by Dill.

Murray descended to depths of 1,030 ft (315 m). Below a depth of 150 ft (45 m), the walls increase markedly in height and the channels become much narrower (Fig. 61). In places the walls are so close together that the Saucer could not penetrate along the axis and had to back up to rise over the constricted zone. Bedrock is exposed on the floor in many places, but for the most part during these 1965 dives,

Fig. 62. One of the narrow gorges that form the head of Los Frailes Canyon. Smoothed granite walls with hour-glass profiles in places overhang as much as 50 ft (15 m). Depth 200 ft (61 m). N.E.L. photo by Dill.

there was a layer of mud about a centimeter thick covering a predominantly sand fill. The muddy sediment may have come from the flash floods known to have occurred between September, 1964, and the time of the Saucer dives the following February. Where the tributaries come together at a depth of about 450 ft (135 m), the channel widens and the bottom is completely covered with sediment, including the thin mud cover found at shoaler depths.

At various places along the axis, fans have been built below hanging tributaries. These fans, up to 30 ft (9 m) above the adjacent floor, contain many well-rounded cobbles mixed with leaf and wood debris (Fig. 63). Below these fans, the slope of the sediment in the axis steepens abruptly, indicating that the build-up of the fans has triggered slumping. At depths of 660 and 900 ft (200 and 275 m) the junior author observed a series of slump scars 3 to 10 ft (1 to 3 m) high and approximately 50 ft (15 m) apart. These are indicative of progressive slumping. The toe of most of these slump scars contains a mixture of plants, shell, gravel, and cobbles. In these slump areas even the recent mud cover has been broken by the slumping, emphasizing the present instability of the sediment fill. The slump scars are outlined by large white patches, which apparently are caused by bacterial action on re-exposed organic material contained in the fill (Fig. 64). These outlines show that the slumps are localized within the fill and do not extend all the way across the canyon floor.

The granite walls along the channels show local undercutting. At most places the walls have a continuous organic growth down to the fill. However, in areas of slumping, organic growth ends abruptly and the wall rock is completely free of growth up to heights of 3 ft (1 m) above the fill (Fig. 65). Rock surfaces are relatively smoothed in these places.

The loss of marker stakes placed across the floor of two main tributaries verified that the sediment is periodically carried into deeper water. Because there is no appreciable fill along the axes of the tributaries down to a depth of 780 ft (240 m), the sediment containing the marker stakes must have moved beyond this depth. Another indication of sediment transport was the observation of active small sand falls below two of the hanging valleys that enter the main channel.

So far as Diving Saucer observations have gone, there were no signs of bottom currents. Furthermore, there was no indication of scour around the boulders nor were there any ripple marked surfaces, like those of San Lucas Canyon.

Seaward from where the branches of Los Frailes Canyon unite at a depth of about 820 ft (250 m), a narrow gorge continues for at least a mile. The steep walls of this gorge have fresh unweathered granite, which was obtained in dredges. The axis is somewhat winding, although to a lesser extent than in most other canyons. One possible tributary is located along the south side. There are not enough sounding lines to be sure there are no other small tributaries. The outer canyon has a wider floor than the inner part and has walls up to about 1,500 ft (460 m) in height. On the north side, dredging at a depth of 1,700 ft (520 m) yielded many granitic boulders partly recemented with manganese and limonite crusts. Fossil shells, said by F. L. G. Hertlein to be of Pliocene age, were obtained in the same

Fig. 63. Rounded cobbles up to 6 inches in diameter incorporated in the sandy fill of Los Frailes Canyon. The sediment surface is covered by a thin layer of clay. Depth 130 m (427 ft) below a hanging tributary to the main channel. N.E.L. photo from Diving Saucer by Dill.

dredgings. On the south side, granite was dredged from 4,500 ft (1,370 m). Apparently the shallow ridge that borders the outer canyon on the south owes its relief to a granite core.

The canyon terminates at about 5,200 ft (1,590 m). Beyond, is a fan-shaped deposit but no valley was found cutting into it.

Very little sediment was obtained from the canyon axis. One core of fine to very fine sand was so distorted that it was impossible to tell whether it was graded or had any structure. A dredge pulled along

Fig. 64. White patches of what appears to be a fungus where slump scars break the sedimentary fill and re-expose organic and plant material. These white patches often outline the area of slumping and indicate that the entire fill is not involved in any one slump. Depth 300 m (985 ft) in Los Frailes Canyon. N.E.L. photo from Diving Saucer by Dill.

the canyon axis brought up a large coherent mass of medium-grained sand with definite cross-bedding.

To the north of Los Frailes, the small Salatito Canyon has a head extending parallel to the coast and originating in 1,800 ft (550 m) of water. A dredge pulled along the south wall of the outer portion of this canyon yielded shallow-water shells, suggesting that some depth changes had taken place. There appears to be no shallow source for slide material or turbidity currents that could account for the depth at which the shells were found.

Fig. 65. The sharp break in growth (arrow) approximately 3 ft (1 m) above the sediment surface in Los Frailes Canyon. The wall is undercut and much smoother in the area not covered with growth, a possible indication of erosion by submarine processes at this depth of 250 m (820 ft). N.E.L. photo from Diving Saucer by Dill.

PALMAS BAY CANYONS (Fig. 66)

North of Los Frailes Canyon group, there is a gap of 14 miles without any true submarine canyons, although there is a series of slope valleys off Arena Point, which is discussed in Chapter XII. The next and northernmost canyon group along the eastern side of Baja California centers in Palmas Bay. About ten branches form the broad head and lie within a mile of the shore between Buena Vista and Pescadero Point. Another branch comes in near the shore 4 miles southeast of Buena Vista. This region is renowned for its excellent fishing and the best areas are associated with canyon heads.

All of the canyons that head in close to the coast join seaward and form a main canyon, called Pescadero. This group has a definite dendritic pattern and cuts the slope into a mature drainage form, like that off the San Lucas-San Jose area. On the land just south of Pescadero Point, there is a broad trough-shaped valley cut in sedimentary rocks. South of this valley there is a V-shaped canyon.

South of Pescadero Point, the valley heads are shallow enough for exploration by scuba diving. Here, approximately 1,000 ft (305 m) offshore, sandy slopes as steep as 30° were found by the junior author, and some gravel and cobbles were observed by Conrad Limbaugh (personal communication).

All of the Palmas Bay canyons have winding courses. Walls have heights up to 1,800 ft (550 m). The steepest wall is on the north side of the outer part of Pescadero Canyon where a bank rising from an axial depth of 5,000 ft (1,520 m) to 1,250 ft (380 m) has granitic rocks. Pescadero Canyon has a length of 9.3 miles or, including Palmas Canyon, a total of 13 miles. The Palmas Branch enters Pescadero Canyon at about 5,000 ft (1,520 m). The combined canyon terminates at approximately 6,000 ft (1,830 m). Beyond the canyon, there is a large fan with a fan-valley incised about 450 ft (140 m) below the surrounding levees. This fan-valley was traced seaward for 12 miles, trending in the same direction as Pescadero Canyon. However, the outermost part is not well sounded.

The southeast wall of Pescadero Canyon and Santiago Branch yielded most of the rocks dredged from the Palmas Bay group. Near the head of Santiago Branch, we obtained basalt with a finger-like flow structure. Lower, near the juncture with the main Las Palmas Canyon, a dredge brought up shale with foraminifera, identified by F. L. Parker as probably Miocene. At 4,500 ft (1,370 m) on the wall of Palmas Canyon, the dredge was anchored, but when broken loose had only a small fragment of crystalline rock. The walls of Pescadero Canyon are steep but dredges yielded only gravel, cobbles, and shells.

Piston coring in the canyons was generally unsuccessful, although two short cores of sand were obtained. A box core in the center of the fan-valley at 6,200 ft (1,890 m) retrieved silty-clay with thin sand layers. A core on the nearby levee showed mud underlain at 20 cm by 2 cm of very fine sand.

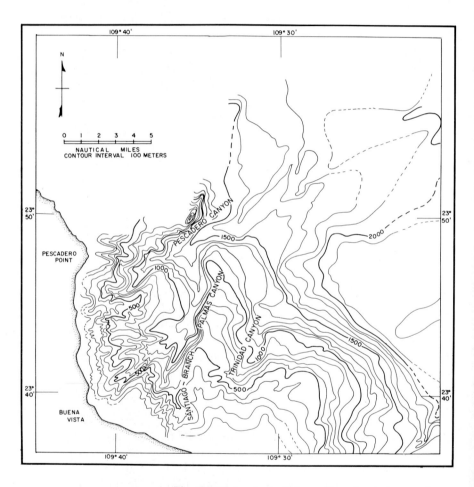

Fig. 66. Canyons in Palmas Bay along the southeast coast of Baja California. Note natural levees outside Pescadero Canyon. From surveys by Shepard.

CHAPTER VI

CANYONS
OF EASTERN HONSHU

T HE SUBMARINE CANYONS in the Tokyo area of eastern Honshu (Chart II) are of special interest because of their location in a zone of active tectonism and volcanism. Furthermore, Tokyo Canyon extends well into the mouth of a bay and has one branch entering a tributary bay. An unusual feature of these Honshu canyons is that, despite their close approach to the land, none have heads coming inside the 50 m (160 ft) contour. This is in contrast to the California and Baja California canyons. Canyons occur all along the east coast of Honshu from the head of Sagami Bay to the tip of Bōsō Peninsula. They are found intermittently along the east side of the peninsula, except for the large canyon that lies off Kamogawa Bay at the eastern end.

The Japanese have referred to the canyons from time to time since the great Tokyo earthquake of 1923 (Yamasaki, 1926; Terada, 1928), when interest in the submarine topography of the area developed. Rocks were dredged by Niino (1952) from several Japanese canyons and compared with those from land formations. In 1961, a cooperative study was made of the canyons by the Japanese University of Fisheries vessel *Umitaka Maru* and the Scripps Institution vessel *Spencer F. Baird* (Shepard *et al.*, 1964).

131

The geological setting for the east Honshu canyons is well known because it is in the most populated part of Japan. The coast in the Tokyo area alternates between mountainous uplands that extend as peninsulas into the sea, and coastal plains found at the heads of interpeninsula bays. Bōsō and Miura peninsulas, forming respectively the east and west sides of Tokyo Bay and Uraga Suido, consist of Tertiary sediments, sandstones, and pyroclastics, along with sediments of undifferentiated Mesozoic age. Izu Peninsula, west of the Sagami Bay canyons, has volcanic cones in various stages of erosion and lavas are associated with sedimentary rocks. The coastal plains at the head of the bays are formed by Pleistocene and Recent alluvium.

In addition to the volcanic activity just to the west of the canyon area, crustal instability is of a remarkably large order. A series of active north-south and east-west trending faults cut the peninsulas and undoubtedly extend out to sea (Chart II). The highly destructive 1923 earthquake, with its epicenter in the head of Sagami Bay, was accompanied by various changes in level of the coast at the bay head and at Tateyama, near the south end of Bōsō Peninsula. Evidence of earlier uplift is provided by wave-cut terraces, which extend up to 1,000 m (3,280 ft)[1] above sea level in Bōsō Peninsula; whereas the coastal area appears to have sunk, drowning the mouths of the river valleys.

TOKYO CANYON

Extensive surveys by the Japanese Hydrographic Office have allowed accurate contouring of the head of the canyon by Masuoki Horikoshi. His contours are used in this portion of our map (see also Nasu, 1964). The soundings of the *Baird* and the *Umitaka Maru,* combined with earlier Japanese surveys, have provided the basis for our contours of the outer part of the canyon.

Tokyo Canyon, with a total length of 30 miles, penetrates for about 20 miles into Uraga Suido, the strait that leads into Tokyo Bay. Here the name *canyon* seems well justified because the valley has steep rocky walls, a winding course, and a large number of dendritic tributaries. However, it is V-shaped only inside a 400-m (1,310 ft) axial depth, and the outer canyon has a flat floor never more than one mile across.

The head of the canyon is a seaward continuation of a broad channel extending up Tokyo Bay with an average depth of about 20 m (65 ft). Where the true canyon begins off Kurihama Wan, in the

[1]Note that because survey results were recorded in meters, meters are given first.

narrow entrance to Tokyo Bay, it has a gradient of 60 m/km. This is much lower than in the heads of most other nearshore submarine canyons. Beyond an axial depth of 300 m (980 ft) this gradient decreases to 20 m/km.

The axis of Tokyo Canyon changes direction at a depth of about 770 m (2,530 ft), bending to the west. This change takes place just north of where Tateyama Canyon enters Tokyo Canyon from the east. Tateyama Canyon is located along the continuation of a land graben, but it shows the winding course typical of canyons and has dendritic tributaries like the main Tokyo Canyon. Sounding lines along the sides of Tokyo Canyon show a surprisingly large number of tributaries.

Near the point where Tokyo Canyon extends seaward of the shelves off Miura and Bōsō peninsulas, it has walls approximately 900 m (2,950 ft) high on both sides. Traced seaward, Tokyo Canyon passes through a deep gorge between shallow banks without losing its flat floor. This gorge has steep walls, 1,300 m (4,270 ft) high on the southeast and 800 m (2,620 ft) on the northwest, comparable to the high-walled canyons off Baja California.

Dredging of the canyon walls has shown that there are occasional rock outcrops. However, several lengthy dredge hauls up the walls failed to retrieve rocks of any type. Rocks were photographed with an Edgerton camera in one place at a depth of 250 m (820 ft), although other camera traverses showed only sediment. Lava was found at two places on the walls. Broken blocks of siltstone and sandstone came up in the same dredge hauls as the volcanic rock. Lower Miocene and Pliocene sediments and volcanic tuffs were found along the west side of Bōsō Peninsula. Near the head of Tateyama Canyon, Lower Pleistocene deposits were encountered similar to the Nagai Formation.

Sediments from the floor of Tokyo Canyon show an interesting contrast between the inner north-south and the outer east-west trending parts. In the inner canyon, several long mud cores were obtained, two with brown oxidized zones on top at depths of 585 and 810 m (1,920 and 2,660 ft). The one at 585 m had a few angular sedimentary rock fragments. At an axial depth of 805 m (2,640 ft), just west of the change in the axial trend, a long core had a series of sand layers interbedded with mud. All of these sands had small percentages of gravel of a volcanic origin, partly pumice and tuff (Fig. 67). Compared to cores from other areas of canyon investigation, the sands in this core were surprisingly free of mica but contained an abundance of pumice and lava. According to F. L. Parker (personal communication), some of the benthonic foraminifera are from shallow water, indicating transport down the axis. At 1,000 m (3,280 ft), a thin mud layer was found overlying rock fragments and clean sand. At 1,300 m (4,265 ft), the core tube was bent, suggesting hard-packed sand or rocks. The outer part of the canyon thus appears to have much more coarse sediment than the inner canyon north of the change in axis direction.

Tokyo Canyon terminates at about 1,500 m (4,920 ft) in Sagami

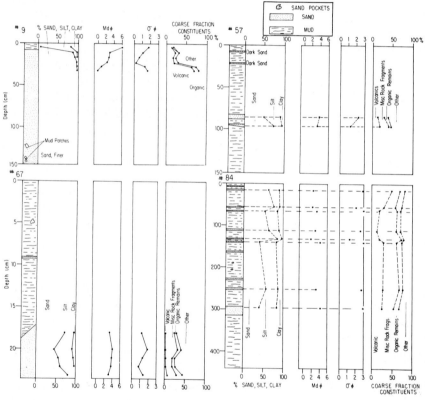

Fig. 67. Nature of sediments in long cores from Honshu canyons and Sagami Trough. Sample numbers given in upper left corner of each block. Sample 9 is from floor of Sagami Trough at depth of 917 m (3,008 ft), sample 57 is from axis of Tokyo Canyon at 800 m (2,625 ft), sample 67 is from axis of Kamogawa Canyon at depth of 2,470 m (8,104 ft), and sample 84 is from axis of Tokyo Canyon at depth of 805 m (2,641 ft).

Trough, the large fault valley (p. 233) that extends down Sagami Bay. In the trough there is evidence of a fan cut by a fan-valley, the latter dying out at approximately 1,600 m (5,250 ft). From available soundings, there is no indication that this fan-valley has steep walls, such as were found in some of the fan-valleys off western North America. In this fan-valley, at 1,460 m (4,790 ft) a piston core obtained only 22 cm of mud, and at 1,545 m (5,068 ft) a gravity core contained only a little sand and some small pieces of gravel in the nose. This is another locality where coarse material has been carried beyond the canyon mouth into the fan-valley.

KAMOGAWA CANYON

The only other large canyon that extends in close to the Japanese coast is located about 20 miles east of Tokyo Canyon (Chart II). It can be traced seaward for at least 25 miles. There is no large estuary inside this canyon, but two of the three small canyon heads point respectively towards the broad bight constituting Kamogawa Bay and the narrower Kominato Bay. The latter bay has a narrow channel of small depth that dies out at the bay mouth. Kamogawa Canyon was first contoured by Hoshino and Sato (1960), who based their map on the Japanese surveys. They made reference to the rocky walls of the canyon.

Kamogawa Canyon, like Tokyo Canyon and its branches, does not extend inside the 50 m (164 ft) contour, but the 100 m (328 ft) contour shows the presence of three inner branches. These merge at about 500 m (1,640 ft) and a V-shaped canyon extends seaward with broad gentle curves, in contrast to the greater sinuosity of Tokyo Canyon. A scarcity of soundings longitudinal to the canyon axis makes it difficult to be sure there are no small tributaries coming in above the juncture of Habuto Canyon. There are enough soundings, however, from the Japanese survey combined with the soundings of the *Spencer F. Baird* to show that no large tributaries enter in this portion. At a depth of 500 m (1,640 ft), the gradient of the canyon head is about 130 m/km, twice as steep as the head of Tokyo Canyon. At greater depth it decreases in slope rather abruptly to 80 m/km out to 1,300 m (4,265 ft). Then it increases to 120 m/km out to its juncture with Habuto Canyon. The outer canyon has a few tributaries of small relief.

The canyon loses its V-shape at 1,300 m (4,265 ft) depth. Beyond this point there is a flat floor about one mile across, similar to that of Tokyo Canyon. Below the juncture with Habuto Canyon the floor widens again, reaching widths of about 1.5 miles. In the V-shaped part the canyon has walls up to about 700 m (2,300 ft) in height, and sedimentary rock has been dredged from them by the Japanese as well as by the *Spencer F. Baird*. Also, photographs with an Edgerton camera showed steeply-inclined layers of rock on the west wall.

The walls of Kamogawa Canyon attain heights of as much as 1,200 m (3,940 ft), greater than those found in Tokyo Canyon. At 2,500 m (8,200 ft), the profiles again become V-shaped. The canyon appears to terminate along a westerly course, running into the outer continuation of Sagami Fault Trough. It is also possible that the canyon bends to the east at this point and continues seaward to depths of at least 3,200 m (10,500 ft). The sounding lines in this outer part were beyond radar control and hence poorly located. The strong, variable Kuroshio Current added to the difficulties of positioning by dead reckoning, and no astronomical fixes were possible at the time when the outer lines were run.

Several attempts were made to dredge the outer walls. At 1,750 m (5,742 ft) one piece of shale was obtained, but otherwise the dredges came up empty. Coring showed that coarse sediment is found even out to depths slightly in excess of 2,400 m (7,870 ft). Sand layers at 2,470 m (8,100 ft) (Fig. 67) in the axis contained shallow-water foraminifera, including *Elphidium* (F. L. Parker, personal communication). Plant material, presumably from shallow water, was also found in the sands. At 2,425 m (7,955 ft), a piston core came up with a bent barrel and only a small amount of gravel.

CANYONS OF NORTHEAST SAGAMI BAY

At least six small canyons cut the slopes on the northeast side of Sagami Bay (Chart II). The valley at the head of the bay may belong in the fault valley category, but the others appear to be true submarine canyons. They have V-shaped profiles (Fig. 68), steep walls with outcropping rock, winding courses, and tributaries with a somewhat dendritic pattern. These canyons head in water with depths of 70 to 120 m (230 to 400 ft). Although the shelf landward of the canyons is narrow, there is no clear evidence that any of the canyons are related to the land valleys of the area. To the south, Jogashima Canyon winds seaward to join the equally twisting Misaki Canyon at a depth of nearly 1,000 m (3,300 ft). The latter has two branches at its head. The combined canyon enters Sagami Trough at a depth of about 1,400 m (4,590 ft). At the head of Jogashima Canyon there is a gradient of

SUBMARINE CANYON CROSS SECTION, EASTERN SAGAMI WAN

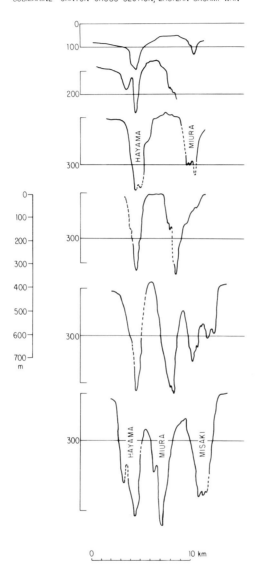

Fig. 68. Profiles of canyons in northeast Sagami Bay, taken directly from fathograms of Japanese Fisheries vessel *Umitaka Maru*. For locations of canyons see Chart II.

about 200 m/km, whereas Misaki drops only 75 m/km. Beyond the juncture, the gradient of the two is reduced to 30 m/km. Shale was dredged from the walls of Misaki Canyon.

Miura Canyon extends in to about one mile (2 km) from the shore, the nearest approach of any of this group. It has several small tributaries and winds seaward to join Hayama Canyon at a depth of about 1,000 m (3,280 ft), approximately the same depth as the juncture of Jogashima and Misaki canyons. The outer continuation extends between two banks where its walls are about 600 m (1,970 ft) high. This is the deepest cut in this group of canyons and, although not as deep as Tokyo and Kamogawa canyons, it has wall heights comparable with those of such land canyons as Zion in Utah. Five miles farther out, the canyon merges into the floor of Sagami Trough at a depth of slightly more than 1,400 m (4,600 ft). Dredging on the walls of Miura and Hayama canyons shows that rock occurs locally. On the north wall of Miura Canyon at 650 m (2,133 ft), a muddy sandstone with animal borings was obtained. Near the head of the canyon, siltstone fragments were dredged. On the south wall of Hayama Canyon, similar material came from 150 and 250 m (492 and 820 ft). Cores were largely mud, but one gravity core at 580 m (1,903 ft) contained 15 cm of gravelly sand and hard clay.

Enoshima Canyon heads with two small branches 3 miles off Eno-shima Island in water about 120 m (390 ft) deep. The canyon is joined by a tributary from the north at a depth of 850 m (2,790 ft). Above this juncture it is V-shaped, but broadens below and enters a very broad trough at a depth of 1,030 m (3,380 ft) where it ceases to have any canyon characteristics. The walls of Enoshima Canyon have also yielded siltstone. Cores along the axis show the presence of a sandy mud at 534 m (1,752 ft), and in the trough just outside of the canyon, a core had a black silty sand underlain by gravelly sand with abundant charcoal.

Sagami Canyon, off the large Sagami River, is actually a group of small valleys that all head about a mile from the shore at a depth of about 100 m (330 ft). Most of the valleys come together in a broad trough at 850 m (2,790 ft). Beyond this juncture, the canyon becomes indefinite, but apparently enters Sagami Trough at 1,000 m (3,280 ft). Dredges brought up sandstone from the slope near the head of one branch.

There is some question whether or not the feature called Ninomiya Canyon should be classified as a canyon. It has V-shaped profiles in the inner part where it runs parallel to the shore, but it has no tributaries, and its outer valley enters Sagami Trough along a known fault. Rock was photographed on the southeast wall of the canyon head.

MERA CANYON (Fig. 69)

Mera Canyon, located outside of the narrow coastal plain in the southwest corner of Bōsō Peninsula, is the third largest of the east Honshu canyons. It has a length of approximately 20 miles and is a true canyon in every sense of the word. It heads 1.6 miles off the coast in a depth of about 70 m (230 ft). Unlike many of the others, it has only one head but gathers numerous tributaries along its winding course. The general trend forms a broad curve, starting southwest and bending around to northwest and then back to southwest where it enters Sagami Trough at a depth of about 1,670 m (5,500 ft). Along most of this course it has a V-shaped profile, although the floor may flatten in the outer part where we have no profiles. At rim depths of about 100 m (330 ft), the canyon floor is as deep as 750 m (2,460 ft), somewhat greater than the deepest cuts in the northeast Sagami Bay canyons.

Mera Canyon has two large tributaries, Inoko and Suno canyons. These both enter from the north, which is the landward side of the main canyon in this section. Suno Canyon is very broad in its intermediate section and some of the profiles suggest it is more of a trough than a canyon. However, it has a V-shaped profile near the juncture with Mera Canyon and has tributaries at the canyon head.

Dredging showed that at least the inner part of Mera Canyon has rock walls. A variety of sedimentary types were obtained, including mudstone, shale, sandstone, and breccia. A photograph of the canyon floor showed a rock outcrop at a depth of about 500 m (1,640 ft). Dredging the walls of Suno and Inoko canyons also produced sedimentary rocks. Coring was mostly unsuccessful on the canyon floor near the head of Mera Canyon. One core, however, contained a few rock fragments, and in others only a few grains of sand were found.

Current Ripples in Mera Canyon

Near the head of Mera Canyon, the published nautical chart has a note reading "overfalls occur at certain seasons." This place is approximately at the juncture point of the powerful Kuroshio (Japanese Current) and the outflowing tides from Tokyo Bay. The Japanese often refer to this as the point of greatest turbulence observed in approaching Tokyo Bay. We were fortunate in carrying on operations in this area at a time when the sea was unusually calm and when almost no current was evident at the surface. We lowered the Edgerton camera a short distance from the axis of Mera Canyon and got photographs while the apparatus drifted slowly down the north wall to the floor of the canyon at 500 m (1,640 ft) depth, and then changing direction, drifted up the axis. During most of the traverse, the photographs showed current ripple marks of a type suggesting strong currents (Fig. 70a). Many of the troughs between ripple crests show rock or gravel exposed below the sand (Fig. 70b). We estimated

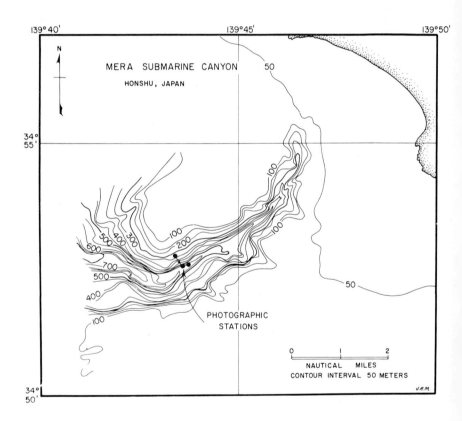

Fig. 69. The head of Mera Canyon off the Bōsō Peninsula. Photograph stations for Fig. 70 indicated by arrow.

a

b

c

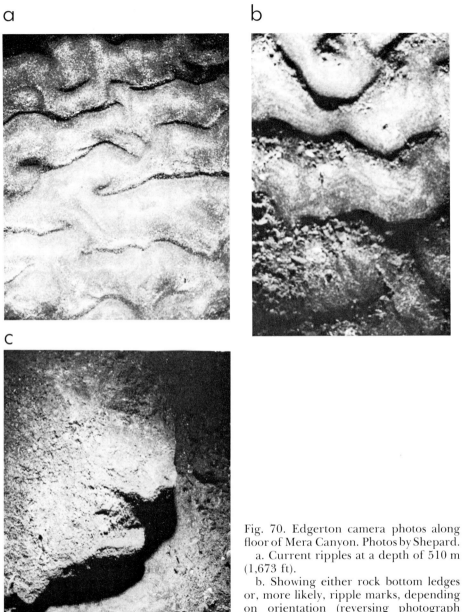

Fig. 70. Edgerton camera photos along floor of Mera Canyon. Photos by Shepard.

a. Current ripples at a depth of 510 m (1,673 ft).

b. Showing either rock bottom ledges or, more likely, ripple marks, depending on orientation (reversing photograph changes its character).

c. Rock outcropping on the floor of Mera Canyon. Depth 495 m (1,625 ft).

that the wave length of the ripples was about 20 cm. A sigmoid ripple pattern prevails. The photographs show no suspended sediment, so it can be assumed that the condition producing the ripples was not present at that time. The photographs also show rock exposed on the floor of the canyon (Fig. 70c).

Some connection seems likely between the pronounced bottom ripples and the confused high-velocity surface currents at the juncture of the Kuroshio and the tidal flow from Tokyo Bay.

CHAPTER VII

SUBMARINE CANYONS
OFF EASTERN
UNITED STATES

SYSTEMATIC FIELD STUDIES have not been as extensive for the submarine canyons off the east coast of North America as for those off California and Baja California. This is because the eastern canyons head many miles from land and there are rough sea conditions during the fall and winter months. However, much general information has been obtained from these canyons by several groups. Of particular importance are the U.S. Coast and Geodetic soundings of the upper continental slope in the area between Georges Bank and Cape Hatteras, made from 1930 to 1937. During the last years of his life, A. C. Veatch became deeply interested in the topography revealed by these soundings. His devoted efforts to the contouring of the eastern continental slopes contined to the time when his increasing illness made work impossible. He was joined in this project by Paul A. Smith, who brought the work to a conclusion after Veatch's death (Veatch and Smith, 1939).

Henry Stetson, pioneer in submarine geology, had begun to study the east coast canyons in 1934. Working from Woods Hole's *Atlantis,* he dredged the walls and cored the floors of most of the principal canyons between Georges Bank and Chesapeake Bay. His success in obtaining sedimentary rock, ranging from Cretaceous to Pliocene in age, represented a milestone in canyon studies (Stetson, 1936, 1949). Also, Stetson (1937) was the first to measure current velocities on the floors of submarine canyons in his investigations off Georges Bank.

Studies by Lamont Geological Observatory personnel, with the field work principally under the leadership of Bruce Heezen, has produced numerous sounding lines seaward of the outer limit of the U.S. Coast and Geodetic Survey coverage. Other lines have been run by ships of the Woods Hole Oceanographic Institution. A compilation of all of these data has been made by Uchupi (in press) and is reproduced in Figure 71. This provides important information on the outer canyon continuations and on the extensive fan-valleys that can be traced seaward from them for many miles down the continental rise. Emery (1965) gives a comprehensive review of the geology of the continental margin off the eastern United States. Many cores were obtained by Heezen in this outer area, but only a few in the valleys. These cores have been described by Ericson *et al.* (1961). In recent years, a number of continuous reflection profiles have been run by Woods Hole scientists across the canyons outside Georges Bank (Roberson, 1964). Also, extensive soundings and bathyscaph dives have been made in the area where the submarine *U.S.S. Thresher* sank (Hurley, 1963). Many papers have been written about the east coast canyons and their origin (Shepard, 1934; Stetson, 1936; Daly, 1936; Bucher, 1940). Johnson (1939) used the East Coast canyons as the chief basis for a book. Kuenen (1953) developed a special classification of sea valleys called "New England Type" to characterize the East Coast canyons, in contrast with other sea canyons such as those off California and Corsica.

EAST COAST CANYONS AS A TYPE

The canyons off the East Coast differ from most of those described in previous chapters in that they head many miles out from shore, near the outer edge of the continental shelf. Inside Hudson Canyon, a shelf valley extends in to the coast (Fig. 3), but this is very different from the slope canyons. At least 18 slope canyons notch the outer shelf margin between Georges Bank and Cape Hatteras. An almost equal number head on the slope beyond. Because Kuenen thought of these valleys as different from other canyons, which he called "ravines," we need to justify including his "New England Type" here under the submarine canyon classification.

Kuenen agrees that both the "ravines" and "New England Types" have similar longitudinal and transverse profiles. However, he was impressed by the fact that the East Coast canyons extend in a relatively straight line down the slope with only widely rounded bends, in contrast to the sharp bends of many of those off California and elsewhere. He also called attention to the fact that the East Coast valleys continue all the way to the bottom of the slope, whereas he stated that the "ravines" off the west coast of Corsica and the Riviera stop part way down the slope. Actually, as discussed in Chapter VIII, we now know that the Corsican and Riviera canyons do go to the base of the slopes. Aside from their lack of sinuosity, the valleys off the East Coast have most or all of the characteristics of typical submarine canyons, including V-shaped profiles, steep walls with rock outcrops, and dendritic tributaries coming in from both sides. They are therefore included here among the submarine canyons.

HUDSON CANYON (Fig. 72)

By far the most completely studied of the East Coast canyons is located off New York Harbor. It was first referred to by Dana (1864) more than a hundred years ago. He described the shallow valley that crosses the shelf almost to the canyon head (Fig. 3). Sounding seaward of this valley, surveyors later found indications of the deep slope canyon (Lindenkohl, 1885). The canyon heads in 300 ft (90 m) of water, with two or possibly three branches coming together at depths of about 600 ft (180 m). Traced seaward, the axis winds gently down the slope with numerous small entering tributaries, none at all comparable in size with the main canyon. The canyon is cut 2,500 ft (760 m) below the shelf edge, and farther down, where the axis attains depths of 6,000 ft (1,830 m), it has walls about 4,000 ft (1,220 m) high.

So far as one can tell from available information, the canyon runs into a fan-valley at a depth of about 7,000 ft (2,130 m). The gradient at the canyon head is about 25 m/km out to 3,500 ft (1,070 m), but it increases to 35 m/km during the next 3,000 ft (910 m) of axis deepening. As Kuenen (1953) has indicated, this increase in gradient occurs near the outer break of the continental shelf in the marginal zone. At greater depths, the slope is decreased to 15 m/km and averages only about 25 m/km for the entire canyon, not counting the

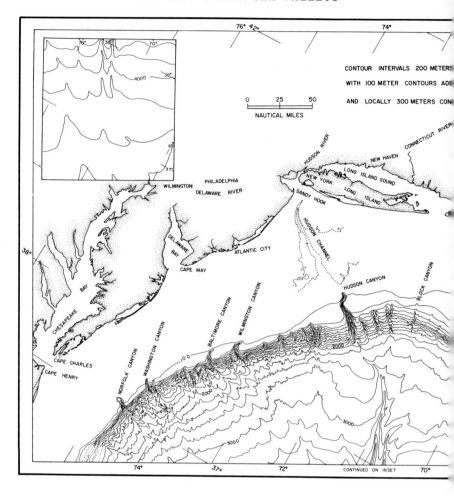

Fig. 71. The canyons off the northeast coast of the
United States. Slightly modified from a map by Elazar
Uchupi, U.S. Geological Survey, Misc. Geol. Investi-
gations Map I-451. (Courtesy of K. O. Emery)

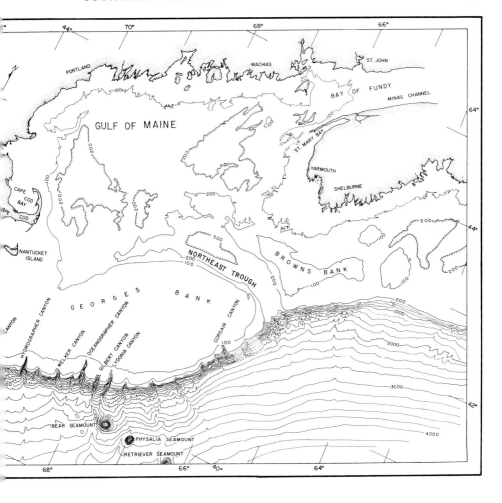

fan-valley that extends beyond. This gradient, it will be noted, is decidedly less than the axial slopes of most Pacific canyons.

Dredging of the canyon wall by Stetson (1949) failed to reveal any rock. Cores obtained by Stetson at axial depths of from 1,340 ft to 5,060 ft (408 to 1,542 m) were largely fine silts, but several of them contained cold-water foraminifera at core depths of about 50 cm. This thick deposit appears to indicate a lack of disturbance (creep, sliding, turbidity currents, etc.) during postglacial times. A core grading downward from coarse silt to very fine sand came from 1,130 ft (344 m). In another core at 1,140 ft (347 m), a very fine sand graded downward to fine sand that overlies silt. Also, at 2,200 ft (670 m) a core showed fine sand overlying silt. The numerous Lamont cores from this general area were taken seaward of the canyons, but the cores provide much information on the fan and the fan-valley outside (Ericson *et al.*, 1961).

Beyond the canyon, there is a very large and extensive composite fan (Fig. 71). The Lamont and Woods Hole soundings show that this

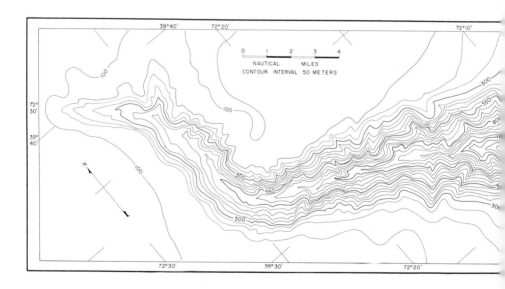

fan is traversed by a fan-valley for at least 200 miles and to a depth of at least 15,000 ft (4,570 m). The sounding lines are not spaced closely enough to determine whether the channel is sinuous, like the valley seaward of La Jolla Canyon, but it does have a gently curving axis. Profiles made by Heezen *et al.* (1959) show that at the head of the fan, the valley walls are only 300 ft (90 m) high, but increase to 1,800 ft (550 m) about 80 miles down the fan. The height then decreases to 600 ft (180 m) or less beyond axial depths of 12,600 ft (3,840 m) (Fig. 73). A similar sequence of changes in wall heights beyond the canyon has already been described for Coronado and Monterey fan-valleys. Another fan-valley cuts the continental rise approximately 25 miles to the northeast. After converging slightly, this valley runs parallel to Hudson Fan-valley and cuts almost as deeply below the surrounding fan.

Lamont scientists have extensively cored the Hudson fan, providing us with a considerable amount of information concerning both the fan and the fan-valley. The latter is referred to as the "Hudson Canyon"

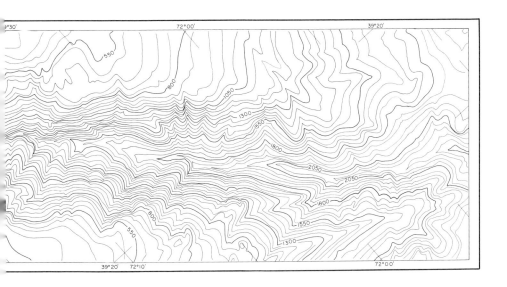

Fig. 72. The Hudson Canyon off New York. For relations to the shelf channel see Fig. 3. Recontoured in meters from an unpublished contour map by K. O. Emery based on unpublished soundings by U.S. Coast and Geodetic Survey.

by Ericson, but the cores come from what we define as a fan-valley. Three cores were obtained from the wall of the fan-valley in the outer gorge at depths between 10,000 and 12,500 ft (3,048 to 3,810 m). All of these cores have only a thin cover of Pleistocene and Recent sediment and continue down to Miocene, described as "marcasite lutite" (Ericson et al., 1961, pp. 234, 235). According to Ericson, the radiolaria from this old sediment were identified by W. R. Riedel as showing that the formations are of Miocene or Pliocene age. Two cores from the floor of the gorge in the fan-valley (Ericson, 1952) contained a confused mixture of gravel, cobbles, and shells with a mud matrix. Richards and Ruhle (1955) described the shells as including shallow-water species mixed with species of moderate depth; some of them are extinct. An examination of this material reveals that at least some of it is not typical of deep water marine sands, because pebbles up to 2 cm in diameter are embedded in a muddy matrix (Fig. 74). However, the shallow-water shells indicate considerable displacement down this gorge. The bottom of one of the fan-valley cores has a green pyritic clay, similar to the Miocene (?) found in the walls (Ericson et al., 1961).

The numerous cores, described by Ericson, from the fan in the vicinity of Hudson Fan-valley have indications that may show the importance of downslope currents. One 12 m (39 ft) core (#164-24) obtained near the fan-valley has a 6 m (20 ft) layer of very fine sand under silty clay, the latter also approximately 6 m (20 ft) thick. According to Scripps Institution analyses, the sand in the bottom layer is one continuous graded bed.

The history of the Hudson Fan-valley is apparently complex. Continuous reflection profiling should be used to determine whether the older formations are nearer the surface of the fan along the outer gorge than in the fan-valley on either side. The suggestion is made that there may have been an uplift of the Miocene (?) under this portion of the fan, producing steepening of the fan gradient and hence greater submarine erosion. We are in complete agreement with Ericson et al. (1961) that erosion has taken place in the fan since the deposition of the deep-water Late Tertiary formation.

GEORGES BANK CANYONS

The canyons off Georges Bank (Fig. 71) include several almost as large as Hudson Canyon. Most of the large ones lie off the southwestern part of the bank and there is only one sizeable canyon on the

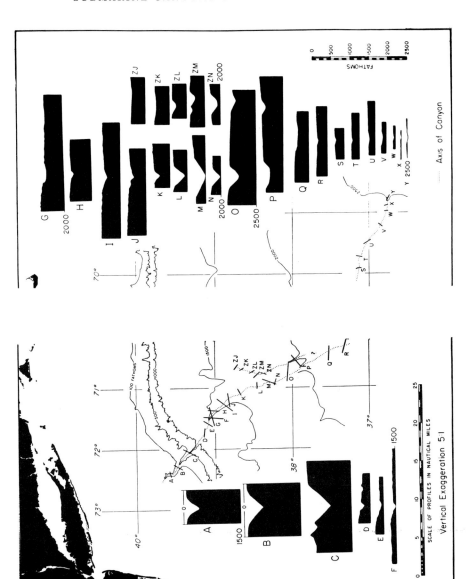

Fig. 73. Cross-sections of Hudson Canyon and Fan-
valley. From Heezen et al. (1959, Fig. 17).

southeast of the shoal part of the bank. It is also notable that there is no large canyon off the deep Northeast Trough, which represents the outlet from the Gulf of Maine. The series of canyons that cut the shelf edge off Georges Bank were first described by the senior author (Shepard, 1934) shortly after accompanying the U.S. Coast and Geodetic Survey on a trip to the area. Stetson investigated the canyons by dredging and coring from the *Atlantis* and described the results in his detailed reports (Stetson, 1936, 1949). The charting by the Coast and Geodetic Survey terminated seaward at depths of approximately 6,600 ft (2,010 m) without getting to the lowest limit of the canyons. Because of positioning difficulties, the outer part of the survey consists largely of lines run down, rather than along, the slopes.[1] These

[1]These transverse lines allowed the ships to return more frequently to the shelf where they could obtain fixes with their bombs and sono buoys better than on the slopes.

Fig. 74. Pebbles embedded in a muddy matrix of core from the Hudson Fan-valley. Scale is given in centimeters. Courtesy of D. B. Ericson, Lamont Geological Observatory.

lines that run parallel to the valley axes are not very satisfactory for contouring canyons. The Veatch and Smith (1939) contours (as they frankly admitted) were based on the hypothesis that the slope had been maturely dissected by ancient rivers. The topography of the slope, even beyond where justified by the soundings, was interpreted as typical of stream erosion. Thus, their contours indicate that Oceanographer, Gilbert, and Lydonia canyons are still deep narrow gorges at axial depths of about 8,000 ft (2,440 m). The outermost U.S. Coast and Geodetic Survey crossings, however, are respectively at 6,450, 6,600, and 5,500 ft (1,970, 2,010, and 1,680 m), although Gilbert Canyon may go to 7,800 ft (2,380 m), as shown by a 180 ft (55 m) dip in a transverse line. It now seems more likely that the canyons off Georges Bank stop at about 7,000 ft (2,130 m) depth, but fan-valleys continue seaward off some of the canyons (Fig. 71). The continental terrace profiles off the East Coast shown by Heezen *et al.* (1959, Pl. 24, sec. W12-14) indicate a depth a little shoaler than 7,000 ft (2,130 m) for the top of the continental rise. The surveys run during the search for the sunken submarine *U.S.S. Thresher* show that well-developed fan-valleys off Eastern Georges Bank extend to a depth of at least 8,400 ft (2,560 m) (Hurley, 1963).

It may be pure coincidence, but all of the Georges Bank canyons swing to the right near their heads inside the shelf, and then bend left downslope. All of the canyons of the Georges Bank area lack connection with valleys on land. About half of them head a few miles inside the outer margin of the shelf, and the rest start on the upper slope at or near the shelf margin. The canyons that deeply indent the shelf have higher walls in their intermediate zones than the canyons heading beyond the shelf margin, but beyond axial depths of about 6,000 ft (1,830 m) there is no difference in wall height between the two types. It is as if a series of canyons with more or less the same dimensions existed at first along the slope, and subsequently the heads of a few canyons were cut into the shelf without any further excavation of the outer parts. More examination of this situation would seem to be desirable, because it may indicate piracy of a limited sediment source as sea level rose after the retreat of the glaciers from Georges Bank.

Most of the canyons off New England are named after the Coast and Geodetic Survey ships that operated in the area. They include, from west to east: Hydrographer, Welker, Oceanographer, Gilbert, and Lydonia canyons (Fig. 71). At the extreme west is Veatch Canyon, named after A. C. Veatch, and at the easternmost end, Corsair

Canyon, named after J. P. Morgan's old yacht, which was given to the Coast and Geodetic Survey.

Oceanographer Canyon

The deepest indentation of the continental shelf of the Georges Bank group is found at Oceanographer Canyon, off the southwest part of the bank (Fig. 75). This canyon penetrates for 12.5 miles into the shelf, almost as far as Hudson Canyon. Because only the latter appears to be connected with a major land valley, this comparison suggests that depth of shelf penetration here may not depend on land drainage, but on the position of shoreline during glacial episodes. At this time, there may have been considerable runoff onto the exposed shelf from the margin of the ice cap that stood at the inner margin of Georges Bank. Also, after the ice margin withdrew, the waves would have reworked the moraines as the sea level rose.

Oceanographer Canyon has only a slightly curving axis and the sounding lines made along the walls of the canyon show many small tributaries. The profiles of the main canyon are apparently all V-shaped, although the outermost crossing at 6,450 ft (1,970 m) shows a terrace on the east side at approximately 6,100 ft (1,860 m). The highest walls, averaging 3,725 ft (1,130 m), are found at an axial depth of 4,600 ft (1,400 m). The walls at this point rise to ridge tops at depths of 1,000 and 750 ft (305 and 230 m). This is almost as high as the walls of Hudson Canyon and is comparable with most of the large West Coast canyons. Only a short fan-valley is indicated seaward of Oceanographer Canyon.

Hydrographer Canyon

Farther to the southwest, Hydrographer Canyon indents the shelf about 11 miles with a three-pronged head at a depth of about 360 ft (110 m). It probably continues seaward as a canyon to at least 6,000 ft (1,830 m). At an axial depth of 5,800 ft (1,770 m), it has walls of 3,600 ft (1,100 m) high on one side and 2,000 ft (610 m) on the other. The general trend is straight or gently curving, like that of the other East Coast canyons. Too few soundings have been made to determine whether or not there are tributaries, but it seems likely that some of the adjacent slope canyons enter the main valley in relatively deep water.

According to available information (Fig. 71) Hydrographer Canyon extends seaward as a fan-valley across the adjoining continental rise to depths of about 14,000 ft (4,270 m). No data are available to show the exact character of this fan-valley.

Lydonia Canyon (Fig. 75)

The easternmost of the closely spaced large canyons, Lydonia, also penetrates for about 11 miles into the shelf and heads at about 360 ft (110 m). The sounding lines that run along the walls of the canyon show many small but no large tributaries. The outer limit of the canyon is very problematic, in both position and depth, due to scarcity of transverse lines. A crossing at 4,650 ft (1,420 m) is the deepest transverse line, but it is likely that a longitudinal line crosses the canyon again at 5,500 ft (1,680 m), as indicated by the Veatch and Smith contours. A fan-valley apparently extends seaward of Lydonia and Gilbert canyons for about 60 miles. This valley is cut just as deep below surroundings as Hudson Fan-valley and extends past two seamounts along its course.

Wall Character of Georges Bank Canyons

The extensive dredging operations by Stetson (1936, 1949) have given a rather good indication of wall material in the Georges Bank canyons. The finding of Cretaceous formations in place on the east sides of Oceanographer and Gilbert canyons is particularly significant because these rocks came from a point just below the outer margin of the shelf. This shows that, despite the gentle dip-slopes indicated by continuous reflection profiling (Roberson, 1964), the shelf in these places has not been built out very far since the Cretaceous. The dredgings contained massive sandstones, suggesting that the canyons were eroded through some durable rock. Eocene marl (Jackson Formation) was dredged from some of the smaller canyons (referred to as "gullies" by Stetson). Talus of highly indurated Miocene sandstones belonging to the Yorktown Formation was found on the walls of Corsair, Lydonia, and Hydrographer canyons. One outcropping rock was broken from the walls of Lydonia. In addition, Pliocene greensands have been taken from Lydonia Canyon and Late Pliocene or Pleistocene silts from four of the valleys.

So far as one can judge, the walls of these Georges Bank canyons are as rocky as most others, although, of course, no crystalline rocks were found in this area where basement is deeply buried (Drake *et al.*

1959). The typical formations are soft rocks with only occasional material firm enough to stop the progress of the dredging vessel. In one place, according to Stetson (1949, Fig. 2), the dredge appears to have been hanging over a vertical cliff, because the wire cut a groove into the rock before the dredge hung up and the rock slab was finally broken loose. This is the only evidence of precipitous cliffs in this region, but they may exist elsewhere.

Continuous Seismic Profile Surveys of Georges Bank Canyons

The results of the sound profiling along the margin of Georges Bank (Roberson, 1964) across Oceanographer, Gilbert, and Lydonia canyons showed that there are a few buried channels at their heads (Fig. 75). There may be some remnants of a Pliocene fill along the canyon walls, indicating an earlier stage of erosion (possibly subaerial) fol-

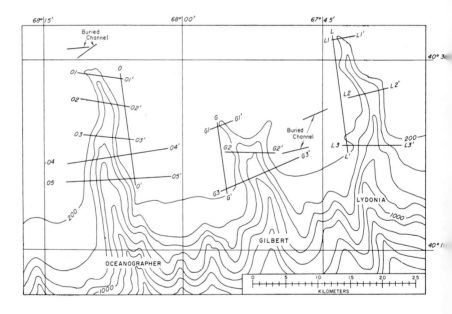

Fig. 75. Three canyons along the margin of Georges Bank. Depths are in meters. Buried channels are indicated from continuous reflection profiles. From Roberson (1964).

lowed by submergence and filling and then re-excavation. The pro-filer also showed that Tertiary and Cretaceous formations, identified by Stetson's dredgings, slope gently seaward but are cut by the steeper continental slope. Locally, the formations may dip slightly into the canyons along the margin, but are in general horizontal in transverse profiles.

Cores from The Georges Bank Canyons

Most of the core data from this locality also was obtained by Stetson (1949, Table 2). Unfortunately, these cores were studied before it was appreciated that deep-sea sand layers were an important item in submarine canyons, and analyses were made from samples taken at random depths in the cores. Therefore, the presence of sand layers and particularly of graded beds may have been overlooked. It is significant, however, that Stetson found the top 8 cm of one core taken at 2,520 ft (768 m) in Gilbert Canyon had fine gravel with a median diameter of 2.72 mm. He also found a fine sand at the top of a core with a first quartile of coarse-grained sand in Gilbert Canyon in 7,180 ft (2,190 m), and a fine sand at the top of a core from Oceanographer Canyon at 4,000 ft (1,219 m). A fine sand was found below a layer of mud at 6,300 ft (1,920 m) in a small valley between Lydonia and Gilbert canyons. A core taken by Lamont from Hydrog-rapher Canyon at 5,880 ft (1,792 m) was described by Ericson *et al.* (1961, pp. 208, 219) as having a series of "sand or silt layers all below the surface." Another Lamont core in the Hydrographer Fan-valley at 7,500 ft (2,286 m), has a sand bed at the top that is almost 3 m (10 ft) thick and overlies silty clays; the sand grades downward from fine-grained to medium-grained (Shepard, 1961, Fig. 2). In the same fan-valley, a third core from a depth of 8,700 ft (2,652 m) contained a series of sand layers.

Another important discovery by Stetson from the Georges Bank canyons was that several cores penetrated through the Recent into Wisconsin glacial age sediments. The evidence for Wisconsin age came from the cold water foraminifera, identified by Phleger (1942). In the canyon axis, the sediment at the base of the cores had a colder planktonic assemblage than that found in the surface layers. The Holocene sediments are greenish silts and silty clays, whereas the Wisconsin clays have a pink or gray color. Based on this evidence, the fill of the Georges Bank canyons, like that of Hudson Canyon, appears to have experienced little slumping and little transportation by strong bottom currents since the beginning of the Holocene. The thick layer of relatively coarse sand (Ericson *et al.,* 1961, p. 208; Shepard, 1961) found in the top of a core from Hydrographer Fan-valley is similar to the sand found on Georges Bank. This suggests that there has been some downslope transportation during the Holocene.

CANYONS SOUTH OF THE HUDSON

Between Hudson Canyon and Chesapeake Bay, the slope is cut by a large number of canyons (Fig. 71). South of Hudson Canyon, most of the slope valleys have heads that begin either at the shelf edge or on the slope a short distance below the break in slope. Four of them, however, cut for about 10 miles into the shelf, three having an initial trend to the south and one to the east. Like most of the other East Coast canyons, they have only one principal head and, except for Wilmington Canyon, only minor tributaries enter each. Nevertheless, so far as one can judge from the sounding lines, there are many small tributaries joining the shoaler parts.

The inner canyons in this section were contoured by Veatch and Smith with sufficient control so that their interpretations do not differ much from those of other cartographers. However, beginning near 6,000 ft (1,830 m), the control became very poor, which made it necessary for them to interpret the soundings extensively in order to draw their 25-fathom (46-m) contours. The sounding lines do not cross very well on these surveys because of difficulties with positions when operating on the slope and because of the rather unsatisfactory character of the echo-sounding devices that were used in the 1930s. Therefore, interpretation of the lines, most of which run diagonal to the slope, is very difficult, and no assurance exists that the contours are nearly as satisfactory as those of most of the West Coast canyons. In this East Coast zone, the interpretation of a maturely eroded stream valley pattern was used by Veatch and Smith. The test lines that were run across this pattern by the Coast and Geodetic Survey do not appear to bear out this interpretation. Probably the valleys do continue seaward to 9,000 ft (2,740 m) depths at the chart limits, but there is little justification for the dendritic pattern developed by Veatch and Smith. An attempt by the senior author to interpret the soundings without assuming this stream valley pattern gives quite different results (Figs. 76a, 76b). It can be expected that if there is a slackening of military demands on the U.S. Coast and Geodetic Survey an opportunity may soon develop to run the necessary lines to delineate this slope accurately.

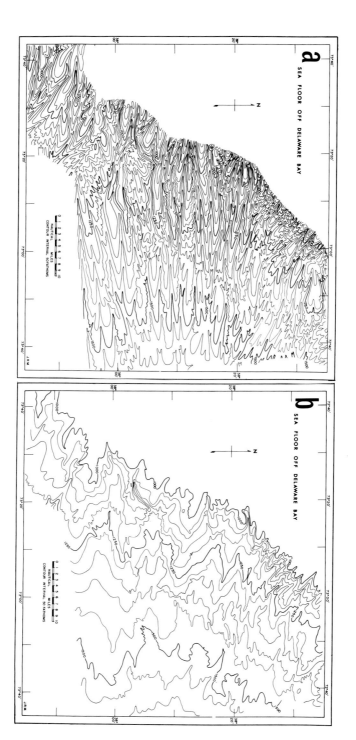

Fig. 76. Comparison of results using different contouring methods. Contour interval 50 fathoms in both maps. (a) Contours by Veatch and Smith (1939) and (b) by Shepard.

The canyons south of the Hudson all show their greatest wall heights near the outer edge of the adjacent shelf. Each of them is incised approximately 3,000 ft (910 m) at this point. Since the lines are run almost entirely diagonal to the axis, it is difficult to ascertain the nature of the transverse profiles of this group. Apparently there is no appreciable flattening of the floors so they probably can be classified as V-shaped canyons.

One of the curious features of the four large canyons south of the Hudson is that part way down the slope they all deflect to the east from the general southeast course at their heads. Some of this change in trend, as shown on the Veatch and Smith contours, is probably the result of the changing direction of the sounding lines which trend to the east in the outer portion (Veatch and Smith, 1939, Chart 2A). The interpretations made here (Fig. 76b) do not show as much of a shift, but some change in direction seems justified. North of Baltimore Canyon, one tributary valley definitely extends northeast, according to both interpretations. The series of northeast-southwest lines on the outer slope outside Washington Canyon shows clearly that the valley on this part of the slope trends to the southeast, but, again, there is some evidence of an east-west trend in the middle of the canyon. Some underlying structure may have caused a shift in the axis of the canyons and this may prevent them from extending southeastward straight down the slope.

The outer part of Washington Canyon is perhaps the best surveyed of any of those of the East Coast canyons, as the sounding lines are nearly parallel to the slope and are close-spaced out to the 9,000 ft (2,740 m) contour. At this depth, Washington Canyon has definitely become a fan-valley with natural levees and a depth below surroundings of about 400 ft (122 m). Adjacent valleys have about the same depth as the outer continuation of this major canyon. It would not be surprising if some of these valleys prove to be distributaries, but the existing soundings allow only an interpretation of a series of independent slope valleys.

The dredgings taken by Stetson (1949) on the walls of these southern canyons yielded mostly soft sediments, except in Norfolk Canyon where a hard, fine-grained sandstone was obtained in two hauls. No fossils were found, but the age was thought to be either Tertiary or Cretaceous. The rocks came from about 2,000 ft (610 m) on the northeast side of the canyon.

Cores from the canyon floors, obtained by Stetson (1949), contained silt for the most part, but one core from Norfolk Canyon at 2,000 ft

(610 m) had a fine sand underlain by a very fine sand. Some of the cores showed Pleistocene cold-water faunas underlying Recent (Phleger, 1942). Here again, the general indication is that bottom currents have not been as active during postglacial time as in the West Coast canyons that head nearshore.

CHAPTER VIII

EUROPEAN CANYONS

L ARGE SUBMARINE CANYONS are found along the Atlantic coasts of Europe and the north side of the Mediterranean. The British have been most active in examining the canyons on the slope south of the English Channel. French investigators have conducted surveys of the series of canyons cutting the slope off western France. They have also added new sounding lines in the valleys off the Iberian Peninsula. However, only a few samples have been taken by either the British or French from the Atlantic canyons.

The French have also studied the canyons of the Mediterranean with special emphasis on those along the Riviera and off western Corsica. This work has included soundings, sampling, and rather extensive bottom photography, both from Cousteau's Diving Saucer and from his towed sled, *Tröika*. The remainder of the Mediterranean is known to have a large number of rather small canyons, but none of them has been investigated more than superficially.

CANYONS OFF THE ENGLISH CHANNEL
AND WESTERN FRANCE

The continental margin of western Europe is divided by a distinct change in the character of the continental slope off the English

163

Channel (Fig. 77). To the north, the slope runs north and south and has very gentle inclinations, with no significant submarine canyons. To the south of the divide, the trend of the slope changes to southeast and steepens progressively. In this region there is a great increase in bottom irregularities and number of sizeable canyons. The canyons off the Channel and directly to the southeast (Fig. 78) have been described by Day (1959), Francis (1962), and Hadley (1964), and the canyons farther southeast off western France are described principally by Berthois and Brenot (1960) and Brenot and Berthois (1962). This group of canyons is comparable to those off the eastern United States. They head near the margin of the continental shelf and extend down to the base of the continental slope. Their trends are only slightly curving and they have relatively few tributaries. Also, like the canyons off eastern United States, the rocks dredged from this group of canyons are sedimentary. In one respect, however, the European canyons differ from their American counterparts by extending to much greater depths. In fact, they include some of the deepest canyons in the world.

Perhaps the best developed canyon of the northern part of this group heads at 1,200±ft (365 m) at 48° N and 8° W. We are calling this Shamrock Canyon. It has several tributaries and winds out to a depth of about 14,400 ft (4,400 m). The length is about 80 miles and the average gradient is about 28 m/km. It has a large fan at its mouth.

A moderately detailed survey of Black Mud Canyon (Francis, 1962) shows that its axis is concavo-convex with a steepening observed at about 5,400 ft (1,650 m). The average gradient is about 57 m/km to 11,400 ft (3,470 m) at the outer end of the close-spaced survey. Walls at least 3,000 ft (910 m) high are shown in some of the transverse profiles. Stride (1963) has shown that sediment is moving across much of the shelf off the English Channel, and evidence of such transport in the form of sand waves is seen on horizontally scanning sonar traces, taken near the head of Black Mud Canyon (Fig. 78). Conversely, it is significant that a general absence of such transport is found at the shelf edge to the north where canyons are missing. The canyons to the south apparently continue seaward as fan-valleys, and, farther out, one continues across an abyssal plain as a deep-sea channel.

Bottom photographs from Black Mud Canyon show that the bottom is sand with well-developed ripple marks at depths of about 5,000 ft (1,520 m) (Fig. 79). These photos are believed to have been taken in the canyon axis (A. S. Laughton, personal communication). The ripple marks appear to indicate that pulsating currents flow both up

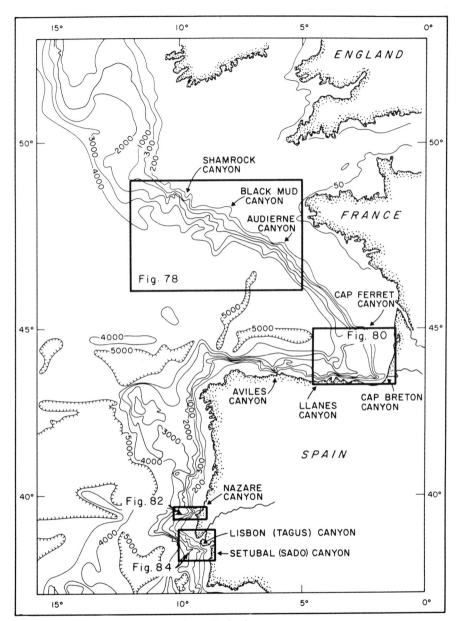

Fig. 77. Outline map showing the principal canyons off western Europe, and blocks showing location of the four contour maps in the area. From Monaco world map.

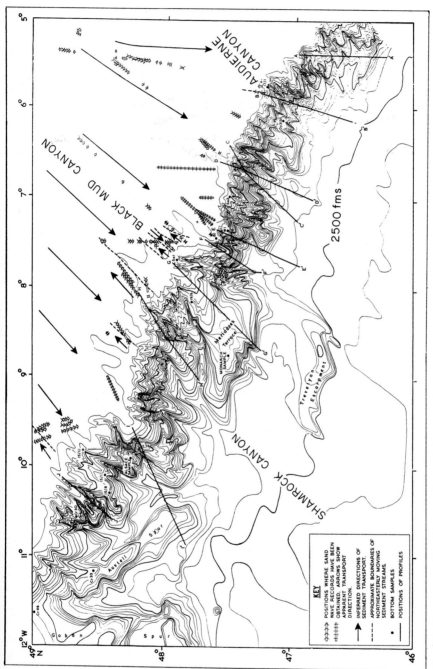

Fig. 78. Canyons cutting the continental slope south-west of the English Channel Contour interval 100 fathoms. From Hadley (1964) with canyon names added.

and down the canyon transporting sediment. Cores in the fan-valley have graded sand layers (Heezen and Laughton, 1963). Dredging of the walls has yielded chalk and chalky limestone of Eocene and Miocene age (Hadley, 1964). Dredging by the French in the northern canyons has brought up cobbles of Amorican rocks similar to those found in Brittany (Berthois and Brenot, 1960).

Farther south, off Cap Ferret, a sizeable canyon is found heading at the edge of the shelf (Fig. 80). This canyon has been described by Berthois and Brenot (1960) and called Gouf de Cap Ferret (here called Cap Ferret Canyon). Hull (1912) thought this canyon was connected with the Gironde Estuary, although it is located 50 miles to the south. A shoreward projection of the canyon trend connects with the main course of the Garonne River above where it turns north and empties into the Gironde Estuary. The Berthois and Brenot contours show that the head of Cap Ferret Canyon has many branches, which join at a depth of about 2,600 m (8,530 ft). Seaward from the juncture, the canyon can be traced for 50 miles trending in a 290° direction, to where it attains a depth of 3,550 m (11,650 ft). Even at this great depth it has wall heights of 500 m (1,640 ft). Ten miles farther out, there appears to be a fan-valley continuation with levees several hundred meters high.

Cap Breton Canyon

located near the southwest corner of France, differs from canyons to the north by extending shoreward across the continental shelf almost to the shore at the town of Cap Breton. This canyon was first referred to by Suess (1900, vol. 3, p. 885) and called the Gouf de Cap Breton (here called Cap Breton Canyon).

Heading a quarter mile out from the beach, this canyon, like others, reduces the height of the surf, often allowing fishermen to launch their boats here when seas are too rough elsewhere along the coast. In the 15th century, the old mouth of the Adour River was located at Cap Breton and later shifted 10 miles. The width of the channel at the canyon head appears to be approximately the same as the width of the present channel of the Adour River in its lower course. This relationship may, of course, be a coincidence but might conceivably indicate a drowning of the canyon head. Another notable feature of Cap Breton Canyon is that its main axis is located directly off a large synclinal fold that is known to have undergone active downwarping until some time in the Tertiary (Schoeffler, 1965).

According to the soundings of the *President Theodore Tissier* and *Thalassa* obtained from 1956 to 1964, with added contour maps up to 1964 by Brenot and Berthois and reported in part by Berthois (1962), Cap Breton Canyon can be traced seaward to a depth of 4,000 m (13,120 ft). The accompanying contour map from Brenot and Berthois (Fig. 80) shows that the canyon has a somewhat twisting course for the first 50 miles, but in general runs approximately parallel to the north coast of Spain for 100 miles, with the last 30 miles having a possible levee on the north, indicating it may be a fan-valley. Beyond 100 miles, it turns north and extends another 35 miles in this direction with no evidence of natural levees. If all of this is a canyon, it is the longest in Europe, 135 miles. The average gradient is 29 m/km for the first 70 miles and 16 m/km for the entire canyon. At a point 83 miles out from the head, the valley has a north wall 1,000 m (3,280 ft) high, and the south wall rises from a depth of 3,120 m (10,240 ft) to the shelf edge at 140 m (460 ft). Forty miles out, the canyon has what may

Fig. 79. Bottom photograph of confused ripples on the floor of Black Mud Canyon at a depth of 4,800 ft (1,460 m). From *R. V. Discovery II*, courtesy of M. N. Hill and A. S. Laughton.

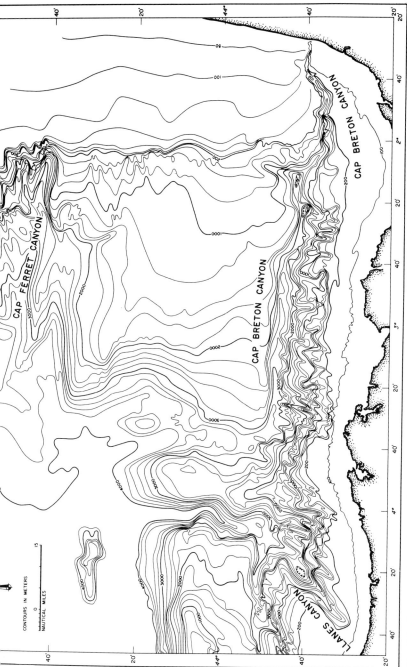

Fig. 80. Canyons along the southwest coast of France and northern Spain. From a 1964 chart of the Institut Scientifique, et Technique des Pêches Maritimes (I.S.T.P.M.) by Leopold Berthois and Roger Brenot. Canyon names have been added.

be its greatest wall heights with 1,650 m (5,410 ft) on the north wall and 2,100 m (6,890 ft) on the south wall. Here the width is approximately 20 miles, somewhat more than the Grand Canyon. If the soundings are correct, this is one of the most deeply entrenched of any submarine canyon in the world. However, the bottom depth of 2,510 m (8,230 ft) seems to be out of line with the rest of the axial depths, so these soundings may well be a mistake. Alternatively, they may indicate tectonic activity. An average wall height of 1,600 m (5,250 ft) is better substantiated. Several indications of deep-silled basins along the canyon, shown by the sounding lines, are disturbing. The fact that all of the canyon surveys made by Scripps Institution have failed to show any clear cases of basins of appreciable depth, causes us to hesitate to accept their existence at Cap Breton. It would be advisable to run a series of transverse lines across the canyon from head to mouth with modern equipment before putting too much credence in the basin contours shown by Berthois and Brenot.

Profiles of the Cap Breton Canyon, made in 1936, indicate that a steep inner gorge incises the floor of more gently sloping canyon walls (Fig. 81). This was found at axial depths of 400 and 1,200 m (1,310 and 3,940 ft) (Bourcart, 1938). However, the profiles reported by Berthois (1962, Fig. 192) only partly confirm this indication of entrenchment (Fig. 81). Most of the Berthois profiles are asymmetrical, being steeper on the south side. As Berthois has observed, the submarine profiles differ from those typical of land canyons in that they do not show a progressive widening and decreasing of wall slope in a seaward direction, but show first a decrease in steepness and then an increase near the outer part of the canyon. This is similar to the order of profile changes found in Monterey Canyon.

The sounding lines along the south side of the canyon show that a series of relatively short canyons come in as tributaries from that side. An indication of a tributary entering from the north is found just beyond the 50-m (164-ft) shelf contour. With more soundings, this tributary may prove to be of the same type as the trough-like valley coming into the north side of Redondo Canyon, off the southern California coast. Another possible tributary is shown on the north side, just outside the edge of the continental shelf, and 10 miles farther out still another possible tributary is indicated. The general lack of longitudinal lines on the north side may be the explanation of the apparent scarcity of tributaries on that side.

Ed. Le Danois found that the walls of Cap Breton Canyon had Eocene limestones (Bourcart, 1952, p. 279). Berthois and Brenot

(1960) also reported rock from the north wall, including limestones of undetermined age.

IBERIAN PENINSULA CANYONS

The recent French surveys continue around the Iberian Peninsula to Cape Saint Vincent, at the southwest corner of Portugal. The 1964 maps of Berthois and Brenot are used here as the principal basis of the discussion.

To the west of Cap Breton Canyon, at least two major canyons cut across the shelf of northern Spain. Of these, Llanes Canyon (Fig. 80), heading at longitude 4°35′ W. off the city of the same name, appears to come in to about 4 miles from the coast with a head at about 150 m (490 ft) depth. It extends out to the northeast for over 30 miles, where axial soundings of 3,670 m (12,040 ft) are given. There, a ridge forms the west wall rising to 2,000 m (6,560 ft), and a plateau at 1,580 m (5,180 ft) borders the wall on the east. The recent Berthois and Brenot contours show a northward continuation for an additional 30 miles, but the basis for the outer area is not clear. The deepest sounding is at 4,125 m (13,535 ft). This apparently is all canyon, so far as one can tell, and hence almost as deep as Great Bahama Canyon (p. 194). Llanes Canyon has walls rising respectively 1,670 and 1,990 m (5,480 and 6,530 ft), making it also one of the deepest entrenched sea valleys in the world.[1] According to the soundings shown by Berthois and Brenot, there may be a basin depression 17 miles out, but again the sounding lines do not have good crossings and another survey is needed. It may be significant that this apparent basin is found along the projection of a long structural low east of the canyon (Schoeffler, 1965). An indentation in the canyon wall at this place suggests alternatively that the depression might be due to slumping. Llanes Canyon extends diagonally across the shelf and slope, giving further evidence of structural control since most canyons cross shelves and slopes more directly.

Llanes Canyon appears to have several tributaries on the east side and one large tributary on the west. The average gradient is 58 m/km, although the head of the canyon apparently has a somewhat steeper gradient.

Farther west, Aviles Canyon comes in to about 8 miles of the coast at longitude 6° W, near the town of Aviles. The canyon extends in a northwesterly direction for 20 miles and then north-northeast for another 17 miles, with the outer line showing an axial depth of 4,750

[1]This, of course, does not include the deep trenches.

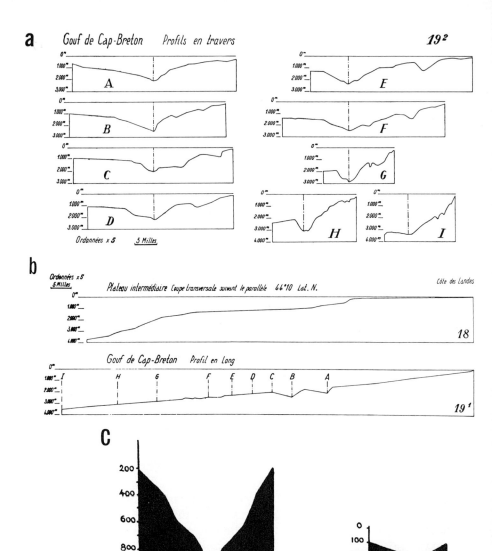

Fig. 81. a. Transverse profiles of Cap Breton Canyon. From Berthois and Brenot (1962).

b. Longitudinal profile of the Cap Breton Canyon. From Berthois and Brenot (1962).

c. Tranverse profile of Cap Breton Canyon from Bourcart (1949).

m (15,580 ft). This makes it the deepest canyon termination in the world, unless the outer part is a fan-valley. The height of the canyon walls is less than in Llanes Canyon, but apparently there are more tributaries. One sounding line, if reliable, would indicate that the canyon has a sill across it, but the line looks suspicious and may not have been well coordinated with the outer lines. Here again, we need surveying with more modern devices.

At least 4 prominent submarine canyons are found off the southern half of the Portuguese coast. Hull (1912) described all but one of these, but included one he called "Greater Cañon of the Tagus," which apparently does not exist. De Andrade (1937) wrote a book about the canyons but did not explore them.

Nazare Canyon

The "Canal da Nazare," here called Nazare Canyon (Fig. 82), lies off the small fishing town of Nazare. It appears to be one of the largest and deepest canyons in the world. It comes in close to shore about 1/3 mile south of a rocky headland. The canyon head produces the same type of crescentic wave pattern along the shore as is found in other places at canyon heads (Fig. 83). Under ordinary wave conditions, this deep re-entry reduces the breaker height sufficiently to allow the fishermen to launch their boats from the beaches inside the canyon. It is likely that one head is located off the small Nazare River.

Traced seaward, the canyon makes two right angle bends, rather like the outer part of La Jolla Canyon. Beyond the second bend, the axis winds out to west-southwest past the Berlengas Islands. At this point, the water depth in the axis is about 2,000 m (6,560 ft). This also represents the approximate height of the canyon walls, because here the canyon is cut below the shallow continental shelf. Farther out, the canyon swings to a more westerly course and reaches a depth of 4,180 m (13,710 ft) a distance of 57 miles from the head. Here the French soundings end, but some Portuguese soundings indicate a northwesterly continuation apparently reaching an axial depth of 4,500 m (14,760 ft) in the outer portion. If this outer part is a genuine canyon, Nazare has a total length of 93 miles and is exceeded in outer depth only by Llanes Canyon.

We do not know much about the walls of Nazare Canyon, but it seems likely that they contain rock, because rocky bottom is reported across much of the shelf on both the north and south sides (Portuguese fishery charts). Also it is likely that the granitic rocks on the

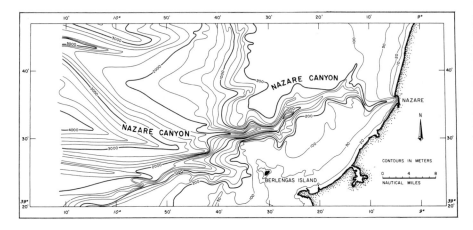

Fig. 82. Nazare Canyon off western Portugal. Note right-angled bends at canyon head. From Berthois and Brenot I.S.T.P.M. maps published in 1964.

Fig. 83. Coast of Nazare, Portugal, showing the crescentic wave pattern shoreward of the submarine canyon head. Photo by Shepard.

Berlengas Islands (De Andrade, 1937) continue north to form at least the south wall of the canyon in that vicinity.

The other Portuguese canyons do not extend in as close to the shore. Two of them, Lisbon (Tagus) Canyon and Setubal (Sado) Canyon, are located on either side of Cape Espichel (Fig. 84). Lisbon Canyon, heading 8 miles south of the Tagus Estuary, extends south along the sandy coast 3 miles out from shore. Pérès dove into this canyon in the French bathyscaph *F.N.R.S. III* and reported seeing bare rock outcrops on the walls (Pérès *et al.*, 1957). Setubal Canyon, by contrast, runs due west, heading 3 miles off the long sandy bight south of Cape Espichel. The two canyons join at a depth of about 1,800 m (5,900 ft) and, on the basis of one sounding line, appear to

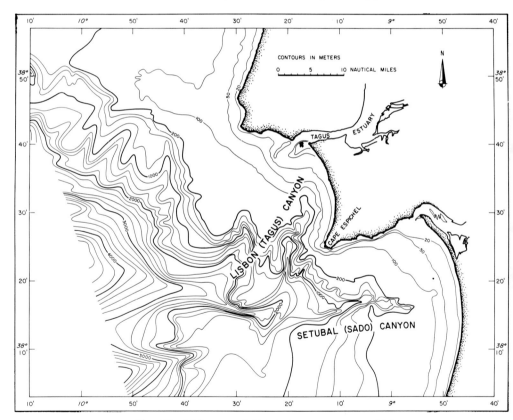

Fig. 84. Lisbon and Setubal canyons near Lisbon, Portugal. From Berthois and Brenot I.S.T.P.M. maps published in 1964.

continue seaward another 33 miles to a depth of 4,640 m (15,220 ft). The outer part may be a fan-valley.

Another canyon extends in a north-south direction 10 miles west of Cape San Vicente, the southwesternmost tip of the Iberian Peninsula, where it curves towards the west. Soundings do not extend beyond axial depths of 2,100 m (6,890 ft).

It is interesting that three of these large Portuguese canyons are all located off the north (or west) sides of prominent points, although in no case do they actually head directly on the upcurrent side of these points, as does Dume Canyon off California. Nevertheless, the relationship may have some significance here, as was suggested by Crowell (1952) for California canyons.

MEDITERRANEAN CANYONS

More submarine canyons are found along the coasts of the Mediterranean than in any other marginal area of comparable length. A few poorly sounded canyons exist off eastern Spain; the entire slope off southern France and the Italian Riviera is cut by rather well-surveyed canyons, as is the slope along the west side of Corsica; scattered canyons are located around the lower part of Italy; the south side of Crete has a few canyons; several are found off Asia Minor; and an almost continuous series of short valleys (probably canyons) are found from Tunisia to Morocco (Rosfelder, 1954). On the other hand, there appear to be rather large areas in the Mediterranean where canyons are conspicuously absent, notably in the Aegean Sea.

Canyons Off Southern France and Northwest Italy

The numerous canyons along the south coast of France (Figs. 85, 86) and the adjacent Italian Riviera (Fig. 87) have been extensively sounded and well sampled. Visual observations have been made by scuba diving, from Cousteau's Diving Saucer, and from the French Navy's bathyscaphs *F.N.R.S. III* and *Archimede*.

Starting in the west, several canyons extend in near the coast at Banyuls, just north of the Spanish-French border. Here, the close proximity of the Arago Marine Laboratory to canyons is similar to Scripps Institution, and has resulted in an extensive examination of the canyons of the area by French scientists. Bourcart (1950) found Upper-Pliocene conglomerates overlying Miocene limestones in the walls of Perpignan Canyon (Fig. 85). He interpreted the Pliocene

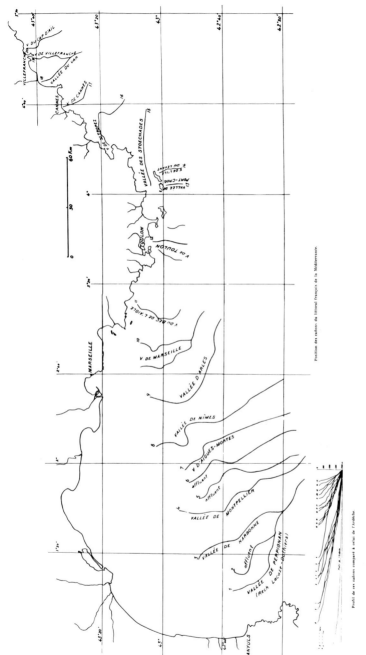

Fig. 85. Longitudinal profiles and axial trends of canyons off southern France. From Bourcart (1959).

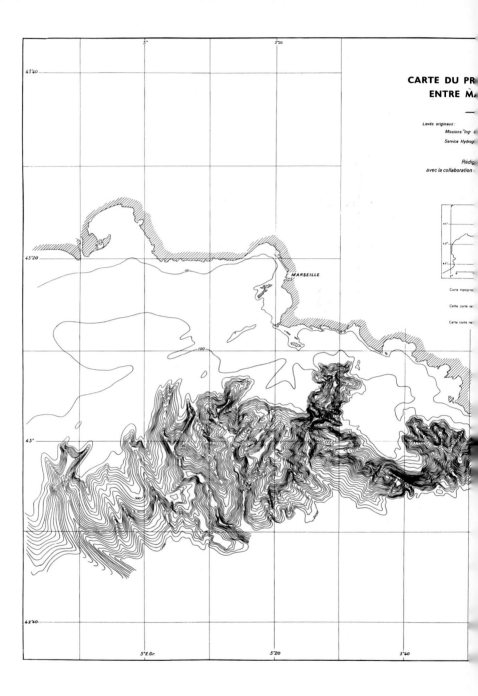

CARTE DU PR
ENTRE M.

Levés originaux :
Missions "Ing-
Service Hydrog

Rédig
avec la collaboration

Carte topograp

Cette carte se

Cette carte ne

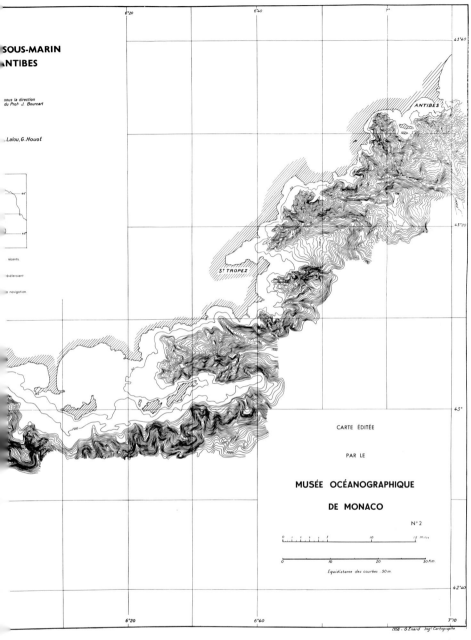

ANTIBES

S.T TROPEZ

CARTE ÉDITÉE

PAR LE

MUSÉE OCÉANOGRAPHIQUE

DE MONACO

N° 2

Équidistance des courbes : 50 m.

Fig. 86. Submarine canyons from the Rhone Delta (20 miles west of Marseilles) to Antibes in southern France. Note change in character of canyons off the hard rock coast east of Marseilles. From Musée Oceanographique de Monaco. Courtesy of J.-Y. Cousteau.

sediments as a deposit filling canyons excavated during the Late Miocene, with renewed erosion producing the present canyons. Kuenen (1953) interpreted the same sequence as one continuous cycle of erosion through a sequence of relatively flat-lying beds. The latter interpretation suggests that the canyons would be entirely of Pleistocene age and much younger than Bourcart suggests. Without more data it is impossible to decide who is correct. The description by Dangeard (1962, 1965) of a Saucer dive into the canyon Rech Lacaze-Duthiers in 250 to 290 m (820 to 951 ft) shows that many features here are similar to those we found in our dives off La Jolla and Baja California. For example, the currents were fluctuating between zero and about 0.3 knots; the sediment on the canyon floor and walls was quite variable but had considerable sand, some of it coarse; worn shells were also common. He encountered a cliff on the southwest side with a notch at the base that recalled the conditions in the American west coast canyons. Locally, furrows were seen in the floor sediment. Also, boulders were found on the floor that evidently had fallen from above. Pleistocene and Recent sediments were mixed together in many places.

The three western canyons off southern France join before reaching the deep floor of the Mediterranean, forming a dendritic system (Fig. 85), but farther to the east, the valleys off the lowlands bordering the Golfe du Lion do not have any known tributaries west of the Rhone River Delta. This, however, may be due to the inadequacy of soundings, because tributaries were found by the detailed *Élie Monnier* surveys of the slope to the east of the Rhone (Fig. 86).

Kuenen (1953) has differentiated between the canyons off the Golfe du Lion, which he called "New England type," and off the Riviera, which he called "ravines." If Kuenen's interpretation of the Riviera "ravines" as drowned valleys, and the Golfe du Lion group as submarine erosion is correct, we should expect a decided change at the boundary between the two types. Figure 86 does not substantiate the existence of any break between the two types. The canyons off the Golfe du Lion have somewhat gentler gradients (Fig. 85) than those to the east and may have fewer tributaries. The lower gradient is usual in canyons off lowlands as compared to those off mountainous coasts.

In the summer of 1962, Menard *et al.* (1965) on the Scripps ship *Horizon* surveyed the outer slope off Marseilles and determined the existence of a huge fan with numerous distributaries (Fig. 88). The volume of this fan can account for the material eroded from the Alps, if it had been carried to the sea by the Rhone River and hence down the canyon to the deep floor of the Mediterranean. According to Menard, the fan has a volume of about 4.6 x 10⁵ km.³ Using this value and the present sediment load of the Rhone, he estimates that the fan started during the Oligocene.

The canyons off the French and Italian Riviera have dissected the entire slope, forming a topography that is similar to that of the neighboring mountains. A number of canyons have walls as high as 1,000 m (3,280 ft). Tributaries are common, at least in the upper parts near land. Many of the canyon heads come in virtually to the coast, and in general the canyons are located off coastal indentations.

Fig. 87. Canyons off Mediterranean coast from Nice to Genoa. Soundings taken by various French and Italian expeditions. From Bourcart (1960). Contour interval 50 m (164 ft). Suggested names of canyons added.

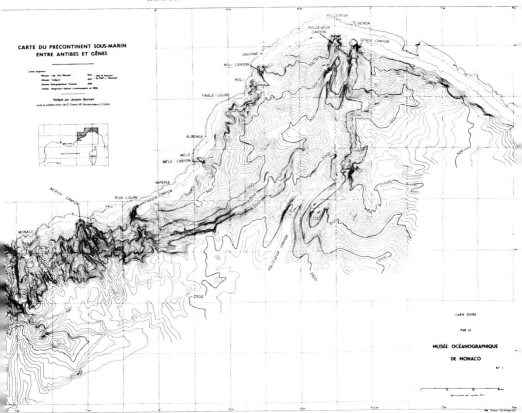

Several of them head directly off the mouths of the larger rivers, such as the Var. Two of the canyons in the vicinity of St. Tropez (Fig. 86, long. 6°40′) parallel the coast along most of their length, like Carmel Canyon off California.

Traced downslope, the Riviera canyons apparently widen, although only contours and not soundings have been published; nor are there any profiles available. Off Nice and Cannes, the continental slope has an inclination of about 100 m/km down to approximately 2,000 m (6,560 ft). Here, the topography changes and it appears likely that

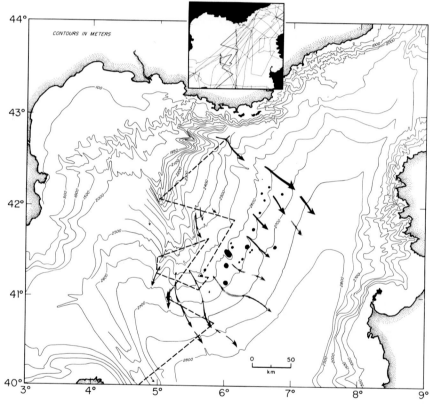

Fig. 88. Fan-valleys off the Rhone Delta. Inset shows location of sounding lines and arrows give presumed direction of movement of turbidity currents down the slope. Note that contour interval is 500 m (1,640 ft) out to 2,000 m (6,560 ft), and then 50 m (164 ft) beyond, in well-surveyed part. Black dots are abyssal hills. From Menard *et al.* (1965).

there is a fan at the base of the eroded slope. The change in topography is similar to that found by Menard *et al.* (1965).

Observations from the Diving Saucer and the photographs from Cousteau's underwater sled *Tröika,* show that the Riviera canyons have an interesting contrast between those to the west and those to the east of Cannes. To the west, the canyons have rock walls and, at least in one place, a rock floor (Fig. 89a); whereas the canyons to the east are cut into unconsolidated or only partly consolidated formations (M. Gennesseaux, personal communication). Off the Nice area, the canyons have sand on the floor with an abundance of gravel (Fig. 89b). This coarse material is locally ripple-marked (Fig. 89c). In three dives in the head of the canyon at Villefranche, the junior author noted a steep sediment-covered slope with slump scars and a narrow V-shaped bottom. Five-inch artillery shells, presumably jettisoned during World War II, were found tipped towards the axis, indicating a slow gravity creep of the sediments. At some localities currents were observed moving upcanyon and at others, downcanyon. Near the axis there was a considerable concentration of Posedonia, the common Mediterranean sea grass, but this grass was virtually missing on the muddy walls. The profile of the canyon is V-shaped and only 3 meters across 1 meter above the floor. Diving in the same area in the bathyscaph *Archimede,* Pérès (1957) encountered extensive mud walls in the canyon and saw no rock.

The cores in the area off Nice and northwestern Italy show sand and gravel layers (Bourcart *et al.,* 1958, 1960). Many of these cores appear to be graded in the upper part, but have gravel at the bottom which is not graded (Fig. 90). One fine-grained sand layer was obtained with a thickness of 1.5 m. The sand layers are found even on the lower fan. According to Bourcart, the sediments from the Var River are carried down the slope to the plain below. Certainly, the close approach of the canyon to the mouth of the Var allows a great deal of sediment to get into a downcanyon circulation.

East of the French-Italian border, the canyons (Fig. 87) continue past the Riva Ligure with heads coming close to shore, and the lower reaches extending to the base of the slope at 2,300 to 2,400 m (7,550 to 7,880 ft). Farther east, the Taggia Canyon, named for a large river at its head, hooks to the left at the base of the slope in a fan-valley. For an additional 18 miles, there do not appear to be any important canyons until just northeast of Cap del Mele, where the first of a series of valleys is found. These come close to shore at their heads and all form tributaries to the long Polcevera Canyon, which extends down

a

b

c

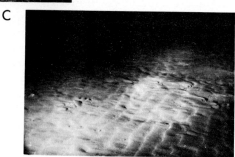

Fig. 89. Bottom photos in canyons off French Riviera.
All taken from J. Y. Couteau's sled *Troïka*.

a. Along the axis of St. Tropez Canyon showing
bedrock and change of axial gradient. Photo courtesy
of R. Vaissiere, Musée Oceanographic de Monaco.

b. Boulders and cobbles the floor of the canyon off
Nice. Courtesy of M. Gennesseaux, Univ. of Paris.

c. Current ripples along the floor of the canyon off
Nice. Photo courtesy of M. Gennesseaux, Univ. of
Paris.

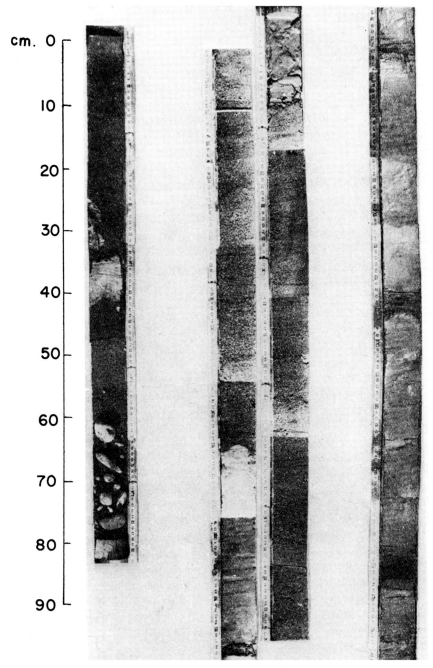

Fig. 90. Cores from canyon floors off Nice, France.
From Bourcart *et al.* (1960).

the slope just west of Genoa. The latter is by far the longest of the Mediterranean canyons, having a total length of 49 miles. It is located off the large Polcevera River and extends in to a point less than 3 miles from the shore. This canyon has many tributaries on both sides, including the parallel trending Genoa Canyon which enters it from the east at 1,850 m (6,070 ft). Another valley with a length of some 25 miles comes in on the east side of Genoa Canyon just above the point where the latter joins Polcevera.

Polcevera Canyon has walls almost 1,000 m (3,280 ft) high, just north of the juncture with Genoa. About 8 miles from the head, the canyon widens at the base and has a floor about 2 miles across in the vicinity of the juncture. However, it is questionable whether the contours are reliable in this section. East and south of Genoa, the canyons appear to have given out, and the continental shelf along the west side of the Italian peninsula is considerably wider than off the Riviera.

Corsican Canyons (Figs. 91, 141)

If geologists were acquainted with only the Corsican submarine canyons, there presumably would be little argument about canyon origin. Even Kuenen (1953) was convinced from the examination of the soundings off west Corsica that here we had true drowning of land canyons. Every bay along the entire west coast has one or more drowned canyons. In most places, relatively deep water extends right up to the bay heads, and tributary valleys come into all of the tributary bays. Outside the bays, the canyons extend down the slope. This group of canyons includes—from north to south—Porto, Sagone, Propriano, Ajaccio, and Valinco. A visit to Pte. Rossa, on the west side of the small Golfe de Girolata, gave the senior author the opportunity to look down from the top of an old Genoese tower and observe the deep blue water coming into each cove in the area. It was as if the land had submerged in historical times and had drowned each small valley.

A comparison between gradients of land valleys (from a rather rough map) inside the canyons and those of the submarine canyons in the deep bays shows the following:

	Average gradient	
	Land canyon	Submarine canyon
Golfe de Porto	70 m/km	90 m/km
Golfe de Sagone	50 m/km	85 m/km
Golfe de Ajaccio	40 m/km	55 m/km
Golfe de Valinco	45 m/km	60 m/km

In all cases, however, the lower ends of the land valleys have gentle gradients due to alluviation, or delta-building, so that the lower average gradients on land are not particularly significant. In fact, these close comparisons between land and sea gradients in the Corsican area are surprising, because virtually all other submarine canyons show much higher gradients than those of adjacent land valleys.

The number of tributaries in the Corsican submarine canyons is certainly comparable to those of the land canyons. The marine canyons appear to have V-shaped transverse profiles. The axes are

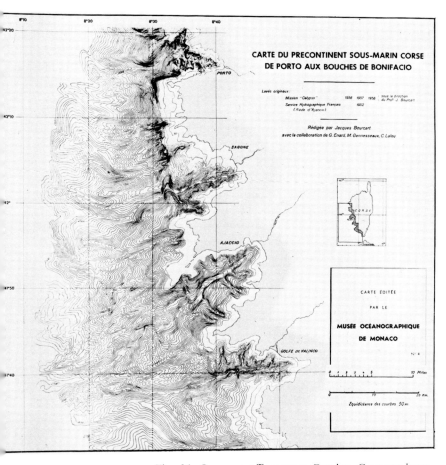

Fig. 91. Canyons off western Corsica. Contour interval 50 m (164 ft). Courtesy of Musée Oceanographique de Monaco.

winding, about like those of the land. The heights of canyon walls are not as great as in many other places; the maximum here rarely exceeds 1,000 m (3,280 ft). The canyon widths are usually less than 5 miles, about like the land canyons in Corsica.

Seaward, the Corsican canyons apparently extend down the steep slope to about 2,500 m (8,200 ft) where they encounter a depositional plain or large fans. The canyons may have fan-valley continuations, but in the absence of adequate soundings this is hard for us to evaluate from the contours alone.

Sampling in the Corsican canyons has yielded sand layers; one taken by the *Élie Monnier* had the sea grass, Posedonia, corals, and Bryozoa, all carried down from shallow water (Bourcart *et al.*, 1958).

It seems probable that the walls of most of the Corsican canyons will yield hard rocks, since the walls of the narrow bays and of the land canyons inside are almost entirely crystalline rock, including granite. A dive in the Saucer into Ajaccio Canyon revealed rock only in shallow water and the deep walls and floor were covered with mud (J. Y. Cousteau, personal communication), but rock walls were found elsewhere (M. Gennesseaux, personal communication).

The really important problem relative to the Corsican canyons is whether it is possible that they could be cut by submarine processes and still so closely resemble land canyons. Another problem of some importance is whether there are canyons on the east side of Corsica. The coast is quite straight on this side and, according to available contour charts, there are no submarine canyons. Small valleys, however, are indicated in two places (Fig. 141).

Crete Canyons

The island of Crete has steep slopes on both west and south sides with depths of 1,000 m (3,280 ft) found at distances of from 2 to 3 miles from the coast. The chart shows canyons along both of these coasts. The senior author investigated one of these canyons while aboard the Greek Navy ship *Ariadne*. A series of sounding lines was run across what appears to be one of the principal canyons on the south side (Fig. 92). The echo sounder was not very reliable in the outer part so that the contour map is somewhat generalized. It shows that this canyon heads directly off a land valley, in fact, one of the largest land valleys on the south side of the island. The canyon is never cut deeper than 200 m (655 ft) below its surroundings. It has at least one tributary which joins the main canyon at about 800 m (2,630 ft) and a smaller

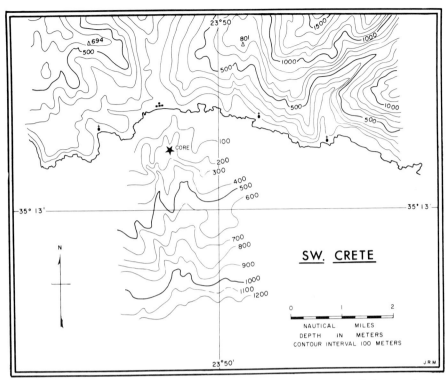

Fig. 92. Small submarine canyon off the southwest coast of Crete, located off land valley. Position of core in axis is indicated. From soundings of Greek Navy ship *Ariadne*.

Fig. 93. Prominent land canyon directly inside submarine canyon along the southwest coast of Crete, location somewhat east of Fig. 91. Photo by Shepard.

tributary that comes in near 1,000 m (3,280 ft). At 1,200 m (3,940 ft) the canyon seems to have come virtually to an end.

A core taken in the center of a Crete canyon showed mud underlain by sand with gravel and small rock fragments at the base. A similar core was taken in another submarine canyon a few miles to the east. This canyon, only partially surveyed, is notable in that it is located directly off a narrow, steep-sided land canyon (Fig. 93).

CHAPTER IX

OTHER
SUBMARINE CANYONS

S EVERAL MISCELLANEOUS CANYONS have not yet been discussed because they do not fit into any particular group. These include a large canyon in the Bahama Islands, some canyons in the southwest corner of Bering Sea, Trincomalee Canyon along the west coast of Ceylon, and Manila Canyon located directly off the entrace to Manila Bay. The only canyons that have been explored around oceanic islands are off Hawaii and these are considered here. Congo Canyon which enters deeply into the Congo estuary is also included, although there is some doubt whether this feature should be considered under the category of submarine canyons.

CANYONS IN THE BAHAMAS

One of the deepest and largest submarine canyons in the world is found in the Bahamas. Spencer (1895) first called attention to the large underwater valleys among these islands and attributed them to drowning of river valleys. As a result of a U.S. Navy survey, Hess (1932) considered that the Bahama valleys were comparable to the great canyons of the land. Actually, the survey made by the U.S.

Navy, using a very early model echo sounder, left much to be desired. The conclusions seemed at the time a little premature, although we have found that they are now thoroughly justified by modern sounding techniques.

During World War II, echo soundings were made off the north coast of Eleuthera. These were shown by Schalk (1946, and an unpublished map) to indicate some very deep canyons extending down the slopes with a high gradient. Again the sounding device was not adequate; consequently the map was considered to be of questionable value. A survey of one of the Bahama canyons with modern sounding devices and Decca navigational equipment was made by Woods Hole Oceanographic Institution (Athearn, 1963). This survey in the Tongue of the Ocean revealed the presence of a relatively straight V-shaped canyon extending for more than 40 miles along the center of this great embayment (Fig. 94). Numerous tributaries enter on both sides.

Additional work on the canyons was begun in 1963 by Miami University personnel. Their first survey revealed an interesting canyon in Northwest Providence Passage. In January, 1964, surveys by Hurley and Shepard (1964) added considerable information to the earlier work.

The charting of the canyons in the Bahamas is still rather incomplete and some sections are quite neglected, requiring broad generalization of the contours. However, the areas that have been adequately sounded show that there are deep submarine canyons (following the definition used in this book). The principal canyon, called here Great Bahama Canyon, has two branches, both unique in that each heads in deep water adjacent to a flat-floored trough. The arm in the Tongue of the Ocean heads at a depth of 4,800 ft (1,460 m), north of the broad trough-shaped depression constituting the southern end of this inter-island passageway (Fig. 94). This main branch extends north, passing west of New Providence Island, and then swinging to the northeast where it extends out through Northeast Providence Channel, attaining a depth of at least 14,060 ft (4,290 m) in the strait between Great Abaco and Eleuthera islands. At this depth the transverse profile is V-shaped and the walls slope down continuously from the low islands on either side. Aside from the somewhat questionable outer depths in two western European canyons, this is the deepest canyon in the world and the walls are by far the highest, nearly 3 miles compared with 1 mile for the Grand Canyon of the Colorado. Fifteen miles farther seaward, a sounding line indicates that the V-shape has given way to two trough-shaped valleys at depths of 14,900 ft (4,540 m) and 14,850 ft (4,525 m), each with relatively flat floors. The total length of the canyon, measured from the Tongue of the Ocean head, is approximately 125 miles. In this distance the axis drops 9,600 ft (2,930 m) with an average gradient of only 13 m/km, almost comparable to the low gradient of Congo Canyon.

The Northwest Providence branch joins the Tongue of the Ocean branch at a depth of about 12,000 ft (3,660 m). Of the two branches, Northwest Providence has a little steeper gradient. Along the axis in Northwest Passage there are clear evidences of basin depressions (Fig. 94, insert). These appeared on two separate surveys, and we have three lines with maximum axis depths of less than 6,000 ft (1,830 m) outside of four lines with depths of more than 6,600 ft (2,010 m). Farther upcanyon, at longitude 78° N, a line shows an axis depth of 5,640 ft (1,720 m) inside 5,300 ft (1,620 m). To the west, the nature of the canyon head has not yet been determined with any accuracy.

Both branches of Bahama Canyon have V-shaped profiles and have many tributaries entering from their sides. The average slopes of the canyon walls are rather gentle, mostly from 9° to 12°, although much steeper zones are shown in some bottom photographs taken near the axis, suggesting that the slopes are far from even. Some of the tributaries apparently extend in close to the steep margins of the coral reefs that border the various islands along the passageways. However, most of the sounding lines were run parallel to the axes of the tributaries, and therefore these side valleys are not well outlined.

Inaccuracies of the chart[1] created difficulties in surveying the canyons along the northeast side of Eleuthera Island. The available soundings indicate a series of three canyon heads two miles out from shore (Fig. 95) with depths of from 4,200 ft (1,280 m) to 6,600 ft (2,010 m). Closely spaced lines showed a drop in the axis of the middle canyon of from 3,960 ft (1,200 m) to 7,200 ft (2,200 m) in about one mile, which means an axial gradient of 540 m/km, by far the steepest so far discovered in submarine canyons, except for short vertical steps observed by scuba divers and in the Diving Saucer during descents into the canyon heads off California and Cape San Lucas. The canyons off Eleuthera attain depths of 12,000 ft (3,660 m) approximately 7.5 miles out from the beach, again a tremendously steep gradient (267 m/km), even allowing for the moderate sinuosity

---

[1]Recently revised by a new edition which shows that the coast on the old edition was locally a half mile or more out of position.

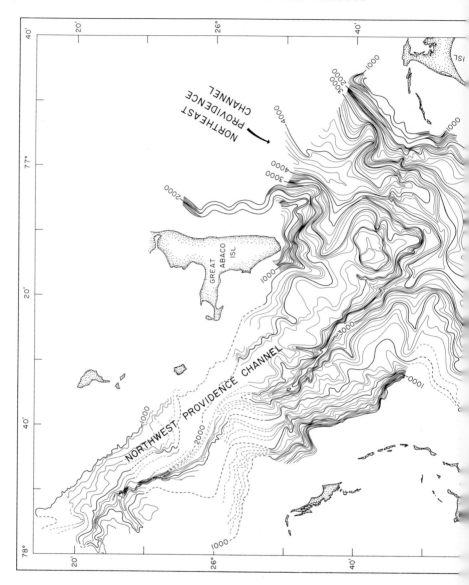

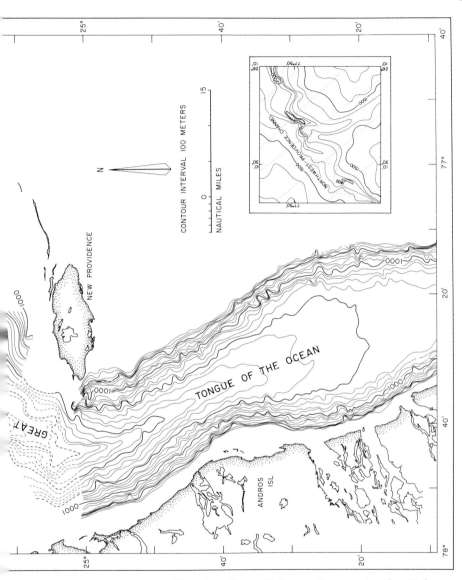

Fig. 94. Great Bahama Canyon in the Bahama Islands. The section of the canyon in Northeast Providence Channel has the highest walls of any in the world. The branch extending up Northwest Providence Channel has probable basin depressions along its course (inset). Note that the head of the main canyon is bowl-shaped in the deep water of the Tongue of the Ocean. Based on soundings by U.S. Oceanographic Office, partly unpublished, and on surveys by Hurley and Shepard (1964) conducted on the *Pillsbury* of the University of Miami.

that is indicated. The sounding profiles at greater depth show fairly flat-floored troughs but with high gradients.

Sampling and photography in the canyons of the Bahamas have yielded additional data that may have a bearing on their origin. In the branch of Great Bahama Canyon coming out of the Tongue of the Ocean, a very successful run of bottom photographs with an Edgerton underwater camera was made while the ship drifted almost directly up the axis of the canyon during a period of two hours.[2] The photographs show that a portion of the sandy floor has current ripples of low relief (Fig. 96), not the interference pattern shown in the Japanese canyon (Fig. 70), or steep-crested ripples in Black Mud Canyon (Fig. 79), but an unquestionable indication of currents mov-

[2]The fathogram did not indicate that the ship ever diverged appreciably from the axis.

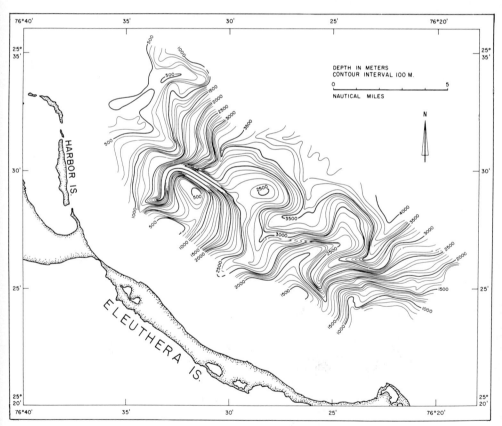

Fig. 95. Steep sloping canyons off the northeast coast of Eleuthera in the Bahama Islands. From surveys by Hurley and Shepard (1964) on the *Pillsbury* of University of Miami.

ing downaxis along the Northwest Providence Branch. Elsewhere, well rounded cobbles and boulders are shown only partly embedded in the sandy floor. Additionally, steep, irregular rock walls are revealed in many of the photographs (Fig. 97). Only a small number of organisms are seen growing on the rocks and life is also scarce on the canyon floor.

Dredging in Bahama Canyon was not very successful, but a few pieces of limestone were obtained from about 11,000 ft (3,350 m), and on one occasion the dredge was hung up for a long time at approximately 12,000 ft (3,660 m), suggesting that it was caught on hard ledge rock. Off Eleuthera, a dredge came up from about 8,400 ft (2,560 m) with limestone fragments, one clearly containing reef corals. This block was coated by a calcareous silt, which M. N. Bramlette determined from the coccoliths to be of Late Tertiary age. A core from Bahama Canyon in 11,500 ft (3,500 m) showed fine calcareous

Fig. 96. Current ripples on the floor of submarine canyon in the Bahamas at a depth of 3,500 m (11,480) ft). Current was moving from northwest to southeast as shown by compass. Photo by deep-sea camera, Hurley and Shepard (1964).

Fig. 97. Photo near axis of Great Bahama Canyon at depth of 11,472 ft (3,497 m). Note rocky walls and rounded cobbles. Direction shown by compass. Photo by deep-sea camera, Hurley and Shepard (1964).

sand overlying coarser sand with scattered pebbles of limestone. As in other canyon cores, these pebbles are not concentrated in the bottom of the deposit.

BERING SEA CANYONS (Figs. 98a, 98b)

At the outer end of the wide Bering shelf, the large Bering Canyon heads at 450 ft (140 m) in a broad bowl north of Unimak Pass. It extends west-southwest along the Aleutian chain for 100 miles past Unalaska and Umnak islands, then swings northwest for an additional 105-mile course and finally bends west, terminating in about 11,000 ft (3,350 m) of water. The total length of about 230 miles is the longest in the world. Unfortunately, the outer part cannot be reproduced, so Figure 98 shows the canyon only to the depths of 9,000 ft (2,740 m). On the south side of the canyon, Bogoslof, an active volcano, is built up to the surface from time to time and then washed away by waves or destroyed by explosions. The canyon is about 20 miles wide near Bogoslof, with a section showing wall heights of 6,600 ft (2,000 m) on the south side and 3,500 ft (1,070 m) on the north side.

Tributaries come into the canyon from both sides, but are especially abundant on the south side. The difference may be only apparent because of the better sounding coverage on the south side. Our contour interpretation of the inner part shows fewer tributaries than in the contours by Smith (1937), but there can be no doubt but what the slopes near the islands have a close-spaced pattern of small valleys.

Soundings suggest that one large tributary, Pribilof Canyon (not shown in Figure 98b), either comes into the outer portion of Bering Canyon from the northeast or forms a separate canyon. Like Bering Canyon, this valley heads near the outer part of a broad shelf with a bowl-shaped head about 20 miles across. The available soundings show several tributaries coming into Pribilof Canyon. One arm heads about 20 miles south of St. George Island in the Pribilofs. A sounding line across Pribilof Canyon at the outer edge of the shelf indicates that it has wall heights of as much as 7,000 ft (2,130 m), but the width is 30 miles at this point so that the average wall slope is relatively low.

Just west of the large bend in Bering Canyon, there is another wide marine valley, Umnak Canyon (Fig. 98b). Several heads of this canyon come in close to the north shore of Umnak Island, one coming within 2 miles of the shore near the center of the island, and another large head with numerous branches extends to within 10 miles of the west side. These heads have a typical dendritic drainage pattern. After running north for about 45 miles, these two main branches join. Beyond, the canyon bends, first to a westerly course that is followed for about 55 miles, and then to a northwesterly path where it dies out after a 15-mile course (not shown in Fig 98b). The canyon terminates at a depth of about 10,500 ft (3,200 m), after a total length of 115 miles, one of the longest canyons in the world. There appears to be a flat-surfaced fan extending out from the canyon mouth for another 40 miles. Umnak Canyon does not have as high walls as the other two canyons in the vicinity, but there are places where it appears to be cut at least 3,000 ft (915 m) below surroundings.

Almost nothing is known about the character of the bottom of this group of canyons. Black sand, presumably volcanic, is noted at a few places on the walls of Umnak Canyon, and rock bottom is given at a depth of 2,400 ft (730 m) on the north wall of Bering Canyon.

Fig. 98. a. The inner portion of Bering Canyon north of the eastern Aleutian Islands. This is thought to be the longest submarine canyon in the world. Note relation to Bogoslof Volcano. From unpublished soundings of the Coast and Geodetic Survey. Soundings are much more closely spaced to the south near

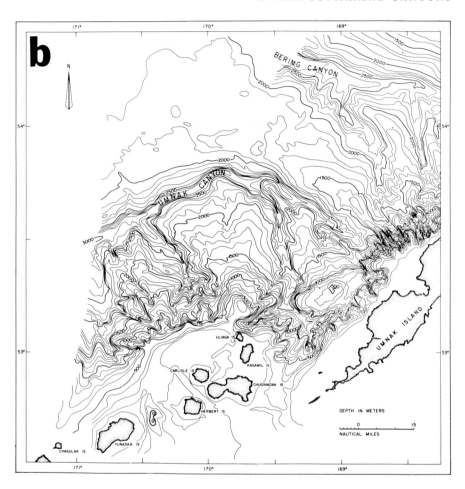

the islands, possibly accounting in part for more tributaries on that side. Continues west on Fig. 98b.

b. Umnak Canyon and intermediate part of Bering Canyon. Joins Fig. 98a. Note the large number of tributaries close to the islands. Outermost Bering Canyon is not included for military reasons.

If it were not for the twisting courses and the numerous tributaries of this group of canyons, one would be inclined to consider classifying them with the fault valleys such as are found on the south side of the Aleutians (Chapt. XIII).

SAN ANTONIO CANYON, CHILE

Apparently a number of submarine canyons are found along the west coast of South America, but only one has been surveyed sufficiently to be described here. This canyon is located off the city of San Antonio, 30 miles south of Valparaiso, Chile. It has one head extending in towards the small coastal plain at Cartagena, and the other towards the small promontory just north of San Antonio. The only large river in the area is Rio Maipo, just south of San Antonio. The continental shelf here is 16 miles wide, and the canyon crosses the entire shelf coming in very close to the shore, as indicated by a depth of 202 m (660 ft) at a distance of less than a mile off shore. No soundings are given nearer to the coast in this place.

One tributary enters the south side of this canyon. It may be similar to the tributary entering the north side of Redondo Canyon. A profile at an axial depth of 800 m (2,625 ft) shows walls 650 m (2,130 ft) high. No soundings are given that would characterize the outer canyon, but it is reasonable to assume that the walls are higher at the outer margin of the shelf, which is several miles beyond the 800 m (2,620 ft) canyon depth.

MANILA CANYON

Along the west and north coasts of Luzon, in the Philippine Islands, a number of canyons extend to within a few miles of the coast. The largest of these, Manila Canyon, is located directly off the entrance of Manila Bay, about 6 miles southwest of Corregidor. The canyon head does not come inside the 300 ft (90 m) contour, as is also true of the various tributaries. The situation here appears to be similar to that off eastern Honshu where the canyons head in water 160 ft (50 m) or more in depth.

A notable feature of Manila Canyon is the relatively steep gradient at its head, about 110 m/km. This decreases outwardly and averages about 40 m/km in the 26 miles from 1,200 to 7,200 ft (370 to 2,200 m).

At the outer limit of the continental shelf, the canyon has wall heights of about 6,000 ft (1,830 m), making it one the most deeply entrenched of any submarine canyon in the world. However, the width here is 17 miles and the wall slopes are not as steep as in many other canyons. The axis is somewhat winding and, so far as can be told from the meager soundings, tributaries come in from both sides. Probably the outer part represents a fan-valley, as it seems to have natural levees. The only bottom indications shown on the chart are "mud," but it is likely that the canyon is cut in rock, because the banks at the outer shelf are coral which probably overlies rock.

It would be of interest to make continuous reflection profiles in the shelf at the head of the canyon and in the entrance to Manila Bay, to see whether a buried channel extends into that deep indentation.

TRINCOMALEE CANYON AND OTHER GORGES OFF EASTERN CEYLON

Ceylon appears to have some impressive submarine canyons that were shown on the old British Admiralty surveys. Supplementary information was obtained during the Indian Ocean Expedition of the Coast and Geodetic Survey ship *Pioneer* (Stewart *et al.,* 1964). The largest Ceylonese canyons are found on the east side of the island. The canyon that extends into Trincomalee Bay (Fig. 99) was extensively sounded beyond the 6-mile limit set for us by the Ceylonese. Farther to the south, three canyons cut deeply into the shelf and slope with wall heights of about 4,800 ft (1,460 m) (Fig. 100). One section shows a width of 3 miles and a cut of 4,500 ft (1,370 m) below the outer shelf. Each of these canyons is located off a main river valley that comes from the high mountains of Ceylon.

The head of Trincomalee Canyon (Fig. 99) cuts back into Koddiyar and Trincomalee bays for 6 miles. The *Pioneer* was not permitted to survey inside the 6-mile limit, so that our information concerning the inner canyon comes entirely from the British charts. The two principal heads in Koddiyar Bay are found off small channels crossing the sand barrier that surrounds most of the bay. These heads come to within 0.1 mile (600 ft) of the shore. Three other tributaries extend in towards all the other gaps in this sand barrier. Undoubtedly these heads are related to the present-day tidal currents in the bay.

Perhaps the most spectacular feature of the canyon is the northern head that extends more than 2 miles up Trincomalee Harbor, past the Naval Base. This tributary is a shallow valley only about 350 ft (110 m) deep at the harbor entrance, but it has branches entering most of the coves on the sides of the harbor. Furthermore, this tributary cuts

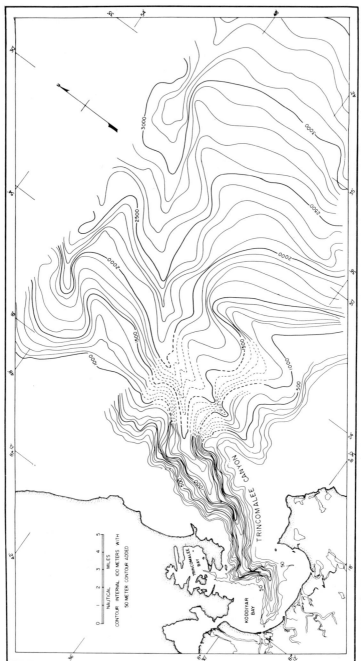

Fig. 99. Trincomalee Canyon off the northeast side of Ceylon. Note the deep re-entrant into Trincomalee Bay. Shoaler soundings indicate a still better fit with the tributary bays and with the openings in the bar inside Koddiyar Bay. Inner part based on soundings from U. S. Oceanographic Office, and outer part on unpublished soundings by the U. S. Coast and Geodetic Survey obtained on the *Pioneer* in 1964. Stewart *et al.* (1964b).

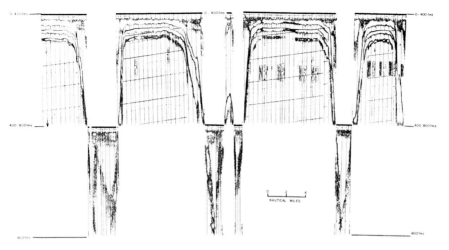

Fig. 100. Profiles of three canyons along the east coast
of Ceylon, south of Trincomalee Bay. From fathograms of U.S. Coast and Geodetic Survey ship *Pioneer*. Stewart *et al.* (1964b).

directly across ridges of quartzite and granitic rocks. The side valleys
develop a fine example of trellis drainage. The senior author, accompanied by R. S. Dietz, observed the upper slopes of this head by
skin diving. They are very precipitous and hard rock is well exposed.

Traced seaward, Trincomalee Canyon has a twisting course. From
available information it appears to have V-shaped transverse profiles.
At the outer edge of the shelf, the canyon has wall heights of 4,500 ft
(1,370 m) and a width of 4 miles.

Farther out, the sounding lines of the *Pioneer* are spaced about 2
miles apart and run diagonal to the canyon. As a result, the topography is not very well developed. However, we can determine that the
canyon continues to a depth of about 11,000 ft (3,350 m), and a fan-
valley is indicated as continuing to at least 11,800 ft (3,600 m). The
total canyon length is 38 miles and the average gradient is 21 m/km.
There are slight suggestions of tributaries in the outer part of the canyon. Our attempt on the *Pioneer* to obtain dredge samples from the
walls did not succeed, although we did obtain granite rock from the
very steep continental slope just south of Trincomalee Canyon. Also,
we took a core in a small canyon just north of Trincomalee and found
mud overlaying clean sand with angular pieces of gravel and fragments of shells scattered through the sand.

Runs with a continuous reflection profiler indicated that there may be sedimentary beds underlying a part of Trincomalee Canyon. Profiles across the fan-valley showed there was a thick mass of unconsolidated sediment at the base of the steep slope.

CONGO CANYON

The river with the largest discharge in Africa, the Congo, debouches into a long deep estuary at the head of Congo Canyon (Fig. 101). This is amazing, because of the enormous sediment load in the Congo that tends to fill the estuary and because of the indication that this part of the African coast is stable, having few other estuaries and being bordered by a shelf of normal marginal depth. The head of the canyon, 15 miles up the estuary, has a depth of 70 ft (21 m) and the inner part has a gradient of 30 m/km, but within a mile this is lowered to approximately 10 m/km. This apparently continues at least out to depths of 2,000 ft (610 m). Beyond, the gradient is slightly lower. At the mouth of the estuary the depth is 500 ft (150 m). No new survey is available for the inner part of the canyon, but seaward of the shelf, Lamont scientists have run a series of echo-sounding lines across the canyon and the fan-valley that adjoins the canyon on the outside (Heezen et al., 1964). According to the Lamont data and the earlier surveys (Fig. 101), the canyon, after extending fairly straight across the shelf, curves slightly to the right and attains its greatest wall heights, 3,600 ft (1,100 m), at an axial depth of 6,000 ft (1,830 m). Here it is still a V-shaped canyon with a width of 9 miles between the upper lip of its walls (Fig. 102). About 15 miles beyond, natural levees are developed on both sides and the wall height decreases rapidly. It thus becomes a fan-valley. At a depth of about 8,700 ft (2,650 m) and 150 miles from the head, it turns about 90° to the left.[3] From there on it crosses a large fan with a curving course and a depth below the surroundings of about 600 ft (180 m), gradually decreasing to about 100 ft (30 m). Some 250 miles from the head, the fan-valley bifurcates and it is difficult to tell which arm is the more pronounced. However, in the soundings of the Lamont ship *Vema* in 1963, a series of crossings were made starting 140 miles out beyond the last crossing of the southern arm, and a distinct fan-valley was found with natural levees on each side. Here, an axial depth of approximately 60 ft (18 m) exists below the surrounding fan.

[3]The left hook in the southern hemisphere is perhaps contrary to the concept of Menard (1955), although this is a low latitude and therefore not a convincing case.

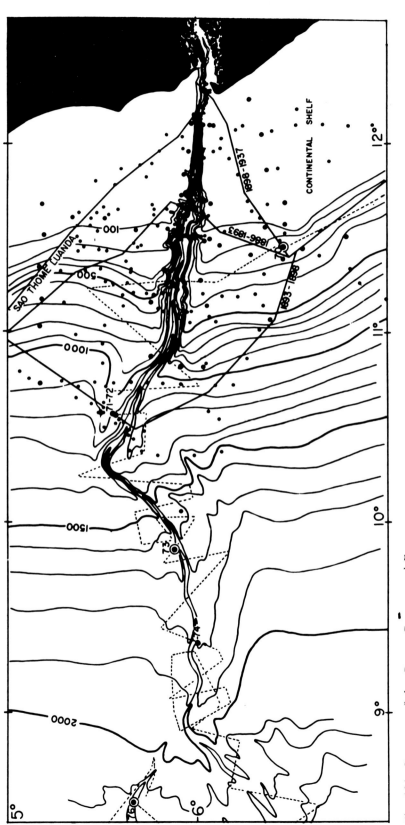

Fig. 101. Contours of the Congo Canyon and Fan-valley. For outer continuation of fan-valley, see Fig. 2. Contours are in fathoms. Positions and dates of cables laid across the Congo Valley are indicated. From Heezen *et al.* (1964).

The inner canyon has at least three tributaries entering from the south side. Marine sediments are introduced on this side by the predominantly north-flowing currents. Whether or not there are tributaries farther out across the shelf, is open to question because the soundings are not adequate.

Unfortunately, no dredgings have been made of the canyon walls, so we do not know if it is a rock gorge. Samples from the estuary are reported by the cable companies as mud, in contrast to the sandy and

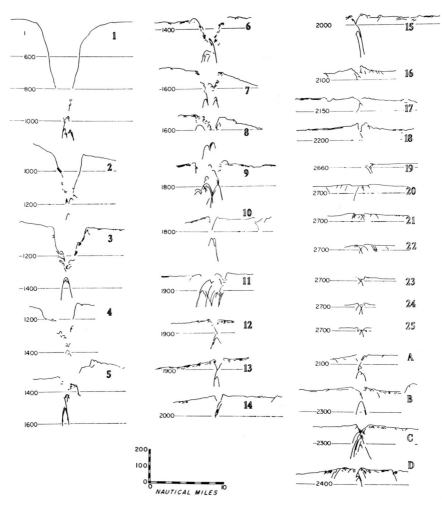

Fig. 102. Transverse profiles across the Congo Canyon and Fan-valley. Depths are given in Fathoms. From Heezen *et al.* (1964).

hard clay river bottom. The cores obtained by Lamont scientists were from the axis of the fan-valley and from the adjoining fan. These show, as usual, that the cores from the axis (V-12-73 and V-12-76) have a number of sand or coarse silt layers (Fig. 103) and that there is an abundance of plant material. Occasional coarse layers were found in the adjoining fans. Thus the situation is very much like that for La Jolla Fan-valley, although the sandy sediments are much finer in the Congo area.

The mud bottom in the estuary suggests quiet water conditions where deposition should occur rapidly. Evidently this indication is deceptive because the estuary is not being filled, and the frequent cable breaks on the outside show that sediment must be moving seaward with sufficient force to rupture strong wires at rather frequent intervals. Milne (1897) and Heezen et al. (1964) give an excellent account of the cable failures along the Congo Canyon and fan-valley. Between 1897 and 1937, when the Saô Thomé Loanda cable was located across the canyon near the coast, it failed 15 times. Five failures were in two tributaries on the south side of the canyon at depths of about 600 ft (180 m) and 1,680 ft (510 m). The breaks were all due to tension and most of the cable in the canyon could not be recovered because of burial. The ruptures were most common during periods of high water discharge. Previously, in 1886, the cable had been laid across the canyon at about 4,000 ft (1,220 m) and then in 1893 in 7,700 ft (2,350 m). At the first location it failed five times and at the second, eight times. Therefore, it apparently broke more often when laid in the deepest water, although this may be purely coincidental rather than related to location. The period between 1893 and 1896 was a time of many breaks. A period of few breaks occurred from 1901 to 1924 when the channel of the river was remarkably stable. The shifting of the channel in the river apparently provides large quantities of sediment, and this in turn develops unstable conditions that lead to mass movements of sediment off shore which break the cables.[4] Although the average time between major movements in the Congo Canyon, one rupture in 2 years, is slightly less than the slides in the head of Sumner Branch of Scripps Canyon, one in 1.3 years, it is evident that disturbances in both of these places are frequent. The data from the Congo is particularly valuable because it shows that the breaks take place along a canyon axis where the slope is very low (< 10 m/km) and that the breaks are probably at least as frequent out in deep water as in shallow water.

[4]For a discussion of the causes see p. 295-309.

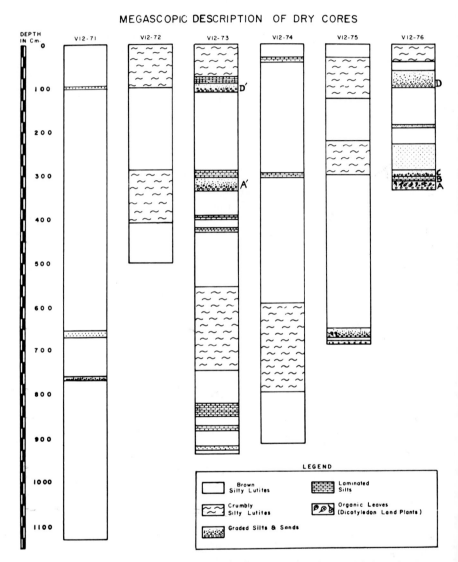

Fig. 103. Diagrams of cores from vicinity of Congo Canyon and Fan-valley. V 12-73 and V 12-76 are from valley axis. See Fig. 101 for locations. From Heezen *et al.* (1964).

HAWAIIAN ISLAND CANYONS

The slopes of oceanic islands are for the most part very inadequately charted. Locally around the Hawaiian Islands, the Coast and Geodetic Survey charts extend deeper than the coastal shelf. One survey off the north coast of Kauai, made in 1927 when echo-sounding methods were just beginning to be used, showed definite indications of submarine canyons. Additionally, in 1947, the senior author—while working on an assignment with the U.S. Navy—had an opportunity to run some sounding lines along the cliffed north shore of East Molokai and along the northeast side of Oahu. Several new canyons were found. In 1962, the opportunity was presented to investigate the canyons of Molokai and Kauai, using the Scripps vessel *Spencer F. Baird.* The surveys made at this time have confirmed the existence of canyons in both places. Samples were taken of the bottom, along with a few photographs. It is worth noting that all of these Hawaiian localities with submarine canyons are off coasts where there has been considerable erosion and where (except at one point off northern Molokai) volcanism is quite remote.

Molokai Canyons

East of longitude 157°03', the north coast of Molokai is very precipitous and cut by deep land canyons with high intervening ridges, whereas to the west there are only low coastal hills with gentle slopes and small valleys. The Molokai canyons occur exclusively off the precipitous deeply eroded rocky coast (Fig. 104). Most of the sea canyons are located directly off prominent land canyons. In making the survey in 1947, it was found that each time we could look up the slot in the westernmost land canyon, Maiwa, we were approximately over the axis of the corresponding submarine canyon. In the more detailed 1962 work, this relationship provided an easy method for coring along the canyon axis. Pelekunu Canyon is a seaward continuation of the land canyon having the same name. Here, the submarine canyon head comes to within a mile of the shore and perhaps much closer. Waikolu land canyon, just east of Kalaupapa Peninsula, has another large gorge which seems to be connected with one of the larger sea valleys. East of Pelekunu Bay, the juxtaposition is not quite as clear. The next marine canyon heads in towards Keanapuka Bay at the mouth of a large land canyon. Finally, the easternmost sea canyon heads directly into Halawa Bay where the easternmost land canyon comes to the sea.

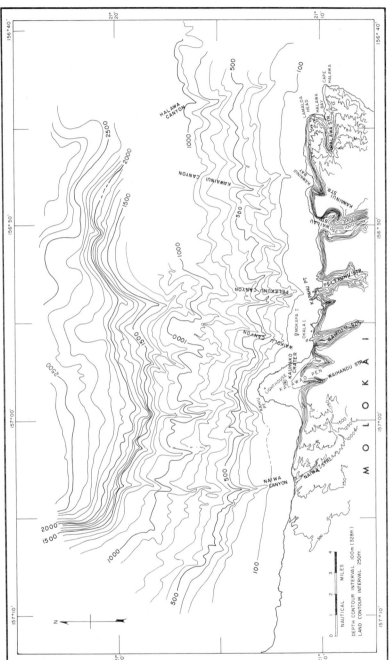

Fig. 104. Canyons along the north coast of Molokai in the Hawaiian Islands. Note apparent relation to land canyons even in the vicinity of Kalawao (Kalaupapa) Peninsula. Waihandu Canyon, not labeled here, is located directly off Kahiu Point. The peninsula is the result of a Pleistocene (?) volcano. From marine surveys by Shepard. Land contours from U.S. Geological Survey.

In order to investigate the significance of this connection between sea and land canyons, we ran sounding lines along the steep submarine slope that represents an easterly continuation of the escarpment of North Molokai, but where no island is found to the south. No submarine canyons were found in this slope, although there is one broad indentation near the eastern end of the lines.

The canyons off northeast Molokai include one valley that is located almost exactly off Kalawao Peninsula.[5] However, this peninsula was built out by the lava cone of Kauhako Volcano, said to be the latest volcanism in the island (Stearns and Macdonald, 1947). Approximately inside this anomalous sea valley, Waihandu Canyon, a relatively large valley, has evidently been deflected from its lower course by the volcano. From comparison between Waihandu sea canyon and the canyons on either side, it will be seen that the contours deeper than 2,300 ft (700 m) all bend in towards the cliffed coast of Molokai to about the same extent. Therefore, it is likely that these outer valleys were cut before the volcano was built. It would be interesting to get subsurface information under Kauhako Volcano to see if the inner part of the submarine canyon can be traced closer to the cliff.

The Molokai submarine canyons have typical V-shaped profiles with no indication of broad flat floors. In some respects, however, these valleys are quite comparable to the canyons off continental coasts. They appear to extend out in fairly straight lines, particularly Naiawa Canyon, the westernmost of the group. Tributaries are found in the Molokai canyons, but they are far less prominent than canyons cutting the continental margins. The height of the canyon walls is definitely lower than that of typical continental types. The deepest cut is in outer Pelekunu Canyon, where the two walls average about 1,150 ft (350 m) high above an axial depth of 4,700 ft (1,430 m). Here, the width is only 2 miles so that the slopes are quite steep. However, most of the profiles show wall heights of less than 800 ft (240 m) (see Appendix).

Another characteristic of the Molokai canyons is that they have rather even gradients. It will be seen that the gradient changes little between the canyon heads and the base of the steep insular slopes where the canyons terminate at depths close to 6,000 ft (1,830 m). There appears to be some evidence of a slightly incised fan-valley forming a gently sloping continuation of Pelekunu Canyon out to a depth of about 8,300 ft (2,530 m), where the soundings end. If this is

[5]Commonly called Kalaupapa Peninsula.

a fan-valley, it bends to the right, contrary to the fan-valleys off western United States described by Menard (1955). Most of the canyons have a gradient of close to 100 m/km out to 3,000 ft (915 m) depths, and either continue at about the same slope or are slightly steeper out to their terminal depths of about 6,000 ft (1,830 m). This is not only different from submarine canyons off continents, which are usually much steeper near their heads, but also strikingly different from land canyons that almost always have steeper heads. The Molokai land canyons have bowl-shaped heads, like most other canyons cut into tropical volcanic islands. This shape combined with extensive fill at the base of most of the land canyons makes their longitudinal profiles very different from those of the adjacent sea-floor canyons.

The earlier survey of the Molokai area indicated the existence of a basin depression along the course of one canyon. This was carefully investigated during the 1962 survey, and no basin could be discovered at the place. Probably one can attribute the basin of the older survey to the inadequacy of the old type of echo sounder used in 1947.

Dredgings of the canyon walls in Molokai showed that the typical canyon slopes east of Kalawao Peninsula were covered with mud, although one dredge from about 1,200 ft (370 m) brought up a block of basalt with a coating of organisms and with many mollusk borings. Most dredgings in Naiwa Canyon, west of Kalawao Peninsula, yielded rock. This rock was partly mudstone, partly basaltic lava with large phenocrysts, and partly a pyroclastic sandstone of definite volcanic material. Some poorly preserved fossils were found in the mudstone.

Cores from the canyon axes showed that coarse sediments exist here. A core from an axial depth of 3,600 ft (1,097 m) in Waikolu Canyon brought up coarse sand overlying gravel covered with red algae, but with clayey sediment in the core nose, indicating that the coarse sediment had been deposited on top of the clay. Sandy sediment underlying mud was obtained in 1,350 ft (410 m) depths in Naiwa Canyon, and a shelly sand came from a depth of 4,060 ft (1,237 m) in Waikolu Canyon. The shells apparently came from shallow water, although they were too broken for definite identification.

Canyons Off Northwest Kauai (Fig. 105)

Scenically even more spectacular than the cliffed coast of northeast Molokai is the Napali Coast of northwest Kauai. This coast is largely inaccessible except from the sea, although a somewhat perilous trail extends from the west end of the road at Haena to Kalalau Canyon, the largest land valley on this coast. Honopu Canyon can be seen from the 4,000-foot (1,220 m) lookout at the top of the Waimea Canyon road.

The contour maps of these Kauai canyons were constructed partly from the old U.S. Coast and Geodetic Survey Hydrographic Sheet 4719, made in 1927, but are based to a greater extent on the 1962 surveys from the *Spencer F. Baird*. The Coast and Geodetic Survey undoubtedly had better positions than we did as they had set up markers all along the coast, and were no doubt more familiar with the peaks and valley mouths on shore. Also, we had rather poor visibility at times due to rain storms, and part of our survey was run at night and had to be based on radar with its questionable accuracy. On the other hand, the very primitive echo-sounding device used by the Coast and Geodetic Survey vessel in that early day of echo soundings

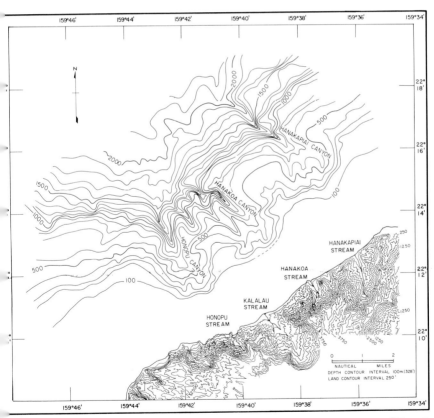

Fig. 105. Canyons along the northwest coast of Kauai, Hawaiian Islands. Possible relation to land valleys is indicated. From marine survey by Shepard. Land contours from U.S. Geological Survey.

was quite clearly inadequate in picking up deep soundings, especially in crossing the deeper parts of the canyons, so the soundings become very questionable in these areas. This inadequacy can be recognized by noting that in crossing the canyons at successively greater distances from shore our precision depth recorder invariably showed greater axial depths, but in several places the Coast and Geodetic Survey soundings indicate shoaler crossings in the outer lines. Also, the large gaps in the Coast and Geodetic Survey sounding lines, where they cross the canyon axes, show that they were having trouble picking up the soundings in this difficult zone.[6]

The submarine canyons along the north coast of Kauai are found exclusively along this Napali Coast (Fig. 105). Small sea valleys of a type difficult to classify lie farther east of Hanalei, where the land valleys are also much smaller near the coast. There is much less certainty about the connections between the land and submarine canyons off the Napali Coast than off Molokai, but it will be seen that one of the two major sea canyons is located off the great cirque-headed valley of Hanakapiai Stream. This submarine canyon has been named for the land valley.

The deeper sections of the other submarine canyons of the Kauai group lie approximately off the large Kalalau Stream Valley. Actually, the two main branches are both located respectively 1.2 and 2.0 miles on either side of Kalalau. The eastern branch is possibly related to Hanakoa Stream, and has been given that name following the usual practice of naming the canyons after the closest stream valley on land. The western branch has been named Honopu Canyon after the valley immediately shoreward of the canyon head.

The Kauai submarine canyons all head about 2 miles offshore, much farther out than those of Molokai. Only small indentations of the shelf margin are observed here, not much greater than one mile. The canyons also differ from those off Molokai in having more branches, at least in the western canyon group. Hanakapiai Canyon extends down the slope just about as straight as the canyons off Molokai, but the others are somewhat more twisting. Honopu Canyon has the deepest cut, with walls approximately 2,500 ft (760 m) high at an axial depth of 5,000 ft (1,520 m). The other valleys are only slightly deeper than the Molokai canyons. Tracing Honopu Canyon seaward, it appears to have become a fan-valley with natural levees on either

---

[6]Even modern sounding devices encounter difficulties in surveys of narrow canyons. See Chapt. II, pp. 19, 20.

side at an axial depth of about 5,800 ft (1,770 m). Neither the valley nor the levees are indicated by the 6,300-ft (1,920 m) contour, but they appear again farther out, and we can hazard the guess that a better survey will show that they are continuous. However, there were no signs of natural levees in the outermost sounding line of the more easterly Hanakapiai Canyon, where the axis has a 7,500 ft (2,290 m) depth. Apparently this canyon goes to still greater depth.

The Kauai canyons are narrow, like those of Molokai. The gradient is steep at the head of Honopu Canyon, about 250 m/km, and then decreases to 190 m/km out to an axial depth of 3,000 ft (910 m). Farther out, from 3,000 to 4,500 ft (910 to 1,370 m), the gradient again steepens to approximately 250 m/km; but beyond that, it decreases to 120 m/km out to the deepest sounding line at 6,000 ft (1,830 m). Hanakapiai Canyon also shows an increase in gradient between depths of 3,000 to 6,000 ft (910 to 1,830 m). The floor of this canyon drops a total of 7,000 ft (2,130 m) in slightly over 6 miles, giving it an average gradient of 190 m/km compared with an average of 240 m/km for Honopu Canyon. These gradients are much steeper than those of the canyons of the continental margin, and they show much less decrease in slope in the outer part. However, the canyons off Hawaii are cut into submarine volcanoes that ordinarily maintain their slope well down toward the deep ocean floor.

The walls of the Kauai canyons were found to have rocks consisting of a combination of lava and mudstone. Some of the mudstone from Honopu Canyon contained foraminifera, which were identified by E. C. Allison as probably Late Miocene in age. These come from a depth of about 2,000 ft (610 m), whereas the foraminifera must have lived in shallow water, showing further evidence of submergence of the area since the formation was deposited (see, also, Menard *et al.*, 1962). The basalt dredged from Hanakapiai Canyon was quite clearly broken off from a ledge at a depth of about 3,500 ft (1,070 m). It is similar to the olivine basalts found also on the island (R. M. Moberly, personal communication).

None of the cores in the canyons contained very coarse sediments, but all had layers of fine sand, and in one core there is some evidence of gradation of sand layers with the coarser sizes beneath. Photographs of the walls of Honopu Canyon, near the axis on a rather gentle slope, showed ripple marks with intersecting patterns (Fig. 106). Unfortunately, during the photographing, the ship failed to drift over the axis of the canyon, so it is not known whether these ripples continue to the floor.

Fig. 106. An intersecting pattern of ripple marks photographed near the axis of Hanakoa Canyon off northwest Kauai at a depth of 1,380 ft (420 m). Photo by Shepard.

Canyons off Northeast Oahu

In 1947, during the installation of SOFAR equipment (an acoustic air-sea rescue system used to locate downed aircraft), close-spaced sounding lines were run off the general approaches to Kaneohe Bay, attendant on anchoring offshore listening gear in favorable localities. These soundings showed the existence of small slope canyons rather similar to those off Molokai. Later, Hamilton (1957) incorporated these early soundings and those of the Coast and Geodetic chart 4116 with soundings from a series of long profiles made between 1950 and 1957 during six expeditions to the Hawaiian region by U.S.N.E.L. and Scripps Institution ships. The resulting bathymetric charts showed at least 14 small slope canyons and gullies seaward of Kaneohe Bay. Two of these can be traced from where they head at a depth of about 300 ft (90 m) down to a depth of at least 6,600 ft (2,010 m), where they die out on a seaward bulge in the bottom contours that may be a fan. The channels are relatively shallow, the deepest with walls less than 1,500 ft (460 m) high and usually much less for the smaller gullies.

Hamilton reports that sedimentation off Oahu is apparently controlled by submarine canyons funneling sediment from shallow water seaward to form delta-like features. Off Kahana Bay, the northernmost fan is found just below the 6,600-ft (2,010 m) contour. To the south, the largest canyon heads in about 300 ft (90 m) and extends seaward with a sinuous course to a fan at a depth of 9,000 ft (2,740 m). Lying directly off Mokapu Peninsula, is one of the few canyons that is located off a point of land. Hamilton concludes that, although the island of Oahu is thought to have been elevated and submerged several times during its geological history, the present depths of the canyon mouth are below any postulated previous estimate of submergence and must have been at least partially eroded by submarine processes.

CANYONS OFF AUSTRALIA, NEW ZEALAND, AND NEW GUINEA

Exploration of the slopes around the Australian subcontinent and the outlying continental islands of New Zealand, New Caledonia, and New Guinea has been quite incomplete, but the few areas that have been adequately covered have revealed a considerable number of canyons. Sprigg (1947, 1963) has called attention to a group of canyons off South Australia near Adelaide, called the Murray Canyons, that head close to the break in slope of a moderately wide shelf, the latter having some high rock islands. Profiles indicate wall heights with a maximum of about 3,000 ft (910 m). The surveys are not sufficiently complete to determine whether there are any appreciable tributary systems, although only a few are indicated on the available contours. At least one canyon may extend out to over 13,000 ft (3,960 m). Sprigg interpreted some of the topography as indicative of the existence of slump blocks.

Along the slope off New South Wales, a few sounding lines have shown that canyons exist between Montague Island and Jervis Bay, but the slope is very even farther north off the vicinity of Sydney Harbor (Phipps, 1963). Ulladulla Canyon has walls about 600 ft (180 m) high at an axial depth of about 1,800 ft (550 m). Dredging of a nearby canyon produced some fragments of consolidated sediment.

Off the east coast of New Zealand, several canyons have been discovered. Some of these are shown in a map of the New Zealand Oceanographic Institute, published in 1963 and compiled by D. C. Krause and A. G. York. A group of small canyons cut several miles into the narrow shelf off South Island's Otago Peninsula. The continental slope ends here at about 1,000 m (3,300 ft), but several of the valleys continue across a broad fan coalescing to form what is called Bounty Channel. This is traced seaward to over 4,000 m (13,120 ft). It has walls averaging about 500 m (1,640 ft) in height. This curious outer valley differs from typical fan-valleys described outside other submarine canyons in that it has tributaries rather than distributaries. Although not shown on the map, the authors have been assured by H. W. Menard (personal communication) that there are several natural levees next to the slightly intrenched channel. Further exploration of this interesting valley should be made. North of Banks Peninsula, two rather large canyons are shown on the same map by the New Zealand Institute. Pegasus Canyon cuts 15 miles into the shelf, extending in a southwest-northeast direction parallel to the coast of the island. After a course of 60 miles, it apparently joins Kaikoura Canyon at a depth close to 2,000 m (6,560 ft). The latter heads near the coast just south of Kaikoura Peninsula. Although Kaikoura Canyon trends at right angles to the coast it has an arm entering from the south that extends along the coast. The combined canyon merges into Hikurangi Trench that runs in an east-west direction. Farther north, a deep canyon extends into Cook Strait. This is being investigated by the New

Zealand Oceanographic Institute. The chart shows strong tidal currents along the inner portion of the canyon, which may have important effects on shaping the floor.

Canyons off New Ginea were discovered in the Morobe area along the north coast of the eastern arm of the island (Sprigg, 1947). A group of three canyons all head within about one mile of the coast. There is some indication from Sprigg's contour map that these canyons lie off small river valleys. They extend normal to the coast and have few tributaries.

CHAPTER X

SUMMARY CHARACTERISTICS AND DIMENSIONS OF SUBMARINE CANYONS

F ROM THE FOREGOING discussion of submarine canyons, it will be seen that, although they do not all follow the same pattern, most of them have much in common. In compiling statistics from described canyons, it should be borne in mind that much more is known about canyons off the coasts of the United States and Baja California than elsewhere, and especially about those canyons with heads coming into the coast. We are actually determining the characteristics of the best surveyed canyons. However, this information should provide a moderately satisfactory picture of canyons in general. In compiling the statistics given in the Appendix, we are referring only to the canyons and not to the fan-valleys that form continuations of many of them. The location of most of the canyons included is shown in the frontispiece.

CANYON CHARACTERISTICS

In the Appendix, we have classified 93 of the canyons according to the following characteristics: (1) Length, (2) Depth of head, (3) Greatest known depth, (4) Character of coast, (5) Relation to points on downcurrent side, (6) Relation to river valleys, (7) Source of sediment for canyon heads, (8) Canyon gradient, (9) Nature of longitudinal profile, (10) Maximum wall height, (11) Channel curvature, (12) Abundance of tributaries, (13) Transverse profile character, (14) Nature of canyon wall material, (15) Core sediment found in axis, and (16) Relation to fan-valleys. In the table, the canyons from the same general area are given in somewhat of a geographic sequence, and at the end of the table are a few of the miscellaneous canyons discussed in Chapter IX. In determining some of the means, each group is averaged and treated as a unit and then these units are in turn averaged. The various parameters appear to be log-normal distributions, thus average values are meaningful descriptions of the group properties.

Lengths and Depths at Extremes of Canyons

The lengths of the submarine canyons have been measured along their axes from the canyon head to the point where the canyon disappears on the slope or enters a fan-valley. These lengths are subject to some uncertainty because many of the surveys do not extend far enough in either direction. Where this is the case, the length is given with a plus sign. For an average length, those with a plus sign are included since they often are the longest. Using this method, the average of the various groups is 30 nautical miles. Probably more complete knowledge would increase this by a few miles. By far the longest canyons are in the southern Bering Sea, where Bering Canyon is of the order of 230 miles in total length. Cap Breton Canyon, of western European canyons, is perhaps the next longest with a probable length of 135 miles. Great Bahama with 120 miles is tied with Congo Canyon for third. If the fan-valleys were included, much greater lengths would be found; for example, about 500 miles for the Congo Valley.

The shortest of the canyon groups are those of the Hawaiian Islands, which average only 6.5 miles although the outer limits are not too well established. Almost equally short are the canyons off southern California that terminate in the inner basins of the continental borderland.

The canyons head at depths of a few feet to more than a thousand feet. The average for the entire group is 350 ft (107 m), but this would be somewhat reduced if better surveys were available. A lower average is found in some of the best surveyed areas. Thus, California canyons average 110 ft (34 m) at their heads, and Baja California has three canyons coming in almost to the beach. By contrast, the East Coast canyons all head at depths of more than 300 ft (90 m).

The depth of outer canyon termination is well known off California and Baja California and for a few other canyons. Elsewhere, it is rather indefinite from the available soundings. However, if we used averages only for those that are well surveyed, the depths would be lower than if we include the estimated depths and the canyons marked with a plus sign. With all included, the average for the group is 6,946 ft (2,117 m). The average for the areas where terminations are well developed is lower, amounting to 5,958 ft (1,816 m). This is lowered particularly by the elimination of the deep Aleutian group and of the canyons of western Europe. The deepest canyon may be Aviles Canyon, off northern Spain, with 15,580 ft (4,750 m), a questionable depth; and the second is Nazare, off Portugal, with a sounding of 14,764 ft (4,500 m) in what appears to be the outer canyon. The deepest that is rather well-established is Great Bahama Canyon with a depth of at least 14,060 ft (4,280 m). It is notable that very few canyons in well-surveyed areas can be traced beyond axial depths of 7,000 to 8,000 ft (2,130 to 2,440 m). On the other hand, the canyons terminating at less than 5,000 ft (1,520 m) are found principally off southern California where they are stopped by the inner basins, and off eastern Honshu where they enter a fault trough. Most canyons continue down to the contact between the relatively steep continental slope and the gently sloping continental rise. There is some evidence that this virtually confines the canyons to the slopes that have rock outcrops or where the rock has only a thin cover of sediment. Such a relationship is well established by continuous reflection profiling off parts of California and Baja California. However, the fan-valleys beyond the canyons may have relatively deep cuts into the sediments of the continental rise and, at least in the Hudson Fan-valley, the cut has extended into Tertiary formations (p. 150).

Land Physiography and Coastal Configuration Shoreward of Canyon Heads

Since the majority of the canyons extend in close to the coast, it is possible to determine whether their heads enter bays, lie directly off bays, off straight beaches, or off straight cliffed coasts. The tabulation for the entire 77 canyons for which such a classification was possible shows that 13 extend into estuaries, 25 lie directly off bays, 26 off straight beaches, including barrier islands, and 13 off relatively straight cliffed coasts. There are, therefore, about an equal number off embayed and straightened coasts inside the canyon heads. It is only off western Corsica that a series of adjacent canyons penetrate deeply into embayments. To date, only two canyons have been found directly off a point of land and at least one is related to recent volcanism.

Because there has been considerable discussion of a relationship of canyons to the upcurrent side of points of land (Davis, 1934), an analysis of the canyon heads was made to look for such a relationship. It was claimed by Davis that these points deflect longshore currents seaward. The result of the analysis was that of the 93 canyons, 73 showed no relationship to such a point, 11 were quite clearly located off the upcurrent side of the point, and nine were close enough to such a point so that a slightly lowered sea level would place them adjacent to it. The best indications of a relationship of this kind were found in southern California and along the coast of Portugal.

The juxtaposition of canyon heads to land valleys has been discussed by many authors. This is, of course, a criteria having significance in the interpretation of canyon origin, both because the drowning of valleys would leave the remaining land valleys shoreward of the drowned areas and, on the other hand, the excavation of submarine canyons by submarine processes should be dependent on a good nearby source of sediment, such as could be provided by an entering river. For this analysis, we have classified the canyon heads as occurring quite directly off river valleys, showing no relation to land valleys, or of an uncertain relationship because of heading far from shore. The result of the analysis is that 46 are located directly off river valleys and 11 have no valleys inside. The remainder head too far seaward to classify. Thus, there appears to be a common relationship to river valleys. In several recent surveys where it had been thought previously that there was no nearshore canyon, the heads of canyons have been traced into the coast at a point where there is a land valley. Perhaps, therefore, the relationship is even better than the figures indicate. However, it should be pointed out that some of the other types of marine valleys are located off river valleys, particularly off deltas. There is only one area where it seems quite clear that the canyons show no relationship to land valleys; that is off Georges Bank, east of New England. Here, it may well be that prior to the glacial excavation of the Gulf of Maine, Georges Bank constituted a coastal plain bordering the New England area.

Sources of Sediment for Canyon Heads

Of the 93 canyons that are included in the table, 34 appear to have a present-day source of sediment carried to them by longshore currents or contributed to them directly by river mouths. Of the remainder, 45 have heads far enough from shore and at sufficient depth so that neither longshore currents nor direct river-mouth supplies are now available. However, we know that considerable transport is taking place over much of the continental shelves, so sediment is probably provided from time to time, and during lowered sea-level stages of the Pleistocene these canyons may have had direct sources. The remaining 14 canyons probably head too deep to have had much supply, even during the lower sea-level stages. Nevertheless, their heads may now be filled, or they may have been depressed by warping or faulting.

Physical Characteristics of Canyons

The gradients of the submarine canyons have been discussed by several authors, most of whom point to the fact that the inclinations are far steeper than those found in adjoining land valleys. As in the case of land canyons, the gradients are closely related to the slope into which the canyons are cut. The average slope of the canyon floors is 58 m/km. This relatively high average gradient is considerably weighted by the preponderance of short canyons, virtually all of these having steeply sloping floors. For example, the Hawaiian Canyon group with an average length of 6.5 miles has an average slope of 144 m/km. Conversely, the long canyons all have low gradients. Thus, Bering Canyon has 7.8 m/km; Congo, 9.6 m/km; Cap Breton, 19 m/km, and Great Bahama, 13 m/km. These four canyons have an average length of 152 miles.

The variation along the longitudinal profiles has been classified in the table as concave upward, convex upward, relatively even, and having a profile with sharp increase in gradient. The analysis shows a great preponderance of concave upward profiles with 56[1] in that

[1]Where the profiles were concave but also showed a sharp step-like steepening, half credit was given to both types, so that actually a total of 66 profiles out of 93 are concave upward, and 8 convex upward.

category and only four with convex upward profiles. Twenty-three profiles showed a sharp step-like increase along the profile, most of these being otherwise concave. A comparatively even profile was shown in 10 cases. The concave profile with steep canyon heads is typical also of land canyons.

The great height of the walls of submarine canyons has always been a feature that has aroused interest among geologists. It is rather difficult to determine the maximum height of the walls of each canyon. Since one wall is ordinarily higher than the other, the two wall heights were averaged and the greatest height has been given to the nearest 1,000 ft (305 m). Averaging the various groups, we find that the average greatest height is just over 3,000 ft (915 m). This is, of course, far greater than one would find from averaging the same heights for land canyons. One factor that may make this comparison rather meaningless is that small submarine canyons in many areas may have been missed in the surveys, or were insufficiently sounded to be included in the present compilation. For example, there are many indications of short, relatively low-walled canyons along the coast of North Africa, shown in the maps of Rosfelder (1954), but these were not included here because of scarcity of data available to the writers. It is an exceptional land canyon that has walls as high as 3,000 ft (915 m). By far the highest walls of a sea canyon were found near the lower end of Great Bahama Canyon, where the walls slope up on both sides to the low islands from an axial depth of 14,060 ft (4,280 m). So far as we know, this exceeds the height of any canyon wall on the continents. Walls higher than the 5,500 ft (1,680 m) average for the Grand Canyon are found in two of the Bering Sea canyons, probably in Manila Canyon, and perhaps in Llanes Canyon off northern Spain.

The extent to which the canyon axes curve seemed worth determining since erosion valleys on land are much more sinuous than fault valleys. A model was set up as in Figure 107 to show four rather arbitrary classifications, between straight at one extreme and meandering on the other. In addition, a class with one large meander-like bend and a class with right-angle bends as in trellised drainage were included. The majority of the canyons, a total of 52, proved to be sinuous, and 36 of the rest were gently curving. Two canyons have a meandering course; two others showed right-angled bends. No canyon runs in a very straight course.

The statement has been made that the submarine canyons have few tributaries. This condition is certainly true of all the other types of marine valleys discussed in Chapter XI to XIV. To determine the situation for the canyons, four categories were selected: (1) canyons with tributaries as common as in typical land river valleys, (2) tributaries existent but less common than in typical land valleys, (3) tributaries

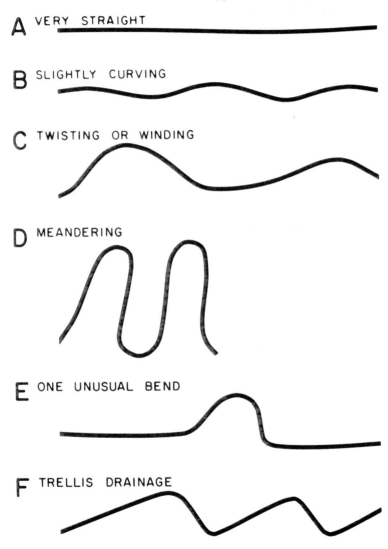

A VERY STRAIGHT

B SLIGHTLY CURVING

C TWISTING OR WINDING

D MEANDERING

E ONE UNUSUAL BEND

F TRELLIS DRAINAGE

Fig. 107. The patterns used for classifying the canyon channel trends used in the Appendix Table.

confined to the canyon heads, and (4) no tributaries. The result shows that the majority have tributaries comparable to land canyons with a total of 50, less common than land canyons with a total of 31, 10 apparently have tributaries confined to the canyon head, and only two do not have any tributaries shown. Thus, there is a very distinct difference between these canyons and the other types of marine valleys.

The character of the transverse profiles was classified in four categories also: (1) predominantly V-shaped with only a narrow floor (as in land canyons), (2) V-shaped in the upper half and trough-shaped (with a broad flat floor) in the lower half, (3) predominantly trough-shaped, and (4) of uncertain character. The analysis shows that 60 valleys have V-shaped transverse profiles, and only 13 have profiles that become trough-shaped in the lower portion, whereas only two appear to be trough-shaped along the entire length. The rest were not sounded well enough to make it possible to determine the nature of the profile.

The walls of the canyons have been dredged in a good many places. In the table, these walls are classified as (1) those having crystalline rock dredged at some place, (2) those with only sedimentary rock (3) those with only mud or other sediment, or (4) those with no information available. Forty-two of the canyons have no available information; virtually all of the rest have rock on their walls, with 22 yielding crystalline rock, mostly granite, and 30 having sedimentary rock alone. Four of the east coast canyons did not yield any rock, although we now know from continuous reflection profiles that rock is found near the surface in some of these canyons.

Many canyons have had cores taken in their axes. These are classified as (1) those with sand layers reported, (2) those with both sand and gravel in the cores, (3) with mud cores only, and (4) unknown. Of the 40 canyons that have core information from the axes, 16 show sand layers, 21 have both sand and gravel, and only four have mud alone. All of the last were found in the east coast canyons that head a long distance from shore.

The nature of termination of 42 canyons has been determined. It was found that 33 of these extend into fan-valleys and only nine terminated at the base of the continental slope without any visible fan-valley. Apparently, fan-valleys extending across the continental rise are ordinarily found outside the canyons. These usually terminate in flat basin floors.

COMPARISON WITH LAND CANYONS

In the preceding descriptions, land canyons have been compared to many of those of the sea floor. Some generalizations relative to this comparison are in order. The submarine canyons are remarkably similar in general character to land canyons cut into slopes of comparable steepness. They have courses that are approximately as winding as land canyons cut in similar slopes. Most of them have comparable V-shaped transverse profiles and a similar dendritic type of entering tributaries. Furthermore, the submarine canyons occur preponderantly outside the mouths of land valleys.

This resemblance to land canyons might suggest that they have the same origin. However, it is clearly evident that most of the submarine canyons are not simply drowned lower sections of land canyons. If they were, one would expect some continuity of the long profile between the land and the sea canyons, whereas, except in Corsica, there is no such relationship. Most of the submarine canyons show concave long profiles with decided steepness at their heads, compared to low gradients at the seaward end of land canyons. This major nickpoint, stressed by Woodford (1951), obviously requires more than a simple submergence and suggests that active marine erosion has taken place in the canyons. Furthermore, the vertical or overhanging walls in several gorges, observed by diving operations, form a remarkable contrast to the type of valley that exists in the landward continuations of the submarine canyons. This certainly suggests marine erosion. Finally, the observations in Scripps, La Jolla, San Lucas, and Los Frailes canyons all leave little doubt but that erosion is taking place in the canyon heads. It is clearly demonstrated that depth changes are also occurring in the canyons, and that sand and gravel are moving seaward along the canyon axes even out onto the fans beyond.

Before going further into the origin of the canyons, it seems advisable to discuss some other types of submarine valleys since these should help lay a background for considering the various theories of origin.

CHAPTER XI

SEA-FLOOR VALLEYS RESEMBLING GRABENS OR RIFT VALLEYS

C ERTAIN VALLEYS that are closely analogous to fault troughs of the continents are found on the continental slopes or borderlands. It should be borne in mind, however, that these valleys may be partly erosional, both on land and under the sea. In this chapter we are not considering the broad troughs off glaciated regions, which have been ascribed to faulting by some early investigators. We do not believe these troughs to be of tectonic origin, and consider a discussion on them more appropriate to Chapt. XIV, under "shelf valleys."

SAGAMI TROUGH, JAPAN

A good opportunity to compare submarine canyons with what is apparently a fault valley exists in Sagami Bay, off the east coast of Honshu, Japan. Chapter VI described the submarine canyons of the Tokyo area, all of which debouch into Sagami Trough. An examination of the contour chart (Chapt. VI, Chart II) shows that Sagami Trough extends south down Sagami Bay and then curves to the east

in a broad arc, finally connecting with the lower trough-like end of
Kamogawa Canyon. Soundings are not sufficient to give assurance
that the trough does not continue seaward beyond the juncture with
Kamogawa Canyon. Spot soundings suggest that the trend jogs to the
south and then back again to the east.

On shore north of the trough head, there is a fault valley where
movement has taken place during recent earthquakes. A total of 44
profiles were run across Sagami Trough (Fig. 108), looking for a
possible reversal of longitudinal slope as in fault troughs on land;
none was found. The axial profile has a steep head with local inclinations of as much as 200 m/km near the shore. The character of the
transverse profiles changes along the trough, but in most profiles
there is a flat floor. Some of the narrower-floored sections are related
to lava flows that have nearly blocked the trough. These have come
out of Ō Shima Island and from Manazuru Si, a cape made by a lava
flow.

Comparison with the nearby submarine canyons shows that Sagami
Trough has some contrasting features. The axis of the trough follows
a broad curve, in contrast to the sinuous courses of all the neighboring
canyons, with the possibble exception of Kamogawa. Also, there are
no indications of tributaries coming into the trough from the west and
south sides,[1] whereas many tributaries are found on both sides of the
submarine canyons of eastern Honshu. The transverse profiles of the
trough are much less V-shaped than most profiles of the submarine
canyons, except for the deeper parts of Kamogawa and Tokyo canyons. Thus, the two types of valleys are distinct in character, although
both may have had the same marine influences working on them after
having been formed in different ways.

TINAJA TROUGH, BAJA CALIFORNIA (Fig. 109)

Along the west coast of Baja California, Mexico, near the southern tip,
there is a valley called Tinaja Trough which differs from the nearby
submarine canyons. This valley extends north and south almost
parallel to the coast. In contrast to the twisting courses of the valleys
to the east, Tinaja Trough is nearly straight. Tributary valleys of the
canyon type enter the trough to the northeast. Another multi-headed
canyon, called Cardonal, trends towards the trough from the coast
but is diverted to the south before joining it. The transverse profiles

---

[1]Admittedly, recent volcanism may have filled the tributaries.

Fig. 108. Transverse profiles of Sagami Trough along its entire length. Note vertical scale does not give depth of profiles. Taken from fathograms of *Spencer F. Baird*. From Shepard *et al.* (1964).

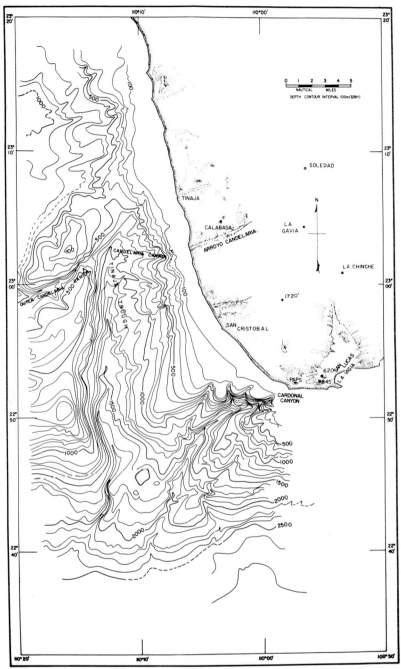

Fig. 109. Tinaja Trough that extends along the southwest coast of Baja California at the southern end of the peninsula. For details of Candelaria Canyon see Fig. 110. From surveys by Shepard.

of Tinaja Trough show a combination of V-shape to the south and trough-shape with a flat floor to the north. The floor of the trough appears to slope towards deep water almost continuously like Sagami Trough. However there is one probable basin depression near the southern end, although not strictly along the main axis of the trough.

The most surprising feature about the trough is its apparent bisection of a small submarine canyon near its northern end (Fig. 110). A detailed survey was made of this severed valley. The contours show that the canyon extends out from the coast, one mile off arroyo Candelaria in about 300 ft (90 m) of water. It runs west for 4.5 miles and then swings south down the trough, being joined by another small canyon coming in from the same side. Directly along the line of continuation of the east-west part of the valley, we encountered a narrow cut in the ridge that borders the west side of the trough. The cut at the high point of the crossing of the ridge is 1,560 ft (475 m) deep, compared to an axial depth of 3,600 ft (1,097 m) at the point where Candelaria Canyon bends south into the trough. To the west-southwest, the cut opens up into a small canyon that was traced seaward to a depth of 3,700 ft (1,128 m), somewhat deeper than the inner canyon where it joins the trough.

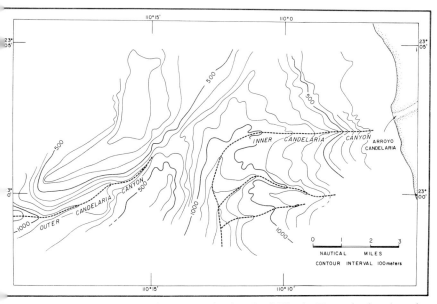

Fig. 110. The head of Tinaja Trough showing the separation of Inner and Outer Candalaria canyons, apparently by faulting. Dotted line follows canyon axis. From surveys by Shepard.

Attempts to core in outer Candelaria Canyon produced only mud-stone with no sediment. However, where Candelaria Canyon enters the trough, a core produced a thick ungraded sand and gravel layer overlain by a graded layer of sand with mud at the top (Fig. 144). Coring along the axis of the trough 8 miles farther south yielded only a hard clay with a conspicuous absence of foraminifera.

Thus, Tinaja Trough has several characteristics which differenti-ate it from typical submarine canyons. It is much straighter, it has few tributaries (all of these on the east side); it has trough-shaped profiles in the upper part; in the lower part its axis apparently lacks the typical sands and gravels of the other valleys of the area, it extends parallel to the coast, and, finally, it appears to cut a submarine canyon in two. All of these characteristics support a fault origin for the trough. A crossing of Tinaja Trough, using continuous reflection profiling, showed evidence of a fault on the west side (J. R. Curray, personal communication). Furthermore, traced to the north, there is a valley on land that seems to have a fault origin. This valley divides the region between a metamorphic sequence to the west and an igneous se-quence to the east. On the other hand, the southern end is curving and there is a fan at the valley mouth, so it may not be entirely explained by faulting. Photographs from Gemini V clearly indicate a large fault running into the head of the trough.

SAN CLEMENTE RIFT VALLEY, CALIFORNIA (Fig. 7)

To the southeast of San Clemente Island, on the continental border-land off southern California, a V-shaped valley extends diagonally down to the bottom of San Clemente Basin. This valley heads along the fault scarp that borders the northeast side of the island. In fact, the valley exists where the southwest-sloping escarpment on the southwest side of Fortymile Bank overlaps the northeast-sloping San Clemente escarpment. The sides of the valley appear to be straight, although halfway along its length one minor side valley may enter from the southwest. The lower end of the valley has a basin with a sill about 900 ft (275 m) above the floor.

The origin of this valley appears to be related to faulting. Since this is an area where faulting is largely of the strike-slip variety, one can speculate on the possibility that Fortymile Bank has been separated from San Clemente Island by a right lateral displacement, such as characterizes the San Andreas fault zone. However, as Emery found from his study of the formations of Fortymile Bank (Emery and Shepard, 1945; Emery, 1960, p. 38), there is no substantial evidence to show that San Clemente and Fortymile Bank have been separated, although both the bank and the island with its adjacent northeast slope have predominantly hard lava rocks, and softer sedimentary rocks of Miocene age occur on both walls of the rift valley. This suggests various possibilities other than right lateral movement, but is not inconsistent with it. In any case, the character of the valley is quite different from that of typical submarine canyons, and the relation to what appear to be two fault scarps suggests a fault origin.

FAULT VALLEYS OF THE ALEUTIAN SLOPES

The Aleutian Island area was charted in great detail after the United States recovered the westernmost islands from Japanese occupation in World War II. As a result of these soundings, we have some of the most complete deep-slope surveys of any place in the world. Many of the unpublished smooth sheets of the Coast and Geodetic Survey have been contoured by Survey officers and by members of the U. S. Geological Survey. Published to date are the maps of Gibson and Nichols (1953), Gates and Gibson, (1956), Fraser and Barnett (1959), Powers *et al.* (1960), and Perry and Nichols (1965). These cover most of the Aleutians from 170° east to 177° west. The contours on the published Coast and Geodetic Survey charts also provide useful information on both sides of this area.

The most notable feature of the contours is the presence of a group of valleys in the western Aleutian region which are strikingly different in character from the three submarine canyons in the Bering Sea, near the eastern end of the Aleutians (pp. 198-202). Most of the marine valleys of the western Aleutians are found on the south side of the islands. Examples of these valleys are shown in Figures 111 and 112. Although similar in some respects, these valleys differ from Sagami and Tinaja troughs in having deep basin depressions, especially along their lower courses. Most of them have straight walls; tributary valleys are almost completely lacking, and trough-shaped transverse profiles are more common than V-shaped ones. The trends of the valleys are principally northeast and northwest, which represent the two main fault patterns on the islands of the area (Gates and Gibson, 1956). Only Murray Sea Valley (Fig. 112) has a possible valley continuation on the north side of the Aleutian Ridge, and even here the two heads are not very clearly connected.

The character of the southwest side of Attu Island (Fig. 111) creates an interesting problem. The coast appears to have two or more bays with submarine contours as deep as 360 ft (110 m) coming into the

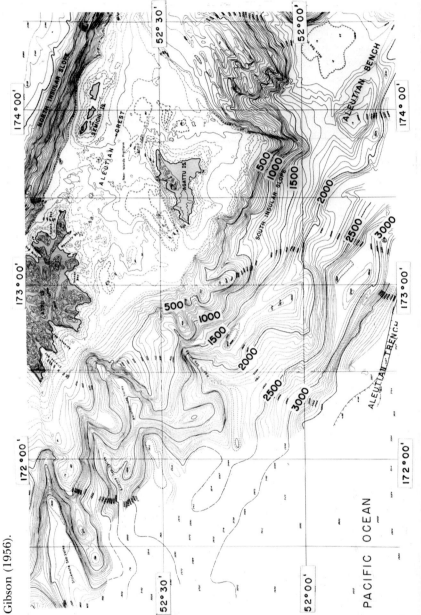

Fig. 111. Trough-shaped valleys near Attu and Agattu, Aleutian Islands, in an area of active tectonism. Note the basin depressions in the sea valleys. Contour interval is 100 fathoms. From Gates and Gibson (1956).

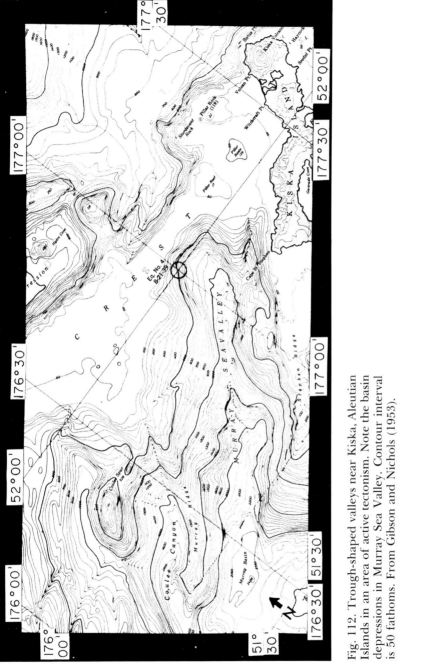

Fig. 112. Trough-shaped valleys near Kiska, Aleutian Islands in an area of active tectonism. Note the basin depressions in Murray Sea Valley. Contour interval is 50 fathoms. From Gibson and Nichols (1953).

embayments. About 4 to 7 miles seaward from the mouth of the bays, there are heads of two submarine valleys, Etienne and Abraham. The situation is somewhat comparable to the embayments in western Corsica with their corresponding submarine canyons. However, the Aleutian valleys have: (1) few if any tributaries, (2) a slight discontinuity between bays and the outer slope valleys, (3) straight parallel courses somewhat, *en echelon,* (4) steep drop-offs in the axis, and (5) closed basins. None of these characteristics are found in the Corsican submarine canyons.

Gates and Gibson also have noted that the western Aleutian sea valleys trend at a considerable angle to the general slope, and they suggest that if the valleys were erosional they would be likely to extend more directly down the slope. Also, they have called attention to the much steeper escarpments on one side of the valleys than on the other, which is particularly characteristic of fault valleys.

If these western Aleutian sea valleys are of tectonic origin, as seems highly probable, one cannot overlook the possibility that the huge canyons in the Bering Sea may also have had at least some tectonic influence. However, all of the Bering Sea canyons have winding courses and have an abundance of tributaries and, so far as we know, lack basins. Therefore, despite some contiguity with the western Aleutian sea valleys, it is doubtful thay they have had the same origin.

According to the contours of Gibson and Nichols (1953), many submarine canyons are also found on the north side of the Aleutians in the vicinity of the Rat Islands, but none are shown by Gates and Gibson (1956) north of the Near Island Group, just to the west. The possibility occurs that Bowie Canyon, shown by Gibson and Nichols (1953) as extending out to a depth of 12,000 ft (3,660 m), may be the result of faulting. The interpretation by Gibson and Nichols shows a stream valley type of topography coming well in towards Semisopochnoi Island, but the chart soundings do not appear entirely to confirm this interpretation. However, quite a few dendritic valleys appear around the 6,000-ft (1,830 m) contour that are puzzling, and these are suggestive of an erosional, rather than fault, origin. It may well be that both faulting and erosion are the formative agents.

CHAPTER XII

SLOPE GULLIES
AND MISCELLANEOUS
SLOPE VALLEYS

M ANY SUBMARINE SLOPES have short valleys that do not penetrate far below the general slope. These are mostly less than 350 ft (107 m) deep, and hence come under a definition given for sea gullies (Buffington and Moore, 1963). These gullies may have several different origins, but they are similar enough in character to be considered together. Most of them have been found on the prograding slope sediments of deltas and on what appear to be submarine fault scarps. A few of these gullies traced seaward extend into valleys that are canyon-like in dimensions.

FORESET SLOPE GULLIES

Mississippi Delta

The surveys off the Mississippi Delta have shown that the shelf has been completely overlapped in places and that the slope is being built forward (Shepard, 1955, Scruton, 1960). The detailed surveys of this advancing slope have revealed the presence of numerous ravines (Fig. 6). These start at various shallow depths and extend down to depths rarely exceeding 200 ft (60 m). This lower limit is not the base of the slope, which continues at about the same angle almost to the deep floor of the Gulf (Fig. 127a). Like most foreset slopes off large deltas, the inclination is very gentle, varying from 7.5 m/km to 11 m/km. As the delta has built forward, approximately the same slope has been maintainded (Shepard, 1955).

The short valleys are so small that the name *gully* is appropriate. The deepest of these gullies has a floor about 50 ft (15 m) below the intervening ridges, but most of them are not more than 30 ft (9 m) deep. The valleys are from 1/3 to 2/3 of a mile in width and ordinarily from 2 to 4 miles long. The valleys differ from typical submarine canyons in being relatively straight, in having virtually no tributaries, in having occasional basin depressions along their length (for details see Shepard, 1955, Pl. 2), and in coming to an end part-way down a slope. A few small hills are found near the lower end of the gullies. Possibly more hills exist and have been missed, because near the outer limits of the gullies soundings are relatively scarce.

The surveys made in 1954 by Project 51 of the American Petroleum Institute, when compared with those of 1940 made by the U.S. Coast and Geodetic Survey, show that off Pass à Loutre the position of the gullies has changed as the delta built forward (Fig. 113). This apparently indicates that old gullies have been filled and new ones developed.

Choosing areas with flat floors, we were able to take cores along the axes of these gullies and from the crest of ridges nearby. Comparing the cores from these two environments showed no difference in general character of the sediment, except that in the valleys the material was often more compact, as if it had been formerly covered by more sediment. In both environments, silty clays or clayey silts are interbedded with thin laminae of very fine sand. There is clearly no indication of a concentration of the coarse fraction, as would be the case if relatively strong currents were flowing down the gullies.

Fraser River Delta

An investigation of the delta of the Fraser River (Mathews and Shepard, 1962) was conducted with the Canadian ship *H.M.S. Oshawa*. The results were combined with surveys by the Canadian Department of Public Works (Fig. 114). Along the front of the Fraser Delta, the slope is somewhat steeper than off the Mississippi, averaging 25 m/km and locally as high as 60 m/km. Near the river mouth the slope has as many gullies as off the Mississippi (compare Figs. 6 and 114), but deeper only two minor valleys were found (Fig. 114). The upper slope gullies are very much like those off the Mississippi, although they have depths of somewhat more than 50 ft (15 m) below the adjacent ridges. Basin depressions are clearly indicated along the floors. In general, there are few tributaries and the relatively straight channels die out at various depths before reaching the base. A sample from the gully

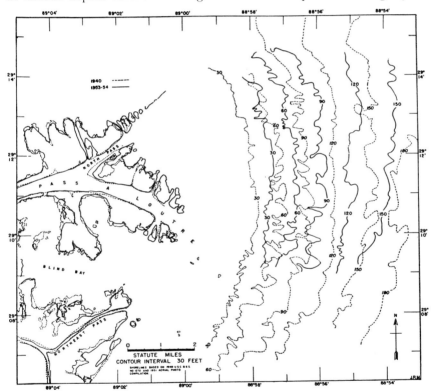

Fig. 113. Comparison of contours from the 1940 and 1953-1954 surveys off Pass a Loutre, Mississippi Delta. Note that valleys in the foreset slope have changed position. The earlier soundings by Coast and Geodetic Survey, and later ones by P. C. Scruton and others of American Petroleum Institute Project 51. From Shepard (1955).

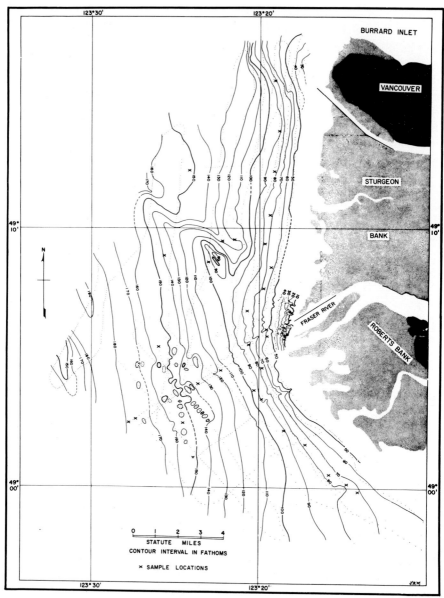

Fig. 114. General character of foreset slope of Fraser Delta. Hills on lower slope are outlined in dotted lines where they do not fit the contour interval. From sounding lines on *H.M.S. Oshiawa.* From Mathews and Shepard (1962).

off the Fraser mouth contained sediment identical with that of the adjacent slope.

The surveys made on the *Oshawa* led to the discovery of a group of small hills near the base of the slope (Fig. 114). These hills with heights up to about 50 ft (15 m) are suggestive of the hills left by land-slides at the base of many slopes on land. Thus here, as off the Missis-sippi, we seem to have good evidence that mass movements have produced the gullies, rather than bottom currents.

Off the Fraser Delta, there are cables which might be broken if active movement is displacing sediment down the slopes at the present time. No breaks have been reported, so we can conclude either that the movement is surficial or that slumps do not break the cables. Another possibility is that the slump features were formed before the cables were laid. Terzaghi (1962) believed the slumping to be a rather rare event and that it occurs in different places and at different times. The close spacing between the hummocks indicated to him that the surfaces of sliding are at very shallow depths.

Valleys Off Arena Point, Baja California

In between the submarine canyons off Los Frailes and Palmas Bay, on the southeast side of Baja California, a long sandy point juts out into the Gulf of California. It is apparently a cuspate foreland built seaward at the juncture of two opposing longshore currents. Outside this point there is a series of irregular valleys and ridges which were sounded in great detail. Both the transverse profiles and the contours (Fig. 115) indicate that these valleys are quite different in character from the canyons on either side, although they are larger than typical foreset slope gullies. Only one of the valleys can be traced well down the slope; the others die out part way down. There is little if any tendency for valleys to join together, as they do in submarine canyons. Possible hills are found near the base of some of the valleys, and probable basin depressions occur along their courses. None of the valleys has walls higher than 500 ft (150 m) and none of the walls was found to have rock. A box core from a valley axis showed that under several centimeters of mud there was an unsorted mass of sand, gravel, and shells—suggestive of mixing during a slump.

These valleys certainly compare closely with those off the Missis-sippi, although they are more deeply incised. Also, the continental slope is much steeper, about 100 m/km; steeper, in fact, than any of the gullied delta-front slopes so far discovered.

Hueneme "Canyon" (Fig. 116)

Off Port Hueneme, along the curving front of the Santa Clara Delta near Ventura, southern California, Hueneme "Canyon" heads within 500 ft (150 m) of the coast. Some question arises whether this valley should be referred to as a canyon. Dredgings by the senior author failed to bring up any rock from the valley walls, so it appears to be comparable to other valleys on the slopes off deltas, although it is continuous down the slope and at one point is cut about 1,000 ft (300 m) below the surrounding slope. Jet borings into the head of the valley, made prior to developing the harbor, penetrated to cobbles and boulders a short distance below the floor and possibly to some rock layers (T. W. Bard, personal communication). Gravel also was found in some of the cores from the "canyon" floor.

The continental shelf on either side of the valley is about two miles wide. Before the harbor was excavated, the head of this valley was

Fig. 115. Slope valleys off Arena Point, a low alluvial fill along the east coast of Baja California. Location is just south of the canyon area in Palmas Bay (Fig. 66). From surveys by Shepard.

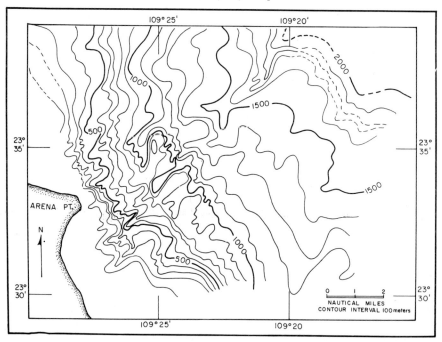

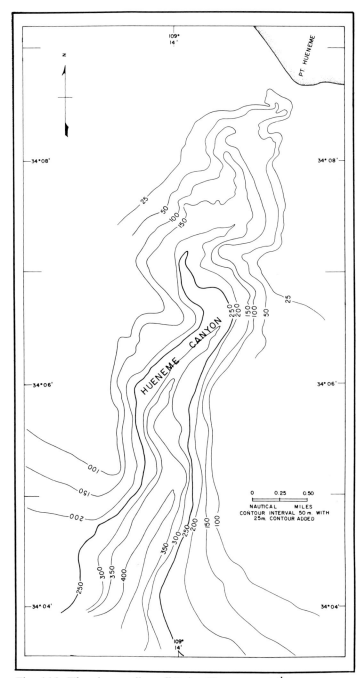

Fig. 116. The slope valley off Point Hueneme at the tip of the Santa Clara Delta. It is not classed a canyon despite the name given on the charts. A harbor has now been cut into the point. From unpublished soundings of the Coast and Geodetic Survey.

only 10 ft (3 m) deep, and it had a trough-shape very much like the head of Redondo and Mugu canyons. One small tributary comes in at the head, but lower down there is no sign of any tributaries. The main channel can be traced seaward for 13 miles to a depth of 2,250 ft (690 m) along a somewhat winding course with an average gradient of 32 m/km.

This valley quite possibly is due to submarine erosion into the delta front. Alternatively, slides may have exposed a layer of cobbles or boulders on the walls.

Small Valleys, of Toyama Bay, West Honshu

The Japanese have made quite detailed charts of several small valleys or gullies that head in very near shore along the south side of Toyama Bay. All are found off an alluvial plain built at the foot of an enveloping mountian range. Most channels start directly off the mouths of rivers (Fig. 117), but off the city of Toyama there are several of these short valleys that do not occur directly off a river. However, an aerial photograph shows a marsh with a meandering course coming to the sea shoreward of the valley that heads at Yakarta.[1] At the town of Fushiki, the valley that comes to the mouth of the estuary, or river, has two principal heads; the one to the east has no apparent connection with a stream mouth. According to the 1934 edition of the chart, at Higashi Iwasi, the valley head comes right into the jetties, whereas, in the 1957 survey, a fill of 12 ft (4 m) had advanced the head seaward. The Japanese charts, with their abundance of bottom notations, show that the sediment in these valleys is predominantly mud. On the ridges between valleys it is a combination of mud and sand, with some increase of sand out from the shore (Shepard, 1948, Fig. 75). This appears to be in contrast to the usual findings in submarine canyons. Because no cores are available, we do not know that the same bottom types continue below the surface.

The outer termini of the Toyama Bay valleys are not known. They evidently go out to at least 1,200 ft (370 m) depths and possibly a little farther. The 600-ft (183-m) contour is about three quarters of a mile offshore in both valleys, and the 300-ft (91-m) contour about one quarter mile from the river mouths. Thus, the gradient here is quite high, averaging about 130 m/km, much more than off most large deltas.

[1]This relationship was pointed out to us by R. L. Hayes, of the Univ. of Calif., Berkeley.

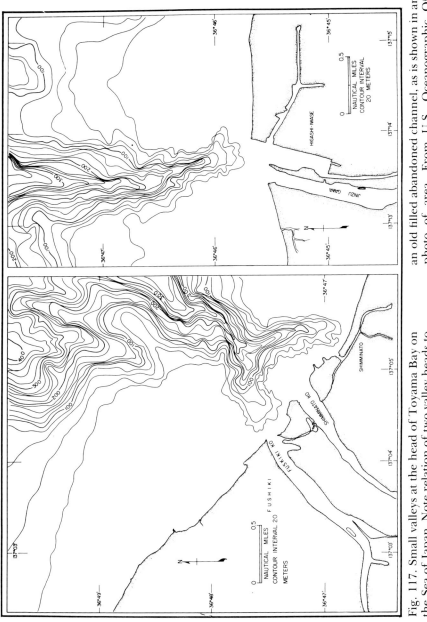

Fig. 117. Small valleys at the head of Toyama Bay on the Sea of Japan. Note relation of two valley heads to present-day river mouths. The exception is found off an old filled abandoned channel, as is shown in an air photo of area. From U.S. Oceanographic Office charts.

Deltas of Northwestern Luzon

Somewhat comparable to the valleys of Toyama Bay are those along the west side of the Island of Luzon, north of Manila. The best developed group is located off the bulge of Abra Delta, near Vigan (Fig. 118). Here, three valleys extend in practically to the shore and can be traced seaward to about 3,000 ft (915 m) depths. All along this part of the coast the continental shelf is virtually missing and many of the rivers have valleys directly off their mouths. Off the Abra Delta, the chart shows water 250 ft (76 m) deep about 1/4 mile from shore and a little farther north of the same delta the water is 1,200 ft (366 m) deep a mile from shore, making an average slope of 200 m/km.

As in Toyama Bay, some of the valleys that come in close to shore are apparently not connected to any stream mouths. The valleys also differ from the typical foreset slope type in having a few more tributaries and extending into deeper water than do most delta-front gullies.

The bottom chart off the Abra Delta area indicates mud near shore, but sand and rock farther out. This would be an interesting area to investigate.

Magdalena Delta

Magdalena River empties into the Caribbean, forming a delta along the north coast of Colombia. Heezen (1956) and Elmendorf and Heezen (1957) have shown the presence of a series of valleys (called canyons) on the submarine slope off the delta. The axes have an average gradient of about 40 m/km. These valleys (Fig. 119a) may differ from those off the Mississippi and Fraser deltas by extending to the base of the slope.[2] Also, they are cut much deeper below surroundings, especially in their outer portions. The pattern of the valleys directly off the Magdalena is very different from that of typical submarine canyons (Fig. 119b). In this area they closely resemble the gullies off the Mississippi. Three heads diverge directly off the river mouth and two come together farther down the slope. The dendritic pattern shown by Heezen in his contours may be somewhat interpretive, since it is based on lines run mostly parallel to the valley axes.

Of special interest in the report by Heezen are the positions at

[2]Soundings taken by the authors in 1966 indicate that some valleys may be discontinuous and may largely disappear on the deeper slopes.

which cables have broken along the submarine valleys (Fig. 119b).
These breaks have occurred 15 times and, according to the map, are

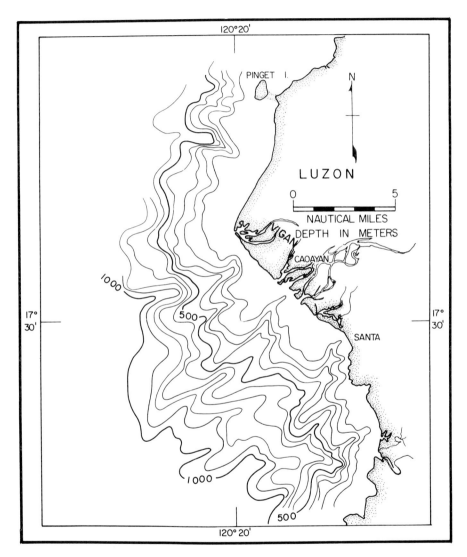

Fig. 118. The slope valleys off a deltaic coast on
northeastern Luzon, Philippine Islands. From U.S.
Oceanographic Office charts.

Fig. 119a. Detail of gullies off Magdalena Delta, Colombia. Depths are in fathoms. From Heezen (1956).

Fig. 119b. Cable breaks in gullies off Magdalena Delta. From Elmendorf and Heezen (1957).

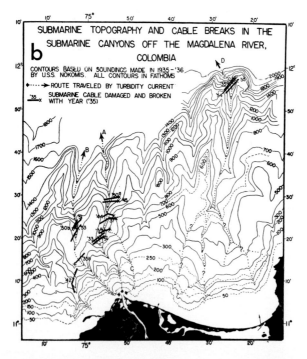

all located near or in the valleys. One group of breaks occurred 55 miles down the slope in water 9,000 ft (2,743 m) deep. Most of the breaks were in or near the valley that lies directly off the river mouth and in a zone from about 15 to 23 miles offshore. Also, in 1935, 1,575 ft (480 m) of the breakwater disappeared and a channel 36 ft (11 m) deep was produced across the bar. Cable breaks were reported the same night 15 miles off the river mouth at a depth of 4,200 ft (1,280 m). Most of these breaks have taken place in August or late November, the periods with the highest runoff in the river and the strongest trade winds. Surveys under the direction of Engineer E. Rico Pulido of Bogota, Columbia, still show frequent changes in depths.

According to Elmendorf and Heezen, the cable breaks have been the result of turbidity currents. They cite the finding of marsh grass wrapped around the deep cable ends after the breaks, as evidence for this origin. Also, some cores from the deep water have coarse silty layers interbedded with clays, suggestive of intermittant current action. In view of the large break in the jetty, it seems likely that mass movements on the slope have been an important factor at this place. The slides of unstable, rapidly deposited sediment at the river mouth may have initiated turbidity currents that moved down the entire length of the channel.

Rhone Delta in Lake Geneva

Where the Rhone River empties into Lake Geneva, at the southeast end of the lake, the slightly greater density of the entering river water than that of the lake water causes the river water to sink below the lake surface. In the summer of 1958, the senior author and B. Dussart used current crosses to determine the depth to which the current had sunk. It was found to lie around 15 m (50 ft), as was also indicated by the reflections of the turbid mass shown in the fathogram. However, in the summer of 1960, the junior author dove in this area and found that the cold river water was following the bottom down to depths of 30 m (100 ft). The strong resulting current pulsated and was in turbulant flow. Small ripple marks, one inch high and with a wave length of 4 inches, were moved along the bottom at an average rate of 0.1 knots (2 inches every 2 min 25 sec). Between the levee walls of the channel, large asymmetrical sand waves up to 1.5 ft (0.5 m) high were developed. Sands on the steep front slope of these waves were actively slumping and overriding slightly coarser sands. The sediments were loosely packed and would slump easily if hit by the diver's hand. It is important to note that upon coming in contact with the still lake water the fine-grained clays were separated from the coarser sands. The fine-grained material spread out along the thermocline as a turbid cloud. The coarse sands settled to the bottom, forming ripples that moved downslope.

Soundings of the submerged delta by Engenieur Hörnliman in 1883 (Collet, 1925, p. 188, Fig. 4) showed that there was a pronounced gully extending along the delta front to the floor of the lake. Parts of this submerged delta were resurveyed with echo soundings by Dussart and the senior author in 1958 and 1960. Unfortunately, the 1960 survey was not completed, but the sounding lines show the general character of the gully (Fig. 120). There are two possible contour interpretations for the lower slope. Either the gully continues down the slope to the bottom after taking a sharp bend, or it may disappear into the trench along the south side of the lake and another gully may come in from the north. The two interpretations are given in Figure 120. The profile shows that the gully reaches a maximum depth of 18 m (59 ft) below the prominent natural levees.

Gravity cores taken in the gully indicate that the bottom is sandy at all depths sampled. On the slopes, however, mud was recovered, but Dussart (personal communication) reports mud with sand layers from portions of the levees. Apparently, the gully is subject to relatively strong currents along its entire length, and the currents decrease rapidly along the sides. From time to time, currents of some strength must go down along the levees and other higher parts of the delta front in order to transport the sand found in layers.

The importance of density flows in producing the valley in Lake Geneva seems to be well established, but in this case we have river water coming into lake water, in contrast to river water coming into heavier ocean water where rivers enter the sea. Therefore, use of the Lake Geneva example as evidence for turbidity current erosion in the sea is not justified. Furthermore, at Lake Zug, in northern Switzerland, a large underwater flow took place, causing the loss of part of the town of Zug. This flow produced a trench 200 ft (61 m) wide and 20 ft (6 m) deep, extending for about 1,000 ft (300 m) along the lake floor (Fig. 121). Beyond the trench there was a debris-tongue 2,500 ft (760 m) long with a hummocky surface. This seems to indicate that mass movements of a mud-flow type are also of considerable importance in lakes in producing valley depressions.

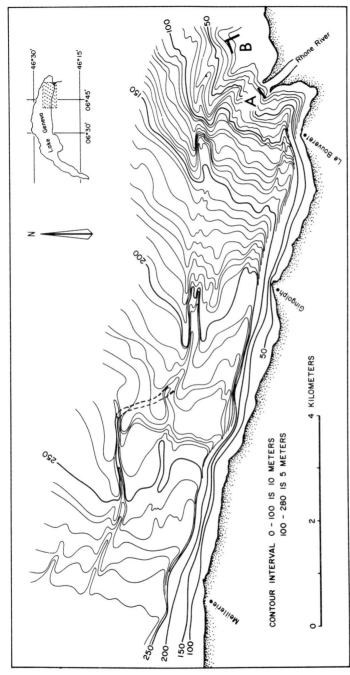

Fig. 120. Leveed channel off the Rhone River Delta in the head of Lake Geneva. Location of scuba dives indicated by solid lines. Contours in meters from surveys by B. Dussart and Shepard.

FAULT SCARP GULLIES

When sounding lines are run along the slopes of the submerged portion of fault scarps, it is a common experience to find valley-like depressions. Several of these slopes have been sufficiently investigated so that they can be described.

Slope Gullies Off San Pedro, California

Emery and Terry (1956) have described a series of gullies cutting the slope off the Palos Verdes Hills, west of San Pedro, California (Fig. 122). Here, the slope is much steeper than off most of the deltas,

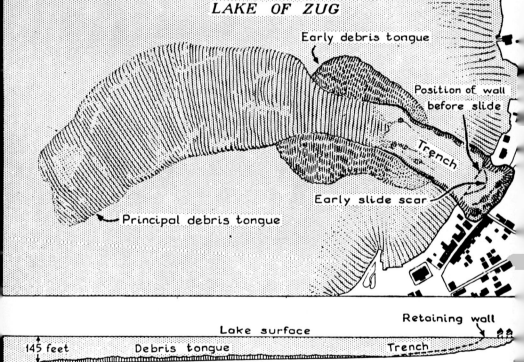

Fig. 121. Showing the slide that took place at the town of Zug in northern Switzerland, carrying a mass of sediment down the floor of Lake Zug and truncating an old debris tongue. From Heim (1888).

varying between 16 m/km and 32 m/km. The gullies range in depth between 30 and 280 ft (9 and 85 m), averaging 75 ft (23 m). They are relatively narrow, about 800 ft (240 m) across. They extend quite straight down the slope with few tributaries and many of them stop above the base. Also, the profiles transverse to the slope show that there are hills near the base, which may be somewhat comparable to those outside the gullies on the Fraser foreset slope. Cores from this slope consist almost entirely of mud, and cores up to 18 ft (5 m) in

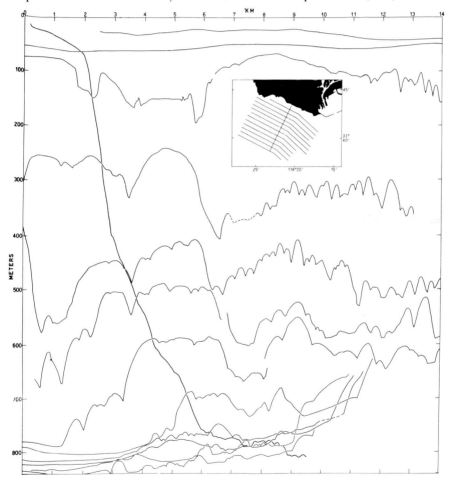

Fig. 122. Profiles along the slope off the Palos Verdes Hills in the Los Angeles area. Courtesy of K. O. Emery.

length appear to indicate that sediment cover on the slope is quite thick in most places.

The origin of the gullies off Palos Verdes is interpreted by Emery and Terry (1956) as being the result of landslides triggered by occasional earthquakes. They believe that these slides may produce turbidity currents carrying away some debris, but that much of it is left at the base of the slope, producing the hummocky topography. It should be interesting to see if turbidity currents are indicated by the presence of coarse sediment in the axis of the gullies. Another interpretation is that movement along faults over-steepens the sediment-covered slope and causes slumping. Once the sediment becomes mobilized it loses much of the internal strength it had, and slides to the bottom of the slope along planes of weakness.

Slope Gullies Off San Clemente, California

A very detailed and careful study has been made of some gullies in the slope approximately halfway between Long Beach and San Diego (Buffington, 1952; Buffington and Moore, 1963). The gullies cutting this slope (Fig. 123) appear to have many points in common with those described previously in this chapter. The setting for these gullies differs from those previously considered in that they do not occur off deltas, nor are they definitely on a fault scarp. Lower sea level during the Pleistocene would place the San Juan River at the shelf edge, and this area would then be quite similar to other present-day deltas with gullies. However, the straightness of the slope and the double escarpment less than a mile below the shelf break rather suggest local faulting at the edge of this two-mile-wide shelf.

The gullies, with one minor exception, are confined to the slope. They head at various depths, mostly near the shelf break. Some of them extend down to the base of the steep part of the slope, but others stop midway. The gullies appear to have widths between 1,000 and 2,000 ft (300 and 610 m), and a maximum depth below surroundings of about 300 ft (90 m). The gradients of the axes average about 80 m/km, but are steeper at the heads. Three basin depressions are indicated in the Buffington-Moore contours, and one or perhaps two minor hills at the mouths of gullies. The trends of the gully axes vary between straight and twisting. Only one good tributary was found. The use of the sonoprobe by Buffington and Moore has shown that rock is present on the sea floor along the outer shelf. Five Saucer dives by Buffington (personal communication) indicated that bedrock crops

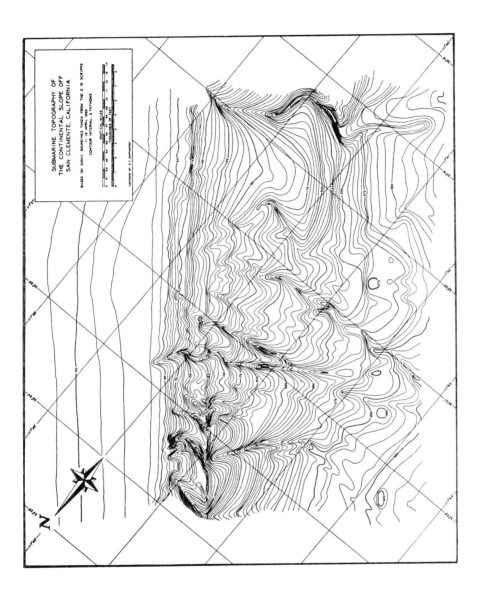

Fig.123. Gullies off San Clemente, California, beyond
a narrow continental shelf. From Buffington and
Moore (1963).

out on the side of at least two of the gullies. Below about 820 ft (250 m), the gullies have been shown to cut into a sediment apron of prograding fine-grained slope sediments. Buffington and Moore found that in most areas a fine-grained fill covers the bedrock floor of the gullies. Buffington believes that, in general, conditions of deposition must now exist, although his Saucer dives revealed some erosional features in areas of slumping. The application of shear tests to core samples from the gullies indicated that the fine-grained sediment accumulated on the walls of the gullies is stable. This is in contrast to unstable conditions in the heads of submarine canyons that are presently receiving coarse-grained sediment and are near shore (p. 301).

The heads of the gullies are explained by Buffington and Moore as being the result of subaerial cutting during a temporary emergence of the slope during the Pleistocene lowering of sea level. Although this may be the case, the valleys certainly are not as typical of stream valleys as many of the much deeper submarine canyons. Furthermore, the gullies are remarkably similar to those found on such recently developed marine slopes as advancing delta fronts and fault scarps where subaerial erosion is highly improbable. One cannot avoid considering the alternative possible origin for the gullies — that slumping of the type shown at the heads of the La Jolla and Cape San Lucas canyons took place during one or more stages of lowered sea level and excavated valleys into these soft rocks. Later, with the rise of sea level, this activity may have ceased and deposition may be occurring now.

A check on these alternative hypotheses could be made by obtaining long cores in the axes. If due to subaerial erosion, shallow-water or bay deposits should be found near the contact with the underlying bedrock.

Ceralbo Island

Several of the submarine escarpments in the Gulf of California have been sounded (Shepard, 1964). All of the lines along the escarpments showed the presence of valleys, some of them as much as 500 ft (150 m) deep. The most complete survey was made off the northeast side of Ceralbo Island in the lower gulf (Fig. 124). Here, the lines were run along a 350 m/km slope at spacing of 0.12 miles, continuing to the base of the scarp. By plotting these soundings, it was possible to determine quite accurately the nature of the slope valleys. Examination of Figure 124 will show that we are dealing here with a type that is even less continuous than the gullies off the Mississippi Delta. The features off Ceralbo Island are of short extent in a downslope direction. Some of them are as broad as they are long, and none reach the base of the slope. The broad depression on the left side of the map appears to be bordered downslope by a considerable bulge, although no hills were discovered. No tributaries were found, nor is there any indication of the twisting courses of canyons. Here, the case for topography resulting from submarine slumps appears to be well established.

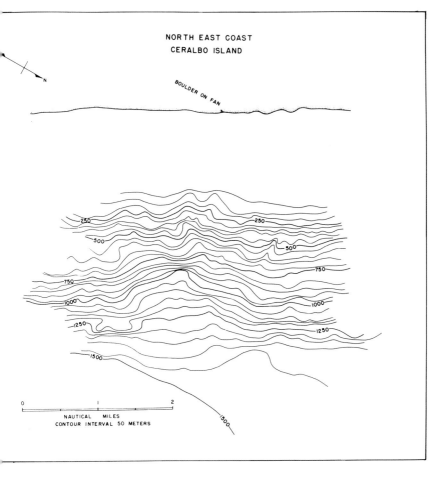

Fig. 124. Small slope valleys off northeast Ceralbo Island in the southern Gulf of California. From surveys by Shepard.

CHAPTER XIII

HYBRID TYPES
OF SUBMARINE VALLEYS

M ANY SUBMARINE VALLEYS are apparently different from those discussed previously, but of a character suggesting that they may have had a rather complex origin. Therefore, they are described separately in the present chapter. It is possible that some of the valleys considered under submarine canyons and others among slope gullies may belong in this group. The delta-front troughs, considered here, are thought to be sufficiently distinct from the delta foreset slope valleys (Chapt. XII) to favor separate consideration. The deep-sea channels, also included, are a particularly problematic group and may have had several origins.

DELTA-FRONT TROUGHS

Off both the Indus and Ganges deltas, there are trough-shaped valleys that cross a wide shelf and extend down the slope beyond. These have striking differences from any of the valleys that have been described previously. The trough off the western Mississippi Delta appears to be another similar feature.

Ganges Trough

The combined delta of the Ganges and Brahmaputra consists of a large plain with an arcuate front built out some 250 miles into the head of the Bay of Bengal. Crossing most of the continental shelf off the middle of this delta, there is a trough-shaped valley generally called Swatch of No Ground. This trough heads about 16 miles off the crenulated delta margin, and extends seaward in a southwesterly direction at almost 45° from the coast and the shelf margin. Detailed soundings of the trough have been made by the Pakistani Navy (Hayter, 1960), and it has also been explored by the *Pioneer*, U.S. Coast and Geodetic Survey (Stewart *et al.*, 1964), and to some extent by ships of the Indian Navy. The southward continuation of the trough has been examined by the *Galatea* and the *Albatross* (Kiilerich, 1958) and, most recently, by the *Pioneer*.

The portion of the trough that crosses the shelf (Fig. 5) has a relatively flat floor 3 or 4 miles across and wall slopes as steep as 12°. These walls are much straighter than those of typical submarine canyons, and only slight suggestions of tributaries are indicated. The Pakistani chart showed one place with a steep dropoff along the floor but a run down the axis on the *Pioneer* failed to discover this step, so it is presumed to have been due to a thoroughly understandable error in relative location of two sounding lines. The bottom apparently slopes outward quite continuously, aside from one small hill and perhaps one small basin depression. Except for a headwall with an incline of 75 m/km, the gradient is close to 10 m/km, much lower than that of most submarine canyons, although comparable to that of Congo Canyon and to the foreset slope off the Mississippi Delta. Near the margin of the shelf, some 70 miles from the trough head, the trough has a depth of 3,540 ft (1,080 m). A core obtained by the *Pioneer* from the center of the trough at a depth of 1,683 ft (513 m) showed fine silt overlying fine- to medium-grained sand. Dredging of the walls showed only a blue-green clay.

Continuous reflection profiles across the trough run on the *Pioneer* 55 miles from its head indicated that it may be bounded by faults, at least on one side (Fig. 125). Faults are said to be common in the Bengal Basin to the north (Morgan and McIntire, 1956), some of them with the same trend as the trough. The same reflection profile showed that the layers of sediment on the north side dip towards the trough, and also that there is a considerable fill of younger sediment within the trough.

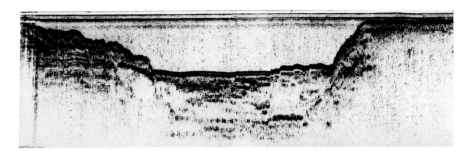

Fig. 125. A continuous reflection profile across the Swatch of No Ground showing the structure under the trough with its deep fill. Faults are indicated at least on the left side and possibly also on the right. Also, slump structures are illustrated along the left approach to the trough. Canyon width is 15 nautical miles, water depth in center of canyon about 750 fms (1,370 m). From continuous reflection profiles obtained on the Coast and Geodetic Survey ship *Pioneer* in 1964. Courtesy of H. B. Stewart, Jr.

Tracing the trough down the continental slope, there was a gradual change to a more V-shaped valley and a rather rapid decrease in wall height. At an axial depth of 4,920 ft (1,500 m), about 100 miles from the head, the walls are approximately 1,000 ft (300 m) high and a slight indication of natural levees appears at the top of the slope. Also, terraces are found on one wall. Thus, the trough appears to be changing seaward into a typical fan-valley. Farther south there can be no doubt but that the trough has become a fan-valley. A core at a depth of 5,764 ft (1,757 m) showed a silty clay with underlying fine sand. About 250 miles from the trough head, the fan-valley begins to bifurcate and was found to be so complex in its distributary pattern that it was impossible for the *Pioneer* to explore very satisfactorily without any electronic positioning device. Crossings of the great fan that extends down the Bay of Bengal show that fan-valleys are still present in the latitude of Ceylon. Very likely these eventually can be tied into a pattern somewhat like that indicated in the Indian Ocean diagram published recently by Heezen and Tharp (1964).

During the work on the *Pioneer* we observed on several occasions a change in the water color when we crossed from the shelf onto the wall of the trough. The water in the trough was less of a brown color and more blue. Slicks were seen also along the same border. Upwelling of clear water along the trough seems probable.

Indus Trough

Off the Indus Delta there is a trough called The Swatch (Fig. 126) that is very similar to the one off the Ganges. This trough heads in about 60 ft (18 m) of water some 2 miles off the Gaghiar Mouth, a principal distributary of the Indus River. The coastal chart shows tidal currents that move parallel to the trend of the trough near shore. Also, the surveyors of the Pakistani Navy told the senior author that current lines can often be seen along the trough margin all across the shelf.

The Indus Trough is even straighter than that of the Ganges. Furthermore, it crosses the shelf normal to its trend. Thirty miles of the trough have been surveyed in detail by the Pakistan Navy, extending from axial depths of 660 to 5,200 ft (200 to 1,585 m). It is notable that there are two small basin depressions along this length. Also, a steepening appears to be indicated at axial depths around 1,200 ft (370 m). The gradient is a little steeper than that of the Ganges Trough. The average is 13 m/km in the well-charted portion, from axial depths of 660 to 3,000 ft (200 to 914 m). However, on the old chart, the outermost crossing is given with a depth of 3,700 ft (1,128 m) almost exactly 60 miles seaward of the head so that, if this is correct, the average gradient is 10 m/km across the shelf, the same gradient as in the Ganges Trough.

Nothing is known about the bottom character of the Indus Trough, nor is there any evidence now available to show if it continues seaward beyond the shelf edge.

Mississippi Trough

Off the western side of the Mississippi Delta, a trough-shaped valley indents the continental shelf for 23 miles. This valley (Fig. 127b) is very similar in shape to those off the Ganges and the Indus deltas. The floor is from 5 to almost 10 miles across, lying between relatively steep walls. The borders are a little more irregular than those of the Indus and Ganges troughs, but this is apparently the result of deformation by salt domes found on both sides (Shepard, 1937; Murray, 1960). The gradient across the well-surveyed portion (Fig. 127a) is 8 m/km, comparable to the other delta-front troughs. In the less accurate chart, farther south (Fig. 127b) the contours show an apparent increase in gradient out to 5,400 ft (1,646 m) with a slope of 10 m/km. Beyond this point there may be a fan and, according to the interpretation by Gealy (1956), the valley may continue along the western margin of the fan.

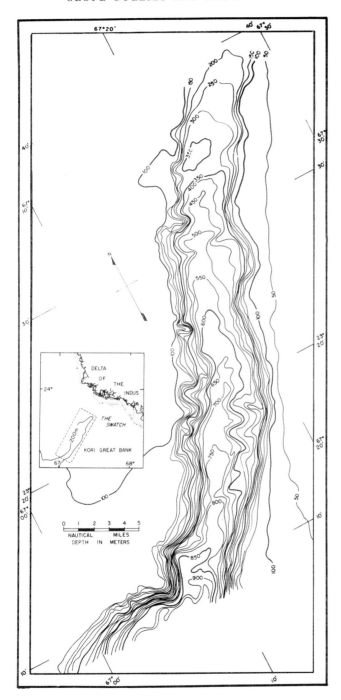

Fig. 126. The Swatch, a delta-front trough off the Indus Delta. Based on close-spaced sounding lines by Pakistani Navy.

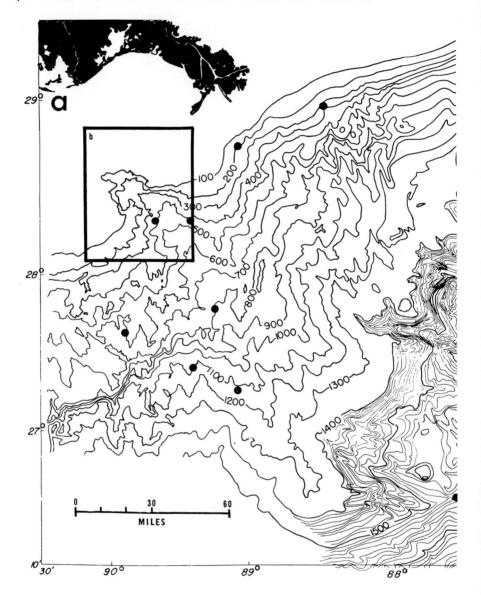

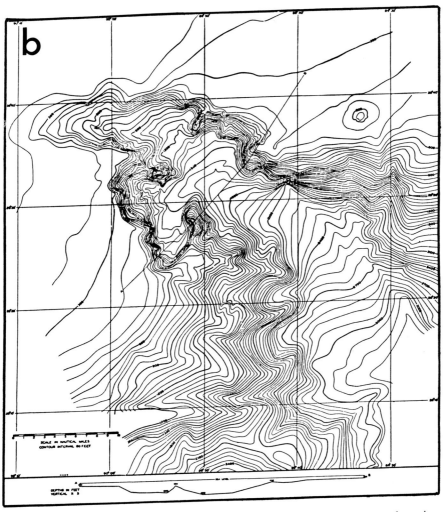

Fig. 127a. The Mississippi Trough and the submarine fan. Depths in fathoms. From Ewing *et al.* (1958).

b. The Mississippi Trough. Geophysical methods have indicated that the head of the trough near the delta has been filled. Note the resemblance to the troughs off the Ganges and the Indus. Based on unpublished soundings by Coast and Geodetic Survey. For location see block in 127a. From Shepard (1937a).

Special interest is aroused in the Mississippi Trough because in-shore borings by oil companies (Fisk and McFarlan, 1955) show that there is a filled valley of the Pleistocene Mississippi River that can be traced into the coast directly shoreward from the trough. This valley is generally supposed to represent an old glacial-stage channel of the Mississippi, cut during lowered sea level.

The cores obtained in the Mississippi Trough have been studied by Phleger (1956). He found that shallow-water benthic foraminifera had been displaced to a depth of 4,250 and 4,500 ft (1,295 and 1,372 m). This movement indicates turbidity current action or other type of downcanyon transport. Also, Ewing *et al.* (1958) have presented evidence that currents have moved down this trough carrying sediment into the Sigsbee Deep. This deposition seems to have stopped when the sea level rose at the end of the last glacial stage and cut off the supply of sediment to the trough from its Mississippi River source (Curray, 1960, p. 259).

An unfortunate inference has been made by Fisk and McFarlan (1955), who considered the depth in the upper part of the trough at 450 ft (137 m) as a measure of the sea-level lowering during glacial stages. In view of the extension of the trough to much greater depths and of evidence for downtrough current action and displacement of shallow-water fauna along the trough, there seems to be little justification for this means of estimating sea-level lowering.

Niger Valleys

The valleys on the shelf and slope off both margins of the huge Niger Delta (Fig. 128) have been studied and called *canyons* by Allen (1964). These are more V-shaped than the delta-front troughs described here previously. However, they may have had the same origin. The only available dredgings made by Allen indicate that the walls are of silty clay. No cores have been described. Avon "Canyon" extends in close to the coast but the others start well out on the shelf. Mahim "Canyon" shows one flat-floored crossing near its head. The profiles of Avon "Canyon" show terrace or slump-block features, which are comparable to those of the fan-valleys in other areas and reveal no matching on the two sides. According to Allen, there are tributaries coming into the head of Avon "Canyon" near the coast. Thus, the marine valleys off the Niger Delta show some resemblance and some contrasts with the delta-front troughs from other areas.

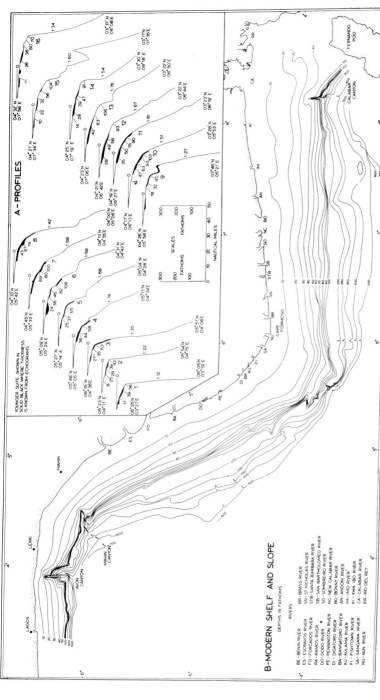

Fig. 128. Valleys cut into the Nigerian continental shelf. Although not contoured, outer slope has numerous gullies. Note that main valley heads are not off the major rivers. From Allen (1964, Fig. 2).

DEEP-SEA CHANNELS

Several valleys have been found on the deep-sea floor. These are of two basic types: (1) those that extend roughly parallel to the continental margins, like the Mid-Ocean "Canyon" that runs essentially parallel to the base of the slope off southeastern Canada, and (2) those that extend across the deep outer fans or continental rises with a direction more normal to the continental margins. Some of these deep valleys are intermediate between these two types.

Mid-Ocean "Canyon"

A valley that follows the continental margin apparently comes down out of Baffin Bay and extends around Newfoundland Banks. It was first described by Smith et al. (1937). Heezen et al. (1959) refer to the same valley as a "canyon," but their profiles show only a long, continuous steep-sided, flat-floored trough with an average depth below the plain of about 300 ft (90 m) and a width of 1.5 to 4 miles (Fig. 8). Such a feature is certainly far different from the usual definition of a canyon, so the use of this valley as the principal example in discussing canyon origin (Heezen, 1956) seems most misleading. The tributaries shown on the Heezen map (Fig. 8) are, as he admits, not at all well established.

The Mid-Ocean Channel (as we shall call it) apparently has an axis that slopes rather continuously southward (Heezen et al., 1959, Fig. 31). One core obtained in the channel had a sand layer, and another, according to Heezen et al., probably had lost a sand layer. To Heezen, these two cores suggested turbidity current action. However, one piece of evidence used by Heezen et al. to indicate such currents as a cause, seems to be questionable. They claimed that the trough margins have natural levees. After examining the sounding profiles, the senior author was not at all convinced of the existence of these levees. In places, the margin may be a little higher than farther out, but not more so than if the trough were due to faulting. Furthermore, the valley extends parallel to the Mid-Atlantic Ridge, with its tectonic origin, as well as to the margin of the North American Continent. One wonders if a rift, such as described by Heezen for the valley that follows at least part of the Mid-Atlantic Ridge,[1] may not be a better interpretation.

[1]For a review of the evidence for continuity of this rift valley, see Shepard, 1963, pp. 373-375.

The very low gradient of the Mid-Atlantic Channel is difficult to understand, if it were excavated by turbidity currents. On the Heezen map, between depths of 14,700 ft (4,480 m) and 16,400 ft (5,000 m) there is a difference of about 840 nautical miles. This is the best-sounded portion of the trough and here we find a gradient of 0.3 m/km. It is conceivable that such a slope (compared to 57.7 m/km for submarine canyon averages) would be sufficient to allow the excavation of this trough-shaped valley, but land rivers with such low gradients ordinarily are loci for deposition.

Cascadia Channel

Another rather well-documented deep-sea channel is found between the two great fans that lie outside the continental slope off the Oregon and Washington coasts of the western United States (Fig. 129). This channel was first discovered by Menard (1955) and later investigated in more detail by Hurley (1960). It is very possible that this feature is simply a fan-valley and represents a seaward continuation of Oregon and Washington submarine canyons (pp. 95-99). However, so far as can be ascertained from the Coast and Geodetic Survey soundings, neither Cascadia Channel nor its tributaries are definitely connected with any of the submarine canyons, and the much less conspicuous Astoria Channel to the east also fails to show any sure connections with a canyon. Furthermore, these channels extend much more to the south than would be expected for oceanward flow across the fans. This bend to the south has been called a "left hook" by Menard (1955) and is explained by him as related to the Coriolis force causing more deposition on the right flank of fan-valleys. However, such a simple explanation does not seem entirely reasonable for the abrupt change in direction in Cascadia Channel at lat. 43°30′ N. Nor is it evident why Astoria Channel should turn directly into the continental slope at 44° north. Both channels appear to have the same tendency to follow continental margins, as does the Mid-Ocean Channel in the Atlantic.

The gradient in Cascadia Channel is somewhat steeper than that of Mid-Ocean Channel. According to Hurley (1960, Fig. 23), it deepens 6,000 ft (1,830 m) in a distance of 1,300 nautical miles, giving it an average gradient of 0.85 m/km. The following increments come from the Coast and Geodetic Survey crossings: In 67 miles it deepens from 8,500 to 9,200 ft (2,591 to 2,804 m), or 1.6 m/km; for the next 55 miles its depth increases to 9,700 ft (2,957 m), also 1.6 m/km; then in the next 90 miles, to a depth of 10,000 ft (3,066 m), or 1.2 m/km. The

Fig. 129. Cascadia Channel cutting an abyssal plain off northwest United States. Note abrupt changes in axial trend where channel approaches mountains to the south. From Hurley (1960).

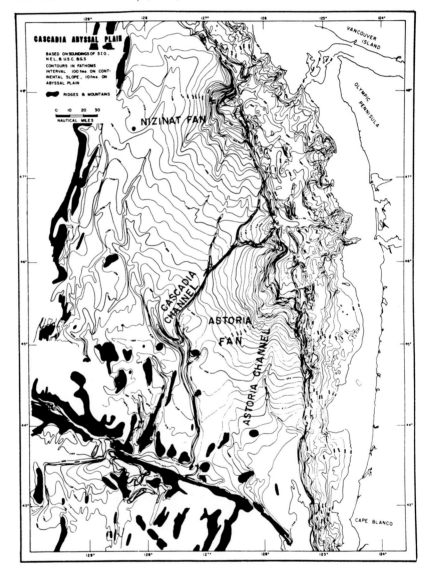

decrease in gradient farther out results in the lower average gradient.

Transverse profiles from Hurley (1960, Fig. 25) show a valley with a V-shape where the channel crosses a ridge, and a trough-shape in crossing the fans. The walls range in height between about 400 ft (120 m) and 1,500 ft (460 m), the highest walls being found in the ridge crossing. One profile, 297 miles from the head of the channel, has a flat floor with a width of 5 miles, but the others are much narrower. Some of the profiles show irregular terraces on the walls, perhaps of the same type as those of the fan-valley off La Jolla Canyon. Natural levees are found on the sides of the channel in most but not all sections.

The greatest contrast between Cascadia Channel and Mid-Ocean Channel is in the possible dendritic pattern shown by the tributaries that enter the former. Also, Cascadia Channel seems less related to a structural pattern than Mid-Ocean Channel. The depth of the channel below surroundings increases downslope, reaching its maximum 330 miles from the head and then decreasing farther out. Thus, the same sequence occurs as in the fan-valley outside Coronado (p. 72) and Hudson canyons (p. 149).

The analysis made by Hurley (1960, p. 41) of possible speeds of up to 20 knots for turbidity currents in Cascadia Channel is based on several assumptions. One of these, that from time to time the channel is filled by turbidity currents overflowing the banks and producing the natural levees, may be reasonable. It is, however, equally possible that the natural levees were formed when the channel was shallower, and that it has since been considerably deepened. If the latter is the case, all of the velocity computations would have to be lowered. To provide the sediment necessary to fill the present large channel with even a very dilute suspension requires a staggering amount of source material. Since no submarine canyon in this area comes into the coast, it would seem improbable that large supplies of sediment could have been provided except during glacial stages of lowered sea level. Equally puzzling is the apparent absence of any slope canyon definitely connecting with the channels.

Connecting Channels between Biscay and Iberian Abyssal Plains

Off the coasts of France and the Iberian Peninsula, there are two abyssal plains that have been investigated by Laughton (1960). There is a gap between these plains with two connecting channels (Fig. 130).

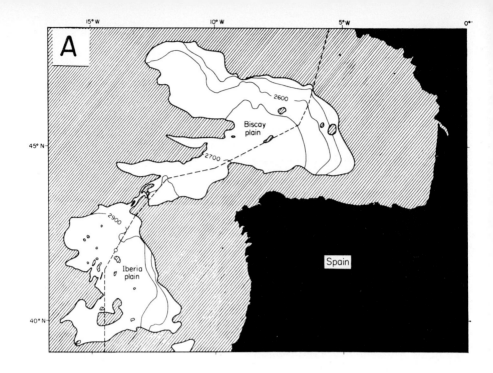

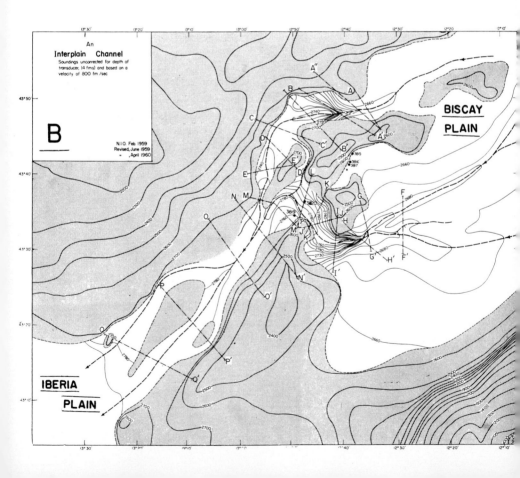

An
Interplain Channel
Soundings, uncorrected for depth of
transducer, (4 fms) and based on a
velocity of 800 fm/sec

N.I.O. Feb 1959
Revised, June 1959
" , April 1960

This has been compared to the Vema Gap south of Bermuda, described by Heezen *et al.* (1959, p. 72). It is believed by Laughton that the sediments of these abyssal plains come mostly from the submarine canyons along the west coast of France and off the English Channel. If so, the sediment must be carried cross the Biscay Plain, and when it crosses the divide separating this plain from the Iberian Plain the transporting current becomes concentrated and cuts the channels with their steep walls as a result of the increasing gradient and confinement of the flow. In the northern channel, a contour detail shown by Laughton has a slope of 7.5 m/km, considerably steeper than the gradients in the other deep-sea channels, but not as steep as that in the gorge in the outer fan-valley off Coronado Canyon (Fig. 34).

Deep-Sea Channel Off Brazil

Heezen *et al.* (1960) reported another deep-sea channel found by the *Vema* off Tortaleza, Brazil, northwest of Cape Sao Roque. This channel extends southeast along the continental rise, parallel to the continental margin and to the Mid-Atlantic Ridge. It is similar in character to the Mid-Ocean Channel. Cores taken along the valley contained both sand and gravel. The Brazilian Channel differs from the Mid-Ocean Channel only in extending along the upper part of the continental rise, rather than along the base. Here again, there are difficulties in reconciling the trough-like valley with a turbidity current origin, particularly since it obviously runs along, rather than down, the slope. In fact, most of these deep-sea channels show an amazing tendency to extend parallel to continental margins, rather than down the slope towards the deeper basins. Part of this parallelism may be due, as Menard (1955) suggested, to the diversion of turbidity currents by deposition on the right side of fan-valleys in the northern hemisphere and on the left in the southern hemisphere.[2] However, the examination of available maps does not make this explanation entirely convincing at present.

[2]The Brazilian Channel is probably a poor test case because Coriolis force decreases to zero at the equator.

Fig. 130. Deep-sea channel off western Europe that extends across two abyssal plains. From Laughton (1960, Figs. 1, 4).
    a. General location.
    b. Detail of the channel between the two plains.

CHAPTER XIV

CONTINENTAL SHELF VALLEYS: CHANNELS AND TROUGHS

T<small>HE NAME</small> *shelf valley* is restricted to sea valleys that are confined to the shelf. In some cases, however, submarine canyons with very different characteristics from those of the shelf depressions extend seaward down the slope in continuity with a shelf valley. Two types are recognized: (1) the shallow discontinuous channels which are found on a few unglaciated shelves, and (2) the relatively deep trough-shaped valleys with large basin depressions which are found on almost all continental shelves that border glaciated land areas.

SHELF CHANNELS

Apparently there is an erroneous impression that channels, like that extending seaward off New York Harbor, are common features on the continental shelves. Actually, similar channels are found in very few places in the world. Several examples will be discussed.

Hudson Channel

The channel off the Hudson (Fig. 3) is virtually continuous all the way across the continental shelf, dying out near the margin and showing no clear surface connection with the head of Hudson Canyon. Near the entrance to New York Harbor, just beyond the dredged Ambrose Channel, there is a natural valley trending in a south-southeast direction. This valley, with a depth of about 20 ft (6 m) below surroundings, can be traced for 8 miles to where it enters a wider shelf channel at a depth of about 90 ft (27 m). The main head of the wide channel trends in a north-south direction for 10 miles along its course before swinging to the southeast. Just beyond the bend the first basin depression appears, and other elongate basins are found all along the channel out to the terminus. None of these basins is more than about 60 ft (18 m) deep. The average depth of the channel below the shelf is about 100 ft (30 m) and the width is between 3 and 4 miles. the gently sloping walls are smoothly curving in outline. There is some indication that the channel is entrenched into a wider less curving valley. Except for the branch coming from the harbor, no appreciable tributaries are apparent. The outer end of the channel lies approximately 5 miles southeast of the head of Hudson Canyon. A subsurface connection, however, has been found by continuous reflection profiling (J. Ewing *et al.*, 1963).

The sediments in Hudson Channel are distinctly finer than those on the shelf on either side (Shepard and Cohee, 1936). The finding of mud bottom in the channel seems to indicate that it is now being filled and is therefore a remnant of earlier cutting, presumably by the Hudson River during the last low sea level stage of the Pleistocene. Considerable information concerning this glacial age Hudson has recently been obtained by Lamont scientists (J. Ewing *et al.*, 1963). Their continuous reflection profiles indicate deltaic deposits that formed an apron during the low sea level stages.

Hurd Deep, English Channel

Somewhat comparable to Hudson Channel is Hurd Deep in the English Channel (Fig. 131). This valley heads just outside Dover Strait where there are two arms extending along the northern side of the channel. Traced to the west, the valley swings toward the French coast, extending in rather close to Cherbourg Peninsula (Cap de la Hague). Off the Alderney Islands, Hurd Deep reaches its greatest

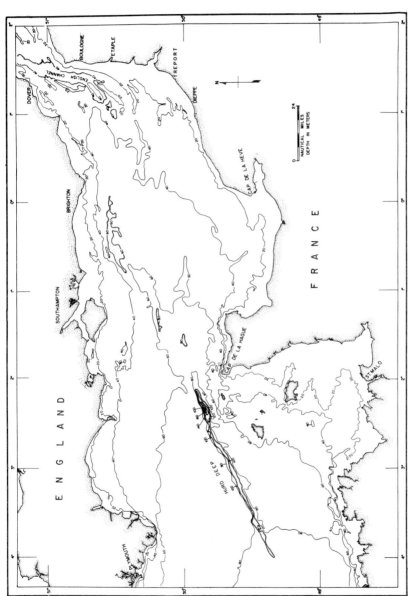

Fig. 131. Hurd Deep, a shelf valley in the English Channel. From U.S. Oceanographic Office charts.

depth below sea level of 570 ft (174 m). Sixty miles farther to the west, the valley dies out at a depth of 300 ft (90 m) and there is no sign of continuation across the remaining 150 miles of shelf. Like the Hudson Channel, Hurd Deep has relatively straight or smoothly curving walls. It is much wider than Hudson Channel, however, with a width of approximating 10 miles along most of its length and at least 20 miles between the Isle of Wight and the east side of the Cherbourg Peninsula. Off the latter, a large tributary comes in from the south. Farther west the valley narrows again to 10 miles or less. Like the Hudson Channel, there are several elongate basin depressions along the Hurd Deep. The greatest depth, 270 ft (82 m) below the rim, is found in the western basin.

Quite possibly there is a partially filled seaward continuation of the Hurd Deep in Dover Strait, although the deeper portion of the strait is not clearly attached to the eastern end of Hurd Deep.

The chief contrast between Hudson Channel and Hurd Deep is in the nature of the bottom. Instead of a mud floor as in Hudson Channel, Hurd Deep has rock, gravel, and coarse sand. Strong tidal currents moving along the English Channel must keep Hurd Deep swept virtually clean of fine sediment.

Whether or not Hurd Deep is a glacial-stage stream valley is not as certain as it is for Hudson Channel. The fact that such strong tides are known in the English Channel suggests that the Hurd Deep may have been excavated largely by tidal action. It is also quite possible that the tidal currents are merely maintaining a portion of an old river valley. The maintenance of Hurd Deep by cold water cascading in winter, as described by Cooper and Vaux (1949), may be important. Apparently, in very cold winters the water is able to move across the shelf with appreciable velocity, and can even slide down the slope to depths of several hundred meters.

St. Georges Channel, Irish Sea

The valley that extends up into the southern end of the Irish Sea between Wales and Ireland is comparable to Hurd Deep. Basin depressions occur along this valley, but unlike Hurd Deep the basins have reports of mud bottom. Evidently the tides are not as strong here, presumably because of the wider entrance to the Irish Sea.

There are various other deep entrances into bays around the British Isles, but these are within glaciated territory and probably have had some glacial excavation or were cut by subglacial streams. The same applies to the so-called North Sea continuations of the Rhine and Elbe rivers.

Sunda Shelf Valleys

Many books and articles refer to the drowned valleys of the Sunda Shelf between Java, Sumatra, and Borneo. The extensions of the channels and their supposed dendritic patterns are shown by Kuenen (1950, Fig. 203). Examination of these contours (Fig. 132) and of the soundings of the Java Sea leads one to question whether there are actually more than a few short drowned valleys. Along the south side of Borneo, soundings indicate an extension into several of the bays of channels about 60 to 80 ft (18 to 24 m) deep, but the soundings do not show any continuation of these channels into the center of the Java Sea. It is possible that high-frequency continuous profilers will show extensions of the channels, but the available soundings show nothing but a very wide, shallow trough with no definite dendritic valley patterns.

The situation in the southwestern part of the China Sea adjoining the Java Sea is somewhat similar, although there appears to be one valley extending in a northeasterly direction from 2° S. latitude. This valley, referred to by Kuenen as the "Sunda River," continues through the Strait between Great Natuna and South Natuna islands, with axial depths ranging from 240 ft (73 m) at the head to 400 ft (122 m) at the deepest point. Farther south, there is a series of basin depressions that may be in line with the valley. However, the tributaries shown in Figure 132 are all very speculative. Actually, the contours given by Kuenen indicate the extent to which speculation has gone in drawing this dendritic pattern. Here again, a high-frequency acoustic profiler survey would be helpful in showing if there is any actual valley pattern under the Holocene sediment cover.

TROUGH VALLEYS OF GLACIATED COASTS

The boundary between glaciated and unglaciated areas of the continents is clearly shown in most places by the change in topography of the adjacent sea floor. This becomes very evident from examination of contour maps of the shelf. The most significant features off the glaciated territory are the trough-shaped valleys extending either across the shelf or along it, although the former are more common. The troughs from several areas will be described.

Laurentian (Cabot Strait) Trough

One of the most impressive troughs of this type extends up the Gulf of St. Lawrence for 500 miles to the Saguenay River (Fig. 4). The trough has relatively steep walls and a broad deep floor with widths up to 50 miles and depths of as much as 1,700 ft (520 m). Elongate basins occur along the trough. Within the Gulf of St. Lawrence, the trough has one large distributary extending for 200 miles northeastward into the Straits of Belle Isle. The main trough extends seaward through Cabot Strait out 150 miles and entirely across the continental shelf. All along the 650 miles of its length — from the Saguenay mouth to the shelf margin — the trough depths are consistently greater than 600 ft (180 m) and in much of the area, greater than 1,200 ft (370 m).

Fig. 132. Sunda shelf valleys. The connections with land valleys are not at all certain. Depths in meters. From Kuenen (1953).

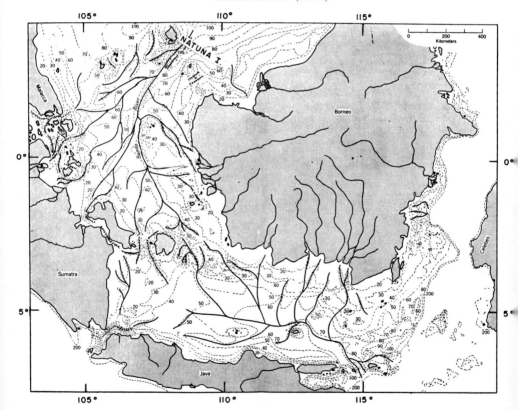

However, this feature is not at all like the delta-front troughs, because it has a continuous series of basin depressions along its length and the greatest depths occur well within the Gulf of St. Lawrence. No continuous outward slope is maintained. This trough has been extensively sounded and sampled by Dalhousie University (Nota and Loring, 1964). Their results show the importance of Pleistocene glaciation in shaping the topography.

Juan de Fuca Trough

Another trough comparable to that of the St. Lawrence is found in the Straits of Juan de Fuca, between northern Washington and Vancouver Island (Fig. 133). This trough can be traced eastward to the fiords of Puget Sound and to the San Juan Island area. Seaward, it crosses the shelf and connects outside with Juan de Fuca Canyon, described previously (p. 99).

The Juan de Fuca Trough is not as wide nor as long as the St. Lawrence Trough. The total length is about 110 miles, of which 45 miles is on the shelf. The width averages about 10 miles. Also, the depths are shallower than in the St. Lawrence, usually less than 700 ft (210 m). Basin depressions occur along the length of the trough and some of the deepest parts are up near the head. The trough, in crossing the shelf, is not as straight as that off the St. Lawrence. It makes one major bend and shows several bifurcations.

Troughs of Southern Alaska

All along the glaciated area of the Alaskan Coast, troughs extend out of the glacial fiords and cross, or partly cross, the continental shelf. Three of these were illustrated by H. Holtedahl (1958, Fig. 4), each located off a fiord. These troughs are not as well charted as are some of the others, so that their shape, as indicated by dashed contours on Holtedahl's map, is not well established. At least one of them has a trough extending along the coast at its head. There does not seem to be any evidence that these features are different from the others described previously, although two of them may possibly slope outward, rather than having the usual basin depressions. No doubt the trough extending along the coast south of Yakutat Bay follows an active fault, and its shape and depth probably are influenced by this structural feature.

Farther south, a well-sounded trough comes out of Dixon Entrance

Fig. 133. The trough coming out of Juan de Fuca
Strait and crossing the shelf. Shows also the Juan de
Fuca Canyon, a seaward continuation of the trough.
The trough extends east beyond the limits of the map
and connects with Puget Sound and the straits east of
Vancouver Island. From U.S. Coast and Geodetic
Survey charts.

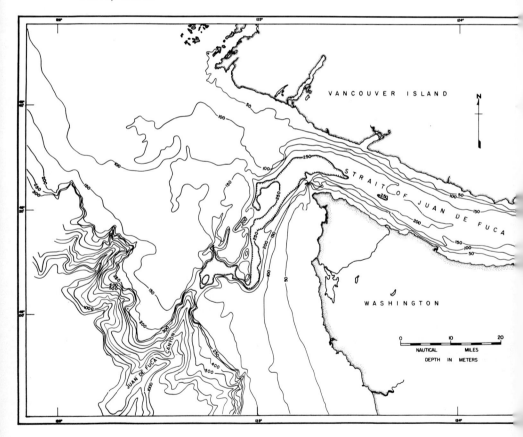

and has two deep distributaries extending across the shelf. The outer portion is not well sounded, but the inner portion appears to be identical with the trough in Juan de Fuca Strait. Depths are greater than in the latter, with large areas in excess of 1,500 ft (460 m). Basins are clearly indicated, and some of the greatest depths are found up the Clarence Strait tributary, a fiord that enters Dixon Strait from the north side.

Norwegian Troughs

The bathymetric maps published by Olaf Holtedahl (1940) show the large number of troughs that occur all along the Norwegian coast. Most of them come out of fiords (Fig. 134) and extend entirely across the shelf beyond. They all have the same general pattern, including broad floors, relatively straight sides, and deep basins. Some of them extend roughly parallel to the general coastal trend, but most of them cross the shelf rather directly. They differ from the fiords within the land only in greater width. In some cases, as shown in Figure 134, several fiords extend into one large shelf trough.

Skagerrak Trough (Fig. 135).

The southern end of Norway is encircled by a trough. This large feature heads in Oslo Fiord, and after a southerly trend swings west and then north, following the coast until it crosses the shelf off Nord Fiord, giving it a total length of 440 miles. The average width is about 45 miles. The sides are smoothly curving. Basins are found all along the trough and the deepest basin has a maximum depth of 2,400 ft (730 m) up near the trough head. Virtually all of the trough is well over 600 ft (180 m) deep.

Aside from its curving path around southern Norway, Skagerrak Trough seems to be identical to the St. Lawrence Trough, and closely resembles all the other troughs off glaciated shelves.

Troughs Along the Labrador Coast

H. Holtedahl (1958) described a series of troughs along the coast of Labrador. He was impressed by the fact that these valleys follow along the coast, rather than extending across the shelf (Fig. 136). Others farther north, however, do cross at least part of the shelf. The Labrador troughs are quite deep, with a maximum reported depth of

2,900 ft (885 m). They are U-shaped with basin depressions. There is no clear indication that they connect with the fiords along the coast, but, aside from trends, they do not differ notably from other troughs off glaciated coasts.

The Antarctic Trough Valleys

The soundings around Antarctica show many deep troughs, some of which are partly covered with ice. Lisitzin and Zhivago (1960) have shown the existence of troughs parallel to the coast of East Antarctica. So far as we know, these have the same characteristics as all of the other troughs found off glaciated areas, although they go to rather

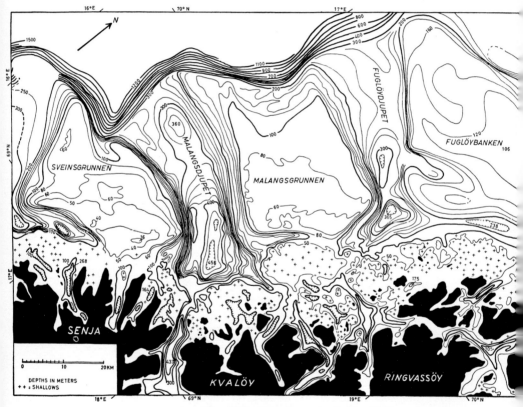

Fig. 134. Continental shelf off Tromso, Norway; depths in meters. Note that the depressions in the large basins lack depression contours. From O. Holtedahl (1940).

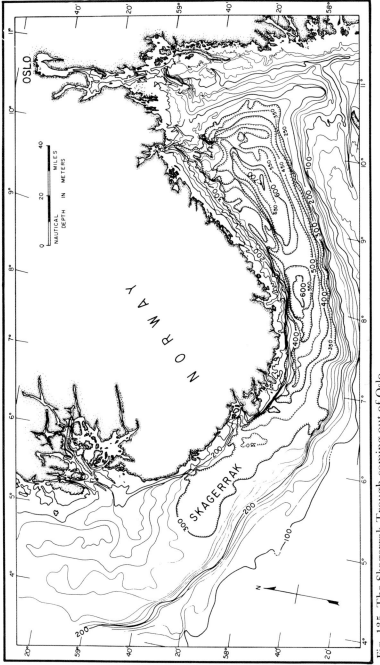

Fig. 135. The Skagerrak Trough coming out of Oslo Fiord and extending around the southern end of Norway. Note similarity to other troughs off glaciated areas. From O. Holtedahl (1940).

Fig. 136. Troughs along the coast of Labrador between South Wolf Island and Belle Isle. Depths are in
fathoms. From H. Holtedahl (1958).

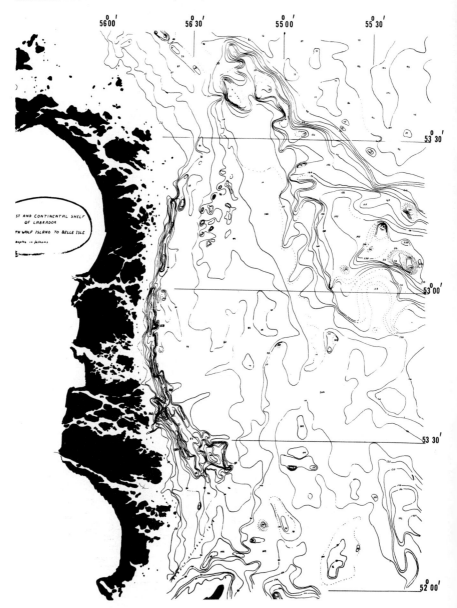

greater depths. Also, the shelf outside is unusually deep, but at least it resembles other shelves more than deep ocean floor plateaus.

ORIGIN OF THE TROUGHS OFF GLACIATED AREAS

The senior author, in studying charts from all over the world, has looked in vain for the existence of troughs on the shevles off unglaciated regions. The troughs off glaciated lands certainly do not compare with the unusual channels (like the Hudson) that cross the shelf or parts of the shelf outside of glacial limits, nor are they comparable to either submarine canyons or delta-front troughs. On the other hand, these shelf troughs are virtually identical to many features on the continents that are generally ascribed to the effects of glacial erosion. Examples are: the Great Lakes, the Swiss lakes (such as the relatively well-sounded Lake Geneva), and Lake Chelan in Washington. All these continental lakes have trough-shaped basins with depths below surroundings similar to those in the troughs off glaciated land areas. Furthermore, there are many indications that the glaciers did not stop at the continental margins, but, like the Antarctic Ice Cap of the present day, moved out beyond the limits of the land, partly onto the shelves laid bare by the lowered sea levels of the time.

Having this information, one wonders why anyone would want to call upon faulting of the shelf to explain these troughs. Yet this has been done repeatedly in the past, probably because studies were confined to one or a few regions. Starting with Johnson (1925, pp. 264-296) the Bay of Fundy was described as being bounded by the "Fundian Fault." Then the Laurentian Trough was called a fault trough after the Grand Banks earthquake broke the ocean cables on the slope (Keith, 1930; Hodgson, 1930). Olaf Holtedahl (1940), referring to the walls of the troughs on the Norwegian shelf, claimed a fault origin. H. Holtedahl (1958) attributed a fault origin to the troughs that run parallel to the Labrador coast and for those of southwestern Alaska, comparing them with those off Norway and Greenland.[1] Lisitzin and Zhivago (1960) added to the accumulated opinions by including the troughs off Antarctica as due to faulting.

So far as the authors can see, the chief argument in favor of faulting used by this considerable group of geologists is that some of the troughs run parallel to the coast, rather than along the direction of

---

[1] The importance of glacial erosion is now well appreciated by H. Holtedahl (personal communication).

major ice movement out from the ice centers. However, an examination of glacial troughs and lake basins on the continents shows that they run in all directions. One has only to look at the trends of the Great Lakes to see that direction means nothing in relation to the general advance of the ice masses. Glaciers, like rivers, follow zones of weakness or areas of soft materials. If these extend parallel to the coasts, the glaciers in moving out over the continental shelves will follow these soft layers. The marginal glaciers have a variety of trends in both Antarctica and Greenland at the present day. Why should glaciers be expected to excavate troughs directly across the shelf when they pass what is only now the coastline, whereas in the interior of the continent they excavate in any direction that is compatible with the structures and the softness of material?

To consider the situation from another point of view, if the troughs are due to faulting, why should they be confined to glaciated territory, and why should they all have characteristics of the glacial troughs of the continents and not of fault troughs? Furthermore, we are confronted with the fact that most of the troughs under consideration are found in areas virtually free from diastrophism. The troughs are as well developed off Norway, Labrador, Newfoundland, and Nova Scotia as they are off such unstable areas as the glaciated portions of Alaska, British Columbia, and Chile.

It used to be common practice to refer to long escarpments on land as *fault scarps,* but geologists gave that up years ago, and now look for independent evidence before invoking faulting. On the other hand, many of the sea floor troughs may have been cut along old faults, making them fault line valleys.

CHAPTER XV

MASS PHYSICAL PROPERTIES OF CANYON SEDIMENTS

P RECEDING CHAPTERS have presented the dominant physical features of submarine canyons throughout the world and, where known, have described the environmental conditions within them. The most striking feature of nearshore canyons is that they have not become filled by the large amounts of sediment continually furnished them from nearby land sources nor by the slow rain of suspended material dropped from above. Regardless of the fact that canyons do not appear to be filling, our studies, along with those of others, show that canyons contain some sedimentary fill, although locally it may be extremely thin or lacking. Furthermore, all canyons that have been adequately and repeatedly sounded in areas where they are receiving sediment show relatively rapid changes in the level of their sedimentary fill, indicating that the fill is unstable. The junior author has therefore investigated the mass physical properties of such sediments because of their importance as indicators of (1) the sedimentary processes that are only periodically active in the canyons, (2) the types of movement and instability preventing the eventual filling of the canyon by sediment, and (3) the limiting parameters for possible types of failure. Another important aspect of the study of physical proper-

295

ties in sediments subject to mass movement is the erosion of canyon walls, which has been observed where the fill moves downslope. The study of mass properties provides a means of predicting the processes capable of such erosion.

Application of the principles of soil mechanics to the study of marine sediments is relatively new (Terzaghi, 1956; Moore, 1956; Hamilton and Menard, 1956; Hamilton, 1959; Moore and Shumway, 1959; Moore, 1961; Richards, 1961, 1962; Chamberlain, 1964). An excellent review of the theory of failure and possible causes of the mass movement of sediment underwater has been presented by Terzaghi (1956). It must be pointed out, however, that the examples he used were from areas of quiet water, and that he lacked adequate data on the *in situ* physical properties of the sediment prior to the failures he discusses. Nor do the data strictly apply to the properties found in the heads of canyons that are subject to the continual movement of bottom currents. Moore (1961) and Richards (1961; 1962) have pointed out the dangers of using assumed physical properties for marine sediments and give several instances of misinterpretation.

The study of undisturbed *in situ* properties of canyon sediments and how they act as a body has led to important new data concerning (1) why sediments accumulate on the relatively steep slopes of a canyon floor; (2) how sediment moves down the canyon after its initial deposition; (3) strength characteristics of the canyon fill; (4) environmental conditions necessary to trigger movement; and (5) the dimensions of sedimentary masses involved in the mass movement of fill after instability has developed (Dill, 1964b). Unfortunately, appropriate data on the physical properties is sparse in all but a few canyons. However, the mass physical properties of the floor sediments found in Scripps, La Jolla, San Lucas, and Los Frailes canyons, representative of different regions and different rock types, are sufficiently similar to warrant the presentation of some of the important data and to point out their value to canyon studies.

One of the difficulties in the application of soil mechanics to the study of marine sediments is the lack of a common terminology between soils engineers and marine geologists. To prevent ambiguity, only those terms applicable to the study of canyon sediments will be discussed here, and then only in the briefest manner. Where pertinent, the reader will be referred to the many excellent texts and papers in the field of soil mechanics, which contain a more complete treatment of this complex subject.

STRENGTH THEORY

Canyon sediments have been shown to contain substantial amounts of silt- to sand-sized particles (Gorsline and Emery, 1959; Ericson *et al.*, 1961; Shepard and Einsele, 1962; Heezen *et al.*, 1964; Shepard, 1964). When stressed, such well-sorted granular sediments either develop significant volume changes or excess pore water pressures. These sediments have physical properties that vary with their rate of deposition, water content, state of packing, sorting, and size and shape of their grains. In addition, canyon sediments contain large amounts of plant and organic detritus mixed in with the mineral grains. Such heterogeneous mixtures do not react in the way predicted from models composed of equidimensional, perfectly round grains sometimes used in developing soil mechanics theory. However, the basic principles do predict certain reactions that can be related to the observed physical properties and the behavior of canyon sediments in nature.

The strength, deformation, and failure of a sedimentary body made up of silt- to sand-sized particles can be understood by visualizing a structural model of loosely contacting particles of varying shapes forming a skeletal framework around interconnected voids. The resistance to stress, or the strength of the sedimentary body, is derived primarily by the frictional forces at contact points and the interlocking between grains. Shear stresses that cause failure can be transmitted only at the point of grain contact. Deformation of the sedimentary body can take place in two ways: (1) by the plastic readjustment of individual grains by bending and distortion, and (2) by failure at contact points. In granular sediments free of large amounts of clay, deformation results largely from slippage between individual grains, and the term *shear resistance* becomes synonymous with *shear strength.*

If failure is restricted to a particular zone in the sedimentary body, nearly all of the deformation is localized along some surface called a *slip surface.* The small element of the sediment mass on a slip surface is referred to as a *failure plane* (Leonards, 1962, p. 177).

Stress is force per unit area and in our usage has units of gm/cm^2 or lbs/in.^{2} Applied to the failure plane, a stress can be resolved into two components: one perpendicular (normal) to the plane and called the *normal stress, σ,* and the other called the *shear stress, τ* (Fig. 137).

Results of extensive tests show that the resistance to failure in cohesionless sediments is nearly proportional to the *normal effective stress, σ ',* on the plane of failure.

The relationship between the normal effective stress, σ ', on every plane through a mass of sediment and the corresponding *shearing resistance, s,* per unit area can be represented by an equation developed from a theory of Coulomb (1776):

$$s = c + \sigma' \tan \phi \qquad (1)$$

where $\sigma' = (\sigma - u_w)$, u_w, is excess pore water pressure and *provided σ* is a compressive stress. Terzaghi (1943, p. 8) uses ϕ to denote the angle of internal friction. It is analogous to the angle of friction between two sliding bodies whose ϕ is the angle of sliding friction and the tan. ϕ is the coefficient of friction. The term, c, represents

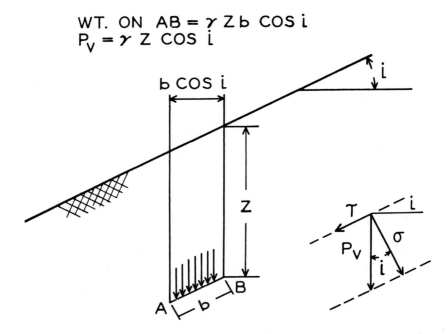

Fig. 137. Schematic example of forces active within a saturated sedimentary slope with an inclination i, and thickness Z, over a potential failure plane AB. The weight on the segment of width, b, on plane AB equals the submerged density of the sediment (gamma γ) times Zb cos. i, where b is the unit area considered. Vertical pressure, P_v, equals Z cos. i, which is the effective weight divided by the unit area b. The vertical pressure has components of shear stress (tau, τ) directed downslope and direct stress (sigma, σ) normal to the shear plane. The direct stress is at the angle, i, to the vertical pressure. From Moore (1961).

cohesion, which is equal to the shearing resistance per unit area when ϕ = zero. Cohesive forces develop mostly from intergranular and intermolecular attraction between grains and are strongly dependent on water content and grain size (Lambe, 1958). Cohesion is usually low or nonexistent for most silt- to sand-sized granular sediments and relatively high for clay-sized particles.

The shear strength for granular sediments is largely determined by frictional forces between grain contact points and the amount of interlocking between grains. Thus, it is often assumed that they are cohesionless sediments (c = 0), and the corresponding equation used in determining their approximate shear strength is:

$$s = \sigma' \tan \phi \qquad (2)$$

Terzaghi (1956) discusses the importance of pore water pressures in submarine slope failures in submerged saturated sediment and gives the following equation for shear strength, s,

$$s = c + (\gamma_s Z - u_w) \tan \phi \qquad (3)$$

Where c is cohesion, ϕ the angle of internal friction, γ_s the submerged unit weight of the sediment, Z the depth below the free surface of the sediment, and u_w the excess hydrostatic pressure in the pore water at the point of stress.

Values of c and $\tan \phi$ can be determined by various laboratory and field tests by measuring the resistance to shear at different values of normal stress (different depths in the sediment), which in the above equation (3) are equal to $(\gamma_s Z - u_w)$.

A generalized set of curves showing the relationship of resistance to shear plotted against normal stress at different grain packings is given in Figure 138. The curves point out the importance of packing and the necessity of distinguishing the difference between the peak strength (s_m) of an undisturbed sediment which develops after consolidation and its residual strength (s_r), which represents its strength after failure. It is important to note for later discussions that the residual strength of a loosely packed and a densely packed sediment approach each other after failure.

If a sediment contains substantial amounts of clay-sized particles it will often relieve outside stresses by plastic deformation without actually failing along a slip zone. This deformation by the readjustment of particles without shear failure is called *creep* (Stokes and Varnes, 1955). The term *creep strength* is used to describe the strength of the sediment at the point where it will deform at a constant volume by plastic flow under a constant shearing stress. According to Terzaghi (1953), creep does not become important until the shear stresses exceed about one half of the shear strength. However, laboratory tests suggest that creep may be initiated at much lower stresses (Gueze and Tan, 1954). The ratio between creep strength and ultimate (residual) shearing resistance has not been extensively investigated, but may be as small as 0.3 for some types of plastic clays (Peck et al., 1953, p. 93). Although the term creep has been used to describe the plastic behavior of clays, it is also useful in describing the behavior of the highly organic silt- to sand-sized canyon sediments.

It is a well-established principle in soil mechanics that a prograding sedimentary body, accumulating at its angle of repose and composed primarily of sand, will remain stable so long as the physical conditions governing its initial deposition do not change. If this were not the

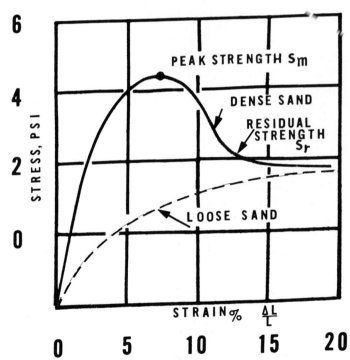

Fig. 138. Stress-strain diagram showing the differences in strength characteristics between loosely and densely packed sediments. From Leonards (1962, p. 178).

case, deposition and growth of the deposit would not have occurred in the first place. The sandy fill in the heads of Scripps, San Lucas, and Los Frailes canyons has been observed to build up gradually as a prograding deposit with its primary source in shallow water. The sediment is initially deposited on a rocky canyon floor that is sloping between 10° and 40°. The upper surface of the fill has a slope that is near the angle of repose of these sandy sediments (approximately 25°). When this critical slope is reached, additional material slides down the upper surface of the fill and gradually progrades the sediment fill into deeper water. Theoretically, the thickness and seaward extent of such a deposit would increase as sediment is added until the canyon becomes completely filled with sediment. The periodic deepenings and downslope loss of marker stakes show that this condition does not prevail in the heads of the nearshore canyons that were investigated. Therefore, some agent, either external or internal, must bring about a decrease in strength characteristics inherent in the canyon sediments at the time of their deposition.

Weekly observations in Scripps Canyon and semi-annual observations in San Lucas and Los Frailes canyons of the sediment level, marker stakes, and large man-made objects placed in the interbedded fill, all show that sandy sediment is lost downcanyon primarily by one or a combination of the following processes: (1) a slow glacial-like gravity creep of the entire sedimentary deposit that accumulated in the canyon head; (2) relatively rapid downslope displacement of a part of the matted fill over short distances by a series of progressive slumps and slides; (3) sediment set in motion by strong bottom currents of various origins; and (4) downslope flow of individual silt- to sand-sized grains that move into the canyon head where slopes exceed their angle of repose. If the downslope flow is caused by a rapid addition of sediment in large quantities, sand flows, (also called 'rivers-of-sand') develop. Examination of the flowing sand (Fig. 55) shows it to contain large blocks of broken rock. Large boulders, some up to 10 ft (3 m) across, with freshly broken surfaces (Fig. 53), have been found in the fans below areas of known sand flows in San Lucas Canyon.

Fine-grained sediment in the silt to clay sizes is also carried deep into the canyon in a dispersed form by water currents of either wave or gravity origin. Dives in deep submersibles show that these 'turbidity currents' of low density and velocity are transporting micaceous silts into great depths. It must be stressed, however, that these micaceous silts are dispersed in clouds of slow-moving 'dirty water' and have not become a part of the consolidated fill observed in the canyon bottom. Once it develops strong cohesion by consolidation or other causes, clay on the canyon floors may become bedded and the mass tends to break into large lumps, which are not easily dispersed even when subjected to relatively high current velocities.

If large amounts of nearshore sands are rapidly dumped onto the marginally stable sediment in the canyon head, a relatively rapid failure in the form of a slump or sediment slide takes place. Several such slumps have taken place in the head of Scripps Canyon (Table 3), and slump scars have been seen in all other canyons investigated visually. Some of the shallow-water slumps may have triggered additional slumps downcanyon where overriding sediment suddenly increases the pore pressure of underlying material; this mechanism has been clearly discussed by Kjellman (1955) and Moore (1961). Thus, once slumping is started in a body of marginally stable sediment it has a tendency to fail as a series of progressive slumps until the sediment slope is decreased sufficiently to allow the shear strength of the sediment to exceed the downcanyon component of the shear stress. In the shallow parts of Scripps Canyon, the maximum distance that sediment has been observed to move in any individual slump or slide is about 400 ft (120 m) (Dill, 1964b, p. 198).

Recalling that the sediments in the poorly bedded layers of the fill are deposited with an initial dip that is near their angle of repose, it can be seen that a small decrease in their internal strength will bring about instability. The critical slope of deposition, or the angle of repose, for a pure sand is very near its angle of internal friction. However, the intertwining strands of plant debris (frequently seen in canyons) increases the strength of the sediment and its critical angle. The plant material adds its maximum strength to the fill when it is first deposited and relatively fresh. Decay decreases the initial strength, and as successive layers of fill are added, the downslope component of overburden stress increases (Dill, 1964b, p. 140; Chamberlain, 1964). Thus, with time, the lower part of the sediment fill becomes weaker while being subjected to a gradually increasing stress from thickening overburden. Under such conditions the remaining intertwining plant detritus distributes the stress throughout the fill, which deforms and begins to creep slowly downslope as it relieves the gravity-induced stresses. If the internal strength is sufficient after mobilization to resist shear failure, creep will continue so long as the downslope gravitational stresses exceed the creep strength of the sediment. The tipping of marker stakes and the slow downslope displacement of large objects, such as an auto body (Dill, 1964b, p. 170), tires, lobster traps, cobbles, and even large boulders, are examples of this type of movement.

During storm conditions, sands, stored in the nearshore areas and on the beaches, move into the heads of the canyon at such a rapid rate

Table 3 OBSERVED OCCURRENCES OF LARGE SLUMPS AND SLIDES IN THE HEAD OF SCRIPPS SUBMARINE CANYON (From Dill, 1964b)

Date	Location	Remarks
Between 12/5-12/13 1959	Sumner Tributary South Branch Intermediate Branch Hanging Valley	Removal followed a severe winter storm which was accompanied by unusually large waves. Large plumes of turbid water mixed with kelp and organic detritus were observed to extend at least one-quarter mile offshore in the surface waters just above the canyon (Dill, 1964a).
Between 3/1-3/3 1961	Sumner Tributary	Large slump removed most of the material from this tributary.
Between 11/15-11/22 1961	Hanging Valley	Large slump removed sediment fill down to bedrock.
Between 11/13-17 1961	Sumner Tributary	Large slump removed sediment fill, bent marker stake (measured 1 week prior to slump to be 4 ft above level of fill).
Between 3/9-3/12 1962	Sumner Branch	Large slump removed sediment fill on the north side of the branch. The northern concrete clump was displaced into the canyon. South side fill unaffected.
3/23/1962	Hanging Valley Intermediate Tributary	Slumps removed sediment fill down to bedrock. Sumner Branch one-fourth full and not affected.
Between 2/8-2/12 1963	Sumner Branch Hanging Valley	Large slump removed south half of fill in Sumner Branch. Slump followed two days of unusually high storm swell. All of the fill of Hanging Valley was removed. Intermediate Tributary and South Branch were unaffected.
Between 3/1-3/5 1963	Sumner Branch	Large slump removed a large part of the fill on the south side of Sumner Branch. Approximately 30 feet of deepening took place during removal of fill in this slump.
Between 11/22-12/2 1963	Sumner Tributary Hanging Valley	Sediment slumped downslope exposing bedrock. The main part of Sumner Branch was unaffected.
Between 12/2-12/13 1963	Sumner Branch	Large parts of the sediment fill slumped into deeper water. South Branch remained full.

that they build a slope which exceeds their angle of repose (between 25° and 30° in Scripps Canyon, and about 30° in San Lucas and Los Frailes canyons). Under such conditions, the individual grains never come to rest, but instead move downslope as a loosely packed surficial layer of flowing grains. Observation of such sand flows show that the underlying sediment, as well as the rock walls confining the flow, are eroded (Fig. 139). This is indicated by the lighter color of the flowing sand, in contrast with the streaks of dark sediment that have been reduced after burial and then brought to the surface by the turbulent overturn accompanying the sand flow.

On occasions, the flow of sand from the tributaries entering Sumner Branch of Scripps Canyon has been sufficient to cut a previously deposited fill down to bedrock. In September, 1962, for example, a narrow channel 10 ft (3 m) across and 6 to 10 ft (2 to 3 m) deep was eroded from the fill over a distance of about 100 ft (30 m). Flow continues only so long as material is added at the head of the flow and the bottom slope exceeds the angle of repose. Usually, small-scale flows entering a canyon from a tributary come to rest when they encounter the main fill of the canyon. The result is the development of a small fan built out over the surface of the sedimentary fill of the main branch of the canyon head (Fig. 140).

The velocity of such gravity flows is variable, ranging from the almost imperceptible creep of individual grains to as much as 0.2 knots (11 cm/sec). The flow pulsates, reflecting the variability of the wave-induced bottom currents that transport sand into the canyon. The velocity of a sand flow increases at constrictions and decreases where the channel widens. Sand flows were observed down to a depth of 1,035 ft (315 m) from the Diving Saucer in Los Frailes Canyon on February 12, 1965, and they may occur at greater depths.

Slumps often create steep scars in the fill of canyons. On several occasions, sand has been seen to flow from within the sediment fill on the upslope side of the slump scar, forming a small fan on the underlying material. The steep slopes observed in slump scars range from 30° to almost vertical. Slopes exceeding the laboratory-determined angle of repose for clean sands must be due to the cohesion derived from clay and the organic content of the fill, and not from intergranular friction between densely packed sand layers. The unstable sands are held in place by the cohesive overlying sediments until they are broken by a slump or slide. Thus freed, the sands will flow until they establish a stable slope.

Critical Density of Canyon Sediments

The critical density or critical void ratio of sand-sized sediments is an important indication of how sediments fail under stress (Casagrande, 1938; Taylor, 1948, p. 354). Sand bodies that are in a state of dense packing tend to dilate and increase in volume as the shearing stresses move the closely interlocked grains up and over each other. In loosely packed sands, the opposite effect takes place. The open structual

Fig. 139. Sand flowing in San Lucas Canyon has eroded an older fill exposing bedrock. Bottles thrown overboard from passing ships are full of sand, indicating re-exposure after burial. N.E.L. photo by Dill.

bridging between the grains collapses, creating a sudden loss of pore volume and, if saturated, an increase in pore water pressure. It can be visualized that there must be some intermediate stage between loose and dense packing where the density (packing) of the sediment will not change as shearing stresses are applied. The density of a sand at this state of packing is its critical density, and the void ratio, the ratio

Fig. 140. A small fan built out and over the older fill in one of the main branches of Los Frailes Canyon. Note how the joint in the granite has been enlarged by sand flows. Nine months after this picture was taken, the marker stakes on the right side of the photo were gone. Depth 95 ft (29 m). Photo taken on Feb. 10, 1962. (From Dill, 1964b).

of the volume of the voids to the volume of solids, is its *critical void ratio.*

The measurement of the critical density of a sediment and its comparison with *in situ* densities is an important factor in determining the type of failure possible in sandy sediments. Some sands that have *in situ* densities less than the critical density are said to be metastable under stress and subject to *spontaneous liquefaction.*

Terzaghi (1956) has lucidly explained the mechanics of liquefaction as a possible explanation of loss of canyon fill and submarine slope failures. For those not familiar with the subject, a brief description follows. If a body of saturated sand, with a void ratio greater than the critical void ratio, is subjected to a suddenly applied shearing stress its structure will collapse. If drainage of interstitial water is restricted, the pore pressure will increase because of the decrease in the volume of the voids. If the permeability of the sediment is low or the deposit large, the dissipation of this localized pressure is not equalized by a loss of water and excess pore pressure develops in the area of collapse (the shear surface). The excess hydrostatic pressure is approximately equal to the buoyed weight of the sediment overlying the shear zone. During liquefaction, part of the weight of the overlying sediments is transferred from intergranular support to support by the excess of pore water pressure (equation 3). This abrupt transfer causes a sudden decrease in the shear strength of the sediment because most of the resistance to stress in relatively cohesionless, sand-sized sediments is derived from the frictional resistance to shear resulting from intergranular contact (Terzaghi, 1950, p. 100; 1956). The loss of strength causes a temporary liquefaction and sand will flow until the excess pore pressure is relieved (by consolidation). In short, spontaneous liquefaction occurs when the shear strength approaches zero during the brief time between loose and denser packing, when the sediment is virtually a suspension of mineral grains in water.

To test the possibility of loss of canyon sediment by liquefaction, the critical density for the sediments in the head of Sumner and South Branch of Scripps Canyon were determined in the laboratory by measuring the change in volume at different densities when sediment from this area was subjected to various shearing stresses in a direct shear test (Table 4). A comparison of the laboratory-determined critical densities and void ratios with the *in situ* density of these canyon sands shows that, although they are not densely packed, the canyon sands are slightly lower or nearly equal to the laboratory-derived critical density. Therefore, when the sediments are subjected to

Table 4. Density, porosity, shear strength, and volume change of a fine grained micaceous sand from the head of Scripps Canyon. Densities were measured after direct shear test and represent the critical density of the sediment. ΔV is change of volume during shear, positive values indicate an increase and dense packing.

Normal Stress lb/in²	Peak Shear Strength s_m lb/in²	Ultimate Shear Strength s_u lb/in²	Wet Density o gm/cm³	Porosity P%	Change in Volume During Shear: ΔV in³
0.10	0.36	0.30	1.849	55.31	+0.044
0.13	– –	– –	1.850	54.17	+0.026
0.37	– –	– –	1.823	54.52	+0.024
0.86	0.82	0.73	1.804	55.79	+0.030
1.73	1.40	1.20	1.810	55.29	+0.024
2.96	2.25	1.95	1.806	55.45	+0.030

Average *in situ* density 1.848 gm/cm³; porosity 50.09%. Increase in volume indicates all samples were denser than the *critical density* prior to shear.

suddenly applied stresses they should react like sediment near its critical void ratio, and should not be expected either to collapse or suddenly expand because the state of packing is not conducive to volume change.

The close agreement between field values of density and the critical density is not surprising, if one considers that in all instances where marker stakes have been placed in the sediment at the head of canyons a slow downslope movement was observed. This movement by gravity creep prevents the development of a dense packing, and would certainly destroy any loose metastable structure that might form as the sediment settled to the bottom from suspension. Metastable structures with loose packing are easily developed in the laboratory in the micaceous sediment commonly found in canyon heads. However, the shear strength (between, 72.5 to 145 gm/cm²) and density of such reconstructed sediments (about 1.60 gm/cm²) is far less than the *in situ* values for any of the samples taken in the same type of sand in the heads of canyons (Dill, 1964b, p. 153).

A review of requirements for metastability and spontaneous liquefaction as defined by Casagrande (1938), Terzaghi and Peck (1948, pp. 100-104), Terzaghi (1956), and others is summarized in Table 5. This summary and the preceding data indicate that the sands in the heads of the investigated canyons are not in a metastable condition that would lead to spontaneous liquefaction under sudden stresses. It cannot be stated that this is the case in all canyons but, to date, all of the tests and observations indicate that in areas of gravity creep and periodic slumps, especially where plant material is incorporated in the canyon fill, liquefaction can only play an extremely limited part in the removal of sediments into deeper water.

Table 5. Comparison of observed and measured properties of sediments from the head of Scripps Submarine Canyon with those needed to develop a state of spontaneous liquefaction (from Casagrande, 1938; Terzaghi and Peck, 1948, p. 100–105; and Terzaghi, 1956, p. 13).

Requirements for spontaneous liquefaction	Characteristics of Scripps Canyon sediments in areas of intermittent mass movement
1. Temporary excess hydrostatic pore pressure.	Temporary excess pore pressure is possible. However, the permeability of the sediment is low enough so that there is some entrapment of gas within the sediment. The high gas content would have a tendency to cushion any sudden shocks and prevent an extremely rapid buildup of excess hydrostatic pressures except in local areas.
2. Sediment must have a metastable structure that will lose most of its internal strength when subjected to a suddenly applied shear stress.	The sand areas in the shallow heads of the canyon have void ratios that are almost equal to or slightly greater than the critical void ratio. Therefore, the change in volume at collapse would be very small and not develop large excess pore pressures if the sediments are subjected to a suddenly applied shear stress. The earthquake of June, 1963, did not cause any substantial collapse and verified at that time the lack of a metastable structure that could lead to spontaneous liquefaction. Large heavy objects (rocks, hammers, and lead weights) placed on the surface of canyon sediments remain supported even when subjected to violent shock or strong blows. However, on slopes greater than 30°, the micaceous sediments will flow or slump when overloaded and carry the objects along with them until a stable slope is reestablished.
3. No creep movement prior to failure (movement relieves metastable structure).	Reference stakes placed in the canyon sediments show that they are slowly moving downslope and that this movement is accelerated just prior to a major slump.
4. Sediment must have low cohesion and be in the silt to sand size.	Undisturbed *in situ* vane shear measurements and laboratory vane shear, unconfined shear, and triaxial shear tests on typical canyon sediments indicate that they have a measurable cohesion. The inorganic portion of canyon sediments range in size from silt to fine sand.
5. Homogeneous in plane of failure.	The mixed origin and interbedded nature of the sediment filling all parts of the canyon preclude it from being classified as homogeneous in any plane of failure (Figures 20 and 22).
6. Slope cannot exceed angle of internal friction nor angle of repose for cohesionless grains (otherwise it has cohesion).	The surface slopes of sediments accumulating in the canyon head often exceed 35° and have been observed on occasion to rest with an angle of repose of 54°. The cohesion necessary to maintain such steep slopes is derived from the sea grass and algae incorporated within the sediment mat.
7. Needs triggering mechanism to start increase in pore pressure.	Triggering mechanisms are available in the form of rapidly deposited sediment brought into the heads of the canyon by rip currents during storms and periods of large swell. Earthquakes are a possible but not a common triggering mechanism (the strongest earthquake shock in 10 years had little effect).
8. Sediment must be 100% *water* saturated.	The high gas content and active bubbling observed just prior to slumps precludes the possibility of a state of 100% water saturation.
9. Spontaneous liquefaction should develop when subjected to rapid buildup of pore pressure.	A series of tests on canyon sediments that had built up over a period of 6 months showed that they do not fail when subjected to rapid increases in pore water pressure. Neither jet boring nor high pressure air applied slowly or rapidly caused spontaneous liquefaction. An increase in bubbling during the air jet tests indicated that the entire sediment fill of the canyon was affected over an area of at least 800 square feet.

CHAPTER XVI

ORIGIN OF SUBMARINE CANYONS AND DELTA-FRONT TROUGHS

T HE ORIGIN OF the large sea-floor canyons and the long delta-front troughs has been left to the last because both are difficult to explain and require a broad background of information for their interpretation. The origin of canyons on the sea floor is today almost as puzzling as it was to the early investigators. Our work has not indicated that any one process or hypothesis can explain the origin of all canyons. The rapid acquisition of information concerning submarine canyons during the period in which this book was written has caused us to change many of our original opinions.

One of the main problems is a lack of data concerning the physical properties and distribution of sediments in the deeper parts of canyons and fan-valleys. In the shallow heads where large numbers of scuba dives permitted repetitive measurements, we have sufficient data to define the erosional processes. Unfortunately, in deep water we were limited in most instances by data taken either by indirect measurements or from samples taken from ships that may be moderately distant from the precise location we wished to sample. We have made many descents in the Diving Saucer and a few reconnaissance dives in the bathyscaph, but the data from these observations are insufficient when compared with the hundreds of scientific dives necessary to prove some of our concepts concerning shallow-water processes.

In view of this lack of information, all we can do in this chapter is offer our interpretation of the data presently available. There is no assurance that present ideas will continue to be tenable in the future. It is only fair to admit that some of the conclusions expressed here are compromises between the personal opinions of the authors. We have presented all of our evidence that both favors and opposes the various hypotheses, thus leaving the reader in a better position to make his own interpretations as to why there are large submarine canyons and other types of valleys on the sea floor.

SUBMARINE CANYONS

Facts Requiring Explanation

The descriptions of the numerous canyons in earlier chapters and an analysis of the data compiled in the Appendix have revealed that many canyons not only have similar features but also create a sedimentary environment that is unique on the sea floor. Any successful hypothesis must be able to explain the following characteristics and pertinent facts:

1. The canyon axes have a virtually continuous seaward slope. Exceptions are rare and mostly not confirmed when older surveys are checked by modern sounding equipment.

2. The longitudinal profiles are usually steeper in the canyon heads than in their lower courses.

3. Canyons are just as common on continental terraces formed of igneous rocks as those formed of sedimentary rock. However, the canyons cut in semi-consolidated sediments usually have broad bowl-shaped tributaries and branches, while those cut in hard consolidated rocks usually form steep-walled narrow gorges.

4. Most canyons can be traced to the base of the relatively steep continental slope, where they either terminate at the contact with the more gently sloping continental rise, or

continue as fan-valleys cut into the sediments forming the continental rise.

5. Most of the canyons have winding courses. These sinuous axial trends continue in the fan-valleys that cross the submarine fans.

6. Most canyons have V-shaped, transverse profiles with narrow flat floors, formed by a sediment fill.

7. In general, tributaries are more common near canyon heads, but some start in deep water far from the present shoreline. Many of the tributaries enter the main channel of a canyon as hanging valleys. Although not strictly comparable, the closest land form for such a system of tributaries would be a dendritic drainage pattern.

8. Many canyons extend below the sill depth of major basins, notably in the Mediterranean.

9. Some canyons terminate part way down the continental slope, where they encounter what appear to be fault troughs.

10. Large sediment fans are usually found at the mouths of submarine canyons.

11. The depths to which canyons are cut below surrounding slopes apparently show no relation to the rock types on the walls.

12. Canyons are as common off unstable coasts as off those with a long history of stability. No apparent relationship exists between the abundance of canyons found off mountainous coasts and off lowland coasts.

13. Aside from the west Coriscan coast, there appears to be no indication that canyons are more prevalent off deeply embayed coasts than elsewhere.

14. Canyons frequently cross narrow shelves, originating almost at the shore.

15. Except for Congo Canyon, which may be incorrectly classified (p. 206), no submarine canyon crosses a continental shelf with a width in excess of 20 miles. Also, except in the southeast Bering Sea, no canyons head more than 20 miles inside the shelf margin. However, delta-front troughs cross shelves up to 80 miles in width, and many shelf-valleys of the glacial-trough type cross even wider shelves.

16. Most canyons are located off river valleys, although some of the largest canyons are found off insignificant land valleys, and several canyons appear to have no connection with land drainage. Others are found off abandoned stream mouths.

17. Although a few canyons head on the upcurrent side of points where currents sometimes turn seaward, they usually show no such relationship and are found off the center of some broad embayments. During glacial-stage lower stands of sea level, the relationship to points would have been more pronounced.

18. Repetition of sounding lines in several canyon heads shows frequent depth changes. Sediment deposited in the canyon heads is transported seaward by a combination of creep, progressive slumps, sand flows, and bottom currents — probably including turbidity currents, at least for the fine-grained sediments. Where the floor has sand sediment, only creep, slumps, sand flows, and transport by bottom currents other than dense turbidity currents, have been observed to date. There is no direct evidence that turbidity currents start in the sand-floored canyon heads, where most observations have been made.

19. The transportation of sand and nearshore organic material down the canyons and their adjoining fan-valleys is also proven by numerous cores. Gravel, rock fragments, and rounded boulders up to 3 ft (1 m) have been found in the fill.

20. Some of the sand layers along canyon axes are graded, but most are not graded, although generally well sorted.

21. Much evidence exists of the transportation of shallow-water foraminifera along the axes of the canyons into great depths. Abundant wood fragments and mats of kelp and sea grass are apparently carried seaward also along the canyon floors.

22. In general, canyon heads that enter long embayments have deposits of mud on their floors.

23. Clear evidence of erosion in the canyon heads is shown by overhanging walls, grooves, truncated burrows of marine organisms, and smooth unweathered rock surfaces both above and below depths known to have been exposed sub-aerially during glacially lowered sea level. This erosion, which resembles glacial plucking, is seen even in granite-walled canyons.

24. Canyon-floor currents with velocities up to at least 0.5 knots have been observed, and comparable velocities are inferred from ripple marks seen during dives and photographed down to 11,480 ft (3,500 m), by lowered cameras. The clean, well-sorted sand samples obtained in many places, even at great depths, add confirmation.

25. Downcanyon currents apparently predominate, except perhaps below drop-offs where upcanyon countercurrents have been reported in several Saucer dives.

26. Canyons receiving large supplies of sediment evidently are not being filled.

27. Bedrock is exposed in the bottom of canyons in a few places.

28. Sediment does not become finer with distance of transport along the canyon axis. Zones of coarsening were found along several canyons.

Hypotheses of Origin

A surprising number of hypotheses have been suggested to explain submarine canyons. Some years ago it seemed as though every well-known geologist had his own hypothesis. In recent years, however, with the gathering of more data, the number has been considerably narrowed, presumably because geologists have accepted the abundant evidence that coarse sediment can be transported out into deep water. The exact method by which this transport and associated erosion is accomplished is difficult to visualize. In general, the main hypotheses of canyon origin include: (1) erosion by turbidity currents starting in the canyon heads, (2) erosion by the slow mass movement of sediment downcanyon by creep, progressive slumps, sandfalls, and later redistribution of sediment by deep-sea bottom currents, (3) erosion by bottom currents other than turbidity currents, and (4) drowning by subsidence of valleys cut subaerially.

Model studies have shown that turbidity currents created in the laboratory are capable of transporting coarse sediments (Kuenen and Migliorini, 1950). As a result, turbidity currents have become one of the most discussed phenomena in the entire field of geology, and are generally credited with the excavation of submarine canyons and with transport of large quantities of sediment into the deep sea. However, as indicated by our observations of the processes operating in the upper canyons, it will be seen that other types of erosion are taking place in the canyon heads and that at the present time turbidity currents do not appear to be a major process operating there. The whole case needs to be reopened with unbiased discussion of the pros and cons of the principal hypotheses.

DISCARDED HYPOTHESES

It is not easy to say which of the many hypotheses have now been discarded, because there has been very little withdrawal of ideas. However, it seems reasonable that when hypotheses have been extensively criticized and not defended, they have been taken out of the running. For example, the Johnson (1939) hypothesis that artesian springs have excavated the canyons was never well documented, and little that has been learned about the canyons from recent investigations seems to support the idea. Continuous reflection profiling of the sub-bottom has helped eliminate this concept. The tsunamis, suggested by Bucher (1940), was an interesting speculation, but again has had little support from field studies — either of canyons or tsunamis. Explanation of the canyons as fault valleys (Lawson, 1893; Wegener, 1924) or at least as having fault control may be more fruitful, but it is obvious that the dendritic tributary system, the sinuous axes, and the failures of most canyons to follow structural trends of the adjacent continent, along with their usual extension directly across and down submarine slopes, form barricades against the hypothesis that make it seem hopeless as a general explanation.

DROWNED RIVER CANYONS

The fact that submarine canyons closely resemble river canyons in many respects, such as their somewhat dendritic tributary patterns, has always been a powerful argument that they represent the result of drowning of valleys cut during a time when the lands stood relatively higher. The submarine canyons that enter the western Corsican embayments seem so clearly to be the seaward continuation of the land canyons that even Kuenen (1953), a firm advocate of turbidity current origin, came to the conclusion that these are true drowned valleys. A few others, like Tokyo Canyon, appear to be almost equally good examples of drowning. If these canyons are submerged river valleys, it seems only reasonable that similar canyons adjacent to them have also been drowned. For example, the series of canyons that can be traced north of Corsica and along the French and Italian coasts would appear to have undergone the same history as west Corsica since there is no topographic break between them (Fig. 141). The mud floors of the canyon heads within most of these bays may indicate that they are now being filled.

Along many coasts of the world, there is evidence of deep submergence. Coastal wells commonly penetrate a thick series of shallow-water marine or terrestrial formations dating as far back as the Cretaceous Period. These formations are now thousands of feet below sea level. The deep borings in the Bahamas have shown nothing but shallow-water formations, indicating that the great depth of the Bahama submarine canyons may be, at least in part, the result of submergence. Furthermore, the closed basins in the northwest branch of Great Bahama Canyon (inset in Fig. 93), may represent submerged karst topography. Perhaps, also, the tunnel found cut into the granite near the floor of San Lucas Canyon (p. 103) could be interpreted as the work of ground water when the canyon was above water. The deep benches with rounded gravel off eastern Honshu (Nasu, 1964) suggest the possibility that the canyons off this coast (Chapt. VI) may have been drowned. The fact that canyons are apparently as well developed in underwater slopes underlain by crystalline rocks as they are in soft sedimentary formations indicates, either that many canyons are drowned valleys, or that submarine erosion is almost as successful in eroding hard rock as are subaerial processes.

An argument of somewhat doubtful validity, but which may favor subaerial erosion, is that the canyon heads are usually located directly off river-cut land valleys, The remarkable alignments in north Molokai (Fig. 104) and west Corsica (Fig. 91) show definite relationship between the land and sea valleys. This connection, however, may indicate only that the sediment provided to the ocean at the mouth of the river has been used by submarine agencies to erode the canyon. Submergence may also be indicated by finding canyon tributaries that head at the shelf break in water several hundred meters in depth (Figs. 78 and 80). Longshore currents, the chief source of sediment for canyon cutting, could not be expected to transport much sediment to the slope at the heads of these tributaries, whether now or during the lowered sea levels of glacial stages. Therefore, these tributaties appear to require a former higher elevation of the sea floor.

OBJECTIONS TO SUBAERIAL EROSION

Probably a common reason why geologists have been opposed to

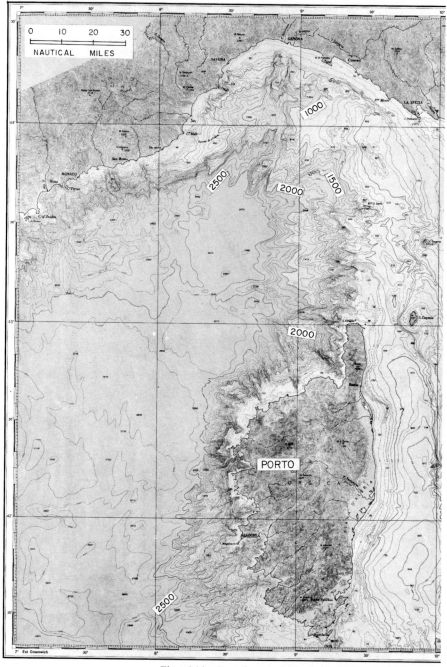

Fig. 141. Deeply eroded slopes off French-Italian
Riviera and Corsica. From E. Debrazzi and A. G.
Segre, publicata dall' Instituto Idrografico della Ma-
rina-Genova, Aug., 1960.

subaerial erosion as the general cause of submarine canyons is because maps showing the distribution of these features (for example,
Shepard, 1948, Fig. 69) have indicated that they are world-wide.
Furthermore, a widespread impression has developed that the canyons extend to depths of 10,000 ft (3,050 m) or more below sea level.
The submergence of all coasts to an amount of that magnitude was
naturally disturbing. However, there are many kinds of submarine
valleys, and many of those on earlier maps are quite clearly not what
we have referred to here as canyons. The map inside the front cover
shows the locations of most of the well-established canyons. Also, the
depths of the canyon termini are rarely as great as 10,000 ft (3,050 m).
Consulting the Appendix Table, we find the figure of 6,946 ft (2,117
m) as an average for the termini, and 5,958 ft (1,816 m) for canyons
that are in the best-sounded areas. These figures are not particularly
out of line with the amounts of submergence indicated in the well logs
of borings in many coastal areas. Admittedly, these submerged piles
of sediment are deeply cut by canyons, for example, along the margin
of the Atlantic Shelf.

On the other hand, the idea that most submarine canyons are
simply submerged portions of stream valleys does violence to what we
know of the relationship between the submarine canyon heads and
the lower ends of the adjacent stream valleys. With the possible
exception of western Corsica, there is such a decided nickpoint
between the land and sea valleys that Woodford (1951) was quite
justified in showing that submergence could not explain this hiatus. It
seems apparent that the typical concave profile of submarine canyons,
with its steepest element in shallow water near the canyon head, is an
indication that the profile is adjusted to the present sea level, or at
least to a sea level close to that of the present day. This does not
disprove an original subaerial cutting of the submarine canyons, but it
does show that some form of submarine erosion must have greatly
reshaped these valleys.

A convincing argument against subaerial erosion as the sole cause is
the finding of smoothed, grooved, and undercut canyon walls with
truncated pholad holes. These provide clear evidence that submarine
erosion is taking place in the canyon heads. The truncation of the
lagoonal sediments in La Jolla Canyon shows that active erosion has
taken place here during the past 8,000 years (p. 57).

Granted that submarine erosion is taking place in the canyons, is
there any reason to bring in the submergence of stream valleys?
Perhaps not, but there is abundant evidence for sinking continental

margins; also the pattern of many of the submarine canyons does not seem to conform with what might be expected from submarine erosion. The dendritic pattern of valleys so well illustrated at the mouth of Tokyo Bay, in the Monterey-Carmel area, and in the southern Bering Sea, is similar to that created by running water on land. Rainwash affects the entire slope but sediment-laden currents appear to be localized. Sea-floor valleys have formed on the fronts of advancing deltas and on recently active fault scarps where no sub-aerial slope submergence seems possible (Chapt. XII). These valleys lack a dendritic pattern and have few tributaries of any sort. However, the dendritic pattern is best developed in the shallow canyon heads, where there can be no doubt that subaerial erosion has taken place during the Pleistocene lowered sea levels.

TURBIDITY CURRENT EXCAVATION

In this discussion we shall assume that turbidity currents result from sediment accumulating along a break in slope until the mass becomes unstable and slumps, throwing the sediments into suspension and thus developing a heavy, turbid mass. As this liquid mass of dense material moves down the slope it may nourish itself by erosion of material over which it flows.

Some type of current must move down submarine canyons and be capable of transporting the sediment and forming the large fans at their mouths. The erosional effectiveness of deep-water currents is indicated by the steep, freshly eroded, cut-bank slopes observed on the outer curves of fan-valleys. That the fan-valleys are in many places bordered by levees implies that the currents fill the entire valley and spill over the edge, just as a river in a flood plain builds a levee at the margin of its channel. The finding of thin beds of well-sorted sand on the levees, as well as on the fans, shows that currents capable of transporting fine sands must exist beyond the confines of the chan-nels. The sands are even carried out considerable distances onto the abyssal plains at the base of the fans. The fact that sands of canyon and fan-valley floors are frequently graded is in line with the grading of sediments deposited by the artificial turbidity currents developed in tank experiments by Kuenen. However, similar grading is possible by a current with a variable velocity. Perhaps of equal importance is the finding that the floors of submarine canyons, and even of many submarine fault troughs, slope continuously seaward, despite the fact that many of these valleys are found in areas where warping and faulting could be expected to develop barriers and basins. This continuous slope indicates that some type of current is very active in cutting away barriers or filling basins behind barriers. The angular blocks of rock in cores along the axes of submarine canyons, especially off Baja California, might suggest that rather powerful currents exist from time to time. Alternatively, the blocks may have fallen from the walls and been rafted by a slowly creeping or slumping sediment fill. Further evidence of the importance of turbidity currents comes from the relatively deep gorges along parts of fan-valleys and deep-sea channels, including Hudson Fan-valley, Cascadia Channel, and Coronado Fan-valley.

DEBATABLE EVIDENCE RELATIVE TO TURBIDITY CURRENTS

(1) *Grand Banks earthquake.* The supposed velocity of 55 knots during the Grand Banks earthquake turbidity current (Heezen and Ewing, 1952; Heezen *et al.,* 1954), if justifiable, would be a convincing argument for turbidity current erosion of canyons. Unfortunately, the evidence, as explained elsewhere, leaves much to be desired (Shepard, 1961; 1963, p. 339). The plotting of the times of cable breaks in relation to distance from the epicenter (Figs. 142a, 142b) shows that the breaks in cables took place for a distance of about 100 nautical miles from the epicenter at the same time as the main earthquake shock. Drawing an arc 100 miles from the epicenter, and assuming that the movements which caused turbidity currents or slides were initiated as far away as that at zero hour, the times of cable breaks can then be plotted beyond the 100 miles. The resulting graph suggests a speed of propagation of 15 knots instead of 55. Actually, it does not even prove such a speed of current flow, because the cables may have parted successively downslope for some other reason, as explained elsewhere.

If speeds of 15 knots are developed by turbidity currents very important erosion could be produced, although perhaps not of a catastrophic nature as would be the case with 55-knot currents. That no such velocity as 15 knots did develop, at least over the wide area indicated by Heezen and Ewing (1952), is signified by the cores obtained by Lamont Geological Observatory in the area where the velocities were supposed to be highest (Fig. 143). It is inconceivable that this great torrent could have raced down the slope and failed to remove the thick masses of silty clay shown at the top of most of these cores. These fine-grained slope sediments must have accumulated

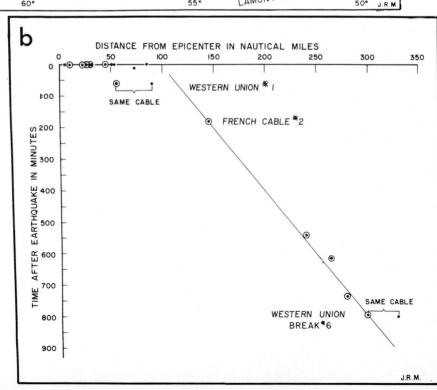

Fig. 143. Diagram showing variation in grain size in cores obtained by Lamont scientists in the Grand Banks cable break area. The black layers represent coarse silt and/or fine-grained sand, and blank areas fine-grained lutite. Note absence of coarse sediments and existence of ordinary deep-sea types of deposit at the surface of four of the cores. From Ericson *et al.* (1961, Figs. 14, 15).

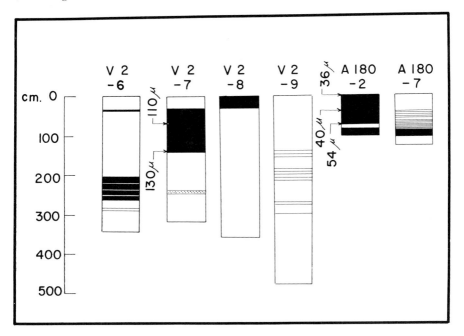

Fig. 142. a. Showing the times of cable breaks after and during the Grand Banks earthquake of 1929. Note that instantaneous breaks occurred out to a distance of approximately 100 nautical miles from the epicenter. Positions of Lamont cores are indicated (1 to 7, V2-6 to V2-9). The contours are not well established because of the absence of accurate surveys.

b. Indicating the relation of time of cable breaks to distance from the earthquake epicenter, assuming an instantaneous break out to 100 miles from the epicenter. Note that the line connecting breaks indicates a uniform velocity of 15 knots.

during thousands of years of undisturbed deposition. Similarly, the material collected by the cable companies directly after the cable breaks was quite inconsistent with the idea that any great torrent of sediment-charged water rushed down the slope (Kindle, 1931). The few pebbles that were reported by Kindle are quite clearly iceberg debris dropped into the clayey sediments, a process still continuing. It is possible, however, that turbidity currents moved rapidly down some canyons along this slope, and that the cable breaks took place where the cables crossed the canyons.

An alternative explanation for the cable breaks was suggested by Terzaghi (1956). He believed that spontaneous liquefaction occurred after the earthquake, and that this spread gradually down the slope as it has in some localities on land, as in the storage dam Swir III in the Soviet Union. Heezen (1963) objected to this idea on the grounds that the cable breaks from such action would have spread along the slope as well as down. A considerable body of evidence also suggests that the cohesive slope sediments would not be subject to spontaneous lique-faction (Moore, 1961).

The possibility that the breaks were due to successive development of slumps, suggested by Shepard (1954) and Moore (1956), may also be a factor to consider. The discovery by Lamont scientists of land-slide slices underlying the slope in this area (Heezen and Drake, 1964) may give some impetus to this idea. It seem rather evident that more investigations are called for before this rather fascinating sequence of cable breaks can be put into its proper perspective.[1]

Theoretical estimates of velocity. Estimates made by Hurley (1960, p. 41) and Inman (1963, p. 140) show the theoretical possibility that under some conditions, suspended sediments could develop turbidity currents attaining high velocities, both in canyons and in deep fan-valleys. Inman's calculations assumed that with a thickness of 35 ft (10 m) and a volume of concentration of fine sand of 5%, flows down La Jolla Canyon could range from 0.26 to 26 kn. It is, however, difficult to understand how the densely packed sand, which is found in a stable state at the head of Scripps Canyon on a 30° slope (p. 301), can be resuspended to form a cloud that is 5% sand by volume and be kept in suspension as it flows down a slope of less than 10°. In any case, the

[1]The polishing of a cable recovered after a break near the Fiji Islands was interpreted as indicating a high-speed current (Houtz and Wellman, 1962). However, scuba observations in Scripps Canyon have shown similar polishing by drag from creeping sediment as stresses built up and eventually broke a semi-buried 2-inch cable stretched across the canyon head.

calculated velocities may be much less at the bottom of the flow and, of course, are dependent on thickness of the flow. Judging from the cores showing that a terrace 13 ft (4 m) high on the sides of inner La Jolla Fan-valley had not received sand from the flows that move down the channel, the estimate of 35 ft (10 m) in thickness may be too large. On the other hand, thin sand layers in the predominantly mud cores on the levees more than 600 ft (180 m) above the channel floor indicate that occasionally there are very thick flows. The usual good sorting and internal flow structure found in the fine-grained sands in La Jolla Canyon (von Rad *et al.*, 1965) suggest velocities at the low end of the range computed by Inman.

The estimates for Cascadia Channel (Hurley, 1960, p. 47), using a modified Chézy formula and assuming that the entire channel was filled with a turbidity current and that the flow had a density of 1.05, indicate that currents conceivably might be as high as 20 kn. The natural levees suggest overflow, but there is no proof that the channel is ever actually filled. It is possible that the channel may have been deepened after the natural levees were formed. However, the finding of sand on the tops of high levees in several other localities implies that currents of the order of 0.5 kn or more[2] may have topped some levees in quite recent times.

Gravel and rock fragments from canyon axes. Until the box corer was employed in sampling the canyon axes, virtually all the evidence seemed to favor slow-speed turbidity currents along the floors. Rarely has coring obtained anything but fine sand (Shepard, 1963, Fig. 164). The gravel and soft rock fragments, described by Ericson *et al.* (1961), from East Coast canyons and sea valleys were found to be incorporated in clayey sediments, and hence were perhaps more suggestive of mud flows than swift-flowing turbulent currents. The gravel from the Monterey Fan-valley, referred to by Menard (1955), was also embedded in muddy sediment.

Several box cores taken in the canyons off the southern end of Baja California (Bouma and Shepard, 1964) might indicate strong currents. The angular, fresh-appearing rock fragments from the bottom of two of these rectangular cores might imply that powerful erosive action had been working on the underlying rock floor. More likely, the rocks have fallen from the walls (p. 109) and later were buried. The ungraded but sorted gravel and sand in two piston cores from this

[2]Judging from currents necessary to move sand on the canyon floor, observed in the Diving Saucer.

same area (Fig. 144) and from a box core signify that a current was moving down these canyons with considerable transporting capacity. This may not have been a turbidity current, if one can judge from the lack of grading. Here again we need more investigations.

The most recent canyon studies have virtually all yielded cores (including some box cores) that had sand with scattered pebbles in the

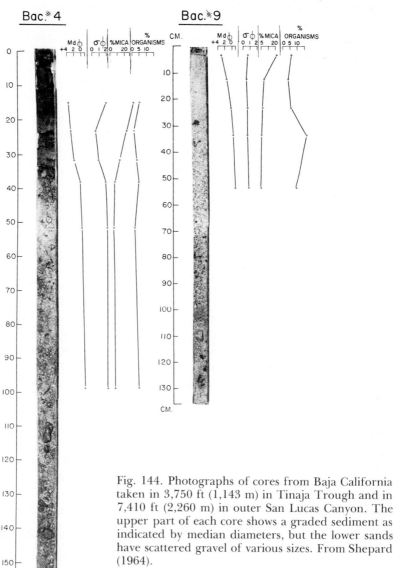

Fig. 144. Photographs of cores from Baja California taken in 3,750 ft (1,143 m) in Tinaja Trough and in 7,410 ft (2,260 m) in outer San Lucas Canyon. The upper part of each core shows a graded sediment as indicated by median diameters, but the lower sands have scattered gravel of various sizes. From Shepard (1964).

lower portion. Examples are: La Jolla Canyon, Monterey Canyon, San Lucas Canyon off Baja California, a canyon off southwestern Crete, Great Bahama Canyon, and a canyon off eastern Ceylon. Similarly, the ancient turbidites found in the Tertiary of southern California and in the French Alps, show many places where such scattered pebbles are found, especially in the lower part of the layers. It is hard to see how these patterns are produced by turbidity currents because one would expect the pebbles to collect at the bottom. Perhaps this indicates that some other type of sediment flow which will carry pebbles is operating and producing what have commonly been called turbidites.

Turbidity currents and even slopes. The experiments of Kuenen (Kuenen and Migliorini, 1950), M. L. Natland (personal communication), and Middleton (in press) demonstrated that sand and mud, when thrown into suspension over the floor of a tank, developed turbidity currents and moved both coarse and fine material down the slope the length of the tank. However, the box release experiments by Buffington (1961) performed on the steep slopes at the head of La Jolla submarine canyon were quite unsuccessful in producing currents on relatively smooth slopes, despite the steep inclines and a variety of mixtures of released material. Similar results were obtained by the junior author and many other divers who have tried to start flows on steep submarine slopes. Also, the small amounts of sediments stirred up by the Diving Saucer on the walls and floor of Scripps and La Jolla canyons generally developed only short-lived turbidity currents. These experiments and observations suggest that on slopes where sediment has accumulated slowly, turbidity currents are not likely to develop. However, as shown by Moore (1960), given an elongate trough with rapidly introduced sediment, the necessary conditions for confining the turbidity currents may exist (as also shown in Kuenen's experiments). Curray's (1964) continuous reflection profiles have revealed that marine slumps may develop on normally stable sediment-covered slopes where they have been over steepened by uplift.

EVIDENCE AGAINST TURBIDITY CURRENTS AS THE MAJOR CAUSE

The extreme confidence placed by so many geologists in turbidity currents as the major or only cause of submarine canyon excavation overlooks many other difficulties. If high-speed turbidity currents were the only cause, the canyons should contain clear evidence of these great floods. The following discussion will serve to focus attention on some complications that should be considered seriously before accepting this hypothesis *in toto.*

For turbidity currents, there are two slope conditions to consider, one being an even slope and the other a slope with an already existing valley. If the slope is even, one would expect the turbidity currents to spread out, lose momentum, and dissipate, as in the experiments by Buffington (1961). On the other hand, if a valley were already cut into the slope, the turbidity current would be confined and hence have a much better chance of continuing to the bottom of the incline. According to this reasoning, the turbidity current is not the initial cause of the valley, but might perpetuate a valley already existing on the slope, or even excavate it to greater depth.

If turbidity currents are the major cause of those canyons cut for thousands of feet into relatively hard rock, they must either have great cutting power comparable to floods and mountain torrents, or the erosion must have continued during a large part of the geological time scale. The available evidence does not seem to justify either of these premises. The numerous cores from canyon floors and from fan-valleys that show an alternation of very fine sand layers inter-bedded with silty clays suggest that the typical currents introducing the sand are not capable of cutting the floor of the canyons. Obviously, strong currents would remove the previous deposits and would transport much coarse debris cut from the walls and floor. According to the estimates of Gorsline and Emery (1959), the turbidity currents along the southern California coast that supply sand to the center of the basins must be quite infrequent, perhaps of the order of one per 400 years. If erosion is produced only by these infrequent currents, the process would have required a much longer period than is available for the excavation of canyons into the walls of troughs initiated since the Miocene. Bathyscaph dives after the more common disturbances on the canyon floors, as for example, annual or biannual deepenings of Scripps Canyon, show they did not develop turbidity currents. However, the short intervals between cable breaks in Congo Canyon (Heezen *et al.,* 1964) may very well have been due to turbidity currents. Even these can be explained by the alternative process of progressive slumping (Moore, 1961; Dill, 1964b, p. 246).

Cores collected from the floors of canyons and fan-valleys and the dredging from the floors have yielded considerable additional evidence that turbidity currents moving along these valleys do not have high velocities. The delicate shallow-water benthic foraminifera from the sand layers are usually well preserved and even include arena-ceous types, which would easily have been broken by dense highly turbulent flows. Dense mats of fragile surf grass interbedded with micaceous sand dredged from the floor of La Jolla Fan-valley are another indication of low velocity emplacements. Similarly, leaf im-pressions and other fragile material were found in the top of the formations at the base of turbidities in the Apennines (Kuenen and Miglorini, 1950) and in California Tertiary beds (Winterer and Dur-ham, 1962).

If the original valleys were due to slumps on the continental slope but the deep canyon excavations were the result of turbidity currents, one would expect to find valleys extending more or less straight down the slopes with few if any major tributaries. The tributaries that extend along the coast, as at Carmel and off the French Riviera, are a serious obstacle to turbidity current origin theories. Furthermore, there are some substantial tributaries that head in deep water where there is no evident supply of sediments to cause turbidity currents either under present conditions or during the lowered Pleistocene sea levels. An example of this type is Great Bahama Canyon where the islands have had no major rivers so far as is known.

Hubert (1964) has argued that the typical sands of deep submarine valleys and bordering fans on the continental rise off the East Coast rarely resemble the sediment types thought to be typical of turbidites. Tank experiments, such as those of Kuenen, Natland, and Middleton, both start and end with a sediment high in silt and clay, but the hundreds of analyses made by Hubert of the sand and coarse silt from deep water seldom showed more than a very few per cent of fine silt and clay. The same is true of the deep-water sands obtained by Scripps Institution (Shepard and Einsele, 1962; unpublished Scripps Institution analyses). This finding led Hubert to question whether the bulk of the deep-water sands were actually introduced by turbidity currents. However, the experiments in tanks may not produce typical turbidites because of scaling problems.

Despite the preceding difficulties with which the turbidity current hypothesis is faced, the evidence remains strong that some type of bottom-seeking current moves down the axes of the canyons beyond the steep headwall slopes, where creep and sand flows are so well documented as the means of transportation. The very gentle gradi-ents in the fan-valleys and deep-sea channels, mostly far less than one degree, must have flows moving along them that are sufficiently powerful to transport sand and to keep in transit the large supplies of sediment which are introduced into the heads of the canyons that come into the coast. The extremely steep, unstable slopes in the fan-valley channels indicate that currents or gravity creep are actively cutting the walls of the semi-compacted sediment of the fans. Furthermore, some type of sediment-charged current is apparently thick enough to spill over the tops of rather deep fan-valleys and produce levees. Either turbidity currents or some other type of currents could play this important role.

The evidence which seems to indicate that turbidity currents may not be important in canyon heads (if we are correct in this interpretation) does not exclude the possibility that turbidity currents are initiated farther seaward. For example, we have abundant evidence that there are many rock falls from the walls of submarine canyons visited by the Diving Saucer. These falls may bring with them sufficient muddy sediment in suspension to set up turbidity currents. One may well imagine the effect of a huge slide, such as that at Vaiont reservoir in northern Italy (Kiersch, 1965), in causing a major turbidity current in a pre-existing valley. However, some agent other than a turbidity current must bring about the instability leading to failure. One of the main problems in the turbidity current hypothesis is how to get one started in sediments which apparently are stable or which will fail by other means prior to being resuspended to the point they can flow as a liquid.

ORDINARY BOTTOM CURRENTS [OTHER THAN TURBIDITY CURRENTS] AS A CAUSE

A common belief is that all of the strong currents of the deep-sea floor are turbidity currents. However, a paper by Heezen (1959) and a summary by Heezen and Hollister (1964) might cause one to doubt this premise. The photographs taken over large areas of the oceans by Lamont Geological Observatory scientists have shown that ripple marks and other indications of relatively strong currents are common on the sea floor. Many of the ripple-marked areas were found where turbidity currents are obviously impossible, as on the tops of seamounts. The senior author observed upcanyon currents of 0.4 kn in a Saucer dive off La Jolla (Shepard, 1965), and various ripple marks have been photographed from other parts of submarine canyons, which seem clearly not to be the result of turbidity currents.

Apparently, temperature and salinity gradients,[3] along with internal waves and tides are quite capable of producing strong flows that will transport sand sediments (approximately 0.2 kn is necessary, according to Sundborg (1956). We shall refer to these as ordinary bottom currents. Hubert (1964) has come to the conclusion that a large part of the deep sand deposits in the Lamont cores are the result of these ordinary currents. He points out that the character of the sands and the sedimentary structures are more typical of such currents than of turbidity currents. However, we really do not know what type of deposits are produced by turbidity currents.

The possibility that ordinary bottom water currents may also excavate submarine canyons, or at least build the submarine fans and keep open the fan-valleys, must be considered. In favor of such an hypothesis are, perhaps, the sediment characteristics discussed by Hubert (1964). Unlike turbidity currents, the other types do not require the large amount of muddy material that has to accumulate and then be set into suspension in order to allow the turbidity current to operate. Ordinary currents are known to exist in the sandy heads of the canyons. A turbidity current might be expected to come to an end due to loss of sediment at the base of the steep gradient, but the ordinary currents not dependent on slope could persist.

The fact that canyon-floor sediments lack properties favorable to spontaneous liquefaction, and hence to developing turbidity currents, does not constitute any obstacle to ordinary currents. Erosion by these currents could account for the tributaries that start at considerable depth on the slope at points where little if any sediment would be available to account for a turbidity current. They also could account for deep abyssal plain gap-valleys (p. 277).

Against an origin by ordinary currents is the difficulty in developing a sufficient density difference to carry a current down along the entire length of a canyon, especially one with a steep slope. Turbidity currents would not have this difficulty. It is also hard to understand why ordinary currents should develop valleys in so many places directly off the mouth of a river. The outflowing low-salinity water might be compensated by slight upwelling, but this should not be sufficient to produce canyons, nor does the upwelling appear to reach any appreciable depth (Sverdrup et al., 1942, p. 501). Finally, there

[3]The cold cascading currents observed in winter outside the English Channel (Cooper and Vaux, 1949) are an example.

appear to be somewhat more downcanyon currents than those flowing upcanyon. The 1938 measurements (Shepard *et al.*, 1939) did not
show any tidal periodicity, but recent measurements 12 ft (4 m) above
the bottom in La Jolla Canyon, in 2,000 ft (610 m), show rapidly
fluctuating water currents up to 0.5 knot, which apparently have a
tidal component (John Isaacs and Richard Schwartzlose, personal
communication).

MASS MOVEMENT AS THE MAJOR CAUSE OF THE CANYONS

Almost all authors who have discussed the origin of submarine
canyons have considered that mass movements on the slopes have
played an important part. However, in the past, only Henry Stetson
(1949, p. 31) went so far as to give submarine landsliding a major role
in the canyon origin. Recent developments may serve to somewhat
strengthen this hypothesis. The observations at the heads of Scripps,
La Jolla, and Mugu canyons, and in three of the canyons off Baja
California, appear to leave little doubt that the glacier-like downcanyon creeping movement of the sediment mat is producing relatively
rapid erosion in the canyon heads. Some indication exists that this
creep may be important much deeper in the canyons, 1,000 ft (305 m)
in Mexican canyons and 2,000 ft (610 m) in La Jolla Canyon. Furthermore, this action must be capable of corrading hard rocks, such as
grantite and massive sandstone. It seems unlikely that the parallel
grooves with inclinations near the angle of repose for the sand, as are
found in the exposed walls of Scripps Canyon (Fig. 25), could be due
to turbidity currents. The powerful drag down the canyon, which
carried the heavy concrete blocks over the cliff in Sumner Branch, fits
perfectly with the glacial type of gouging that is indicated here.
Moreover, the canyon floor sediment was found by Dill (1964b) to
have neither a metastable packing nor other physical properties
necessary for spontaneous liquefaction (p. 307; Table 3). To produce
turbidity currents from sandy sediments during earthquakes, a metastable condition seems to be necessary. The canyon head is probably
more emptied by gravity creep and slump and by occasional sand
flows, such as those observed at Cape San Lucas. How much erosion
slump and sand flows produce is not known, but probably it is less
than the glacial-like creep that occurs when the canyons are full of
sediment.

This creep, at least at the canyon heads, combined with slump
would appear to account for the cutting back of the canyons into

Holocene formations. It also explains erosion at a point in the canyon where it is scarcely possible that turbidity currents could have played an important role, because they presumably would not have had time nor the steep slope to gather momentum sufficient to resuspend the sands and break down the internal strength of the sediment fill.

The possible importance of mass movements in producing what are generally considered as old turbidities can be attested by the incorporation of so many unsorted boulder beds between sorted sands and silty clays of probable deep-water origin (Natland and Kuenen, 1951; Crowell, 1957; Winterer and Durham, 1962; Dott, 1963) (Fig. 145). While the nature of the movement introducing the boulders is uncertain, it seems quite possible that the action which transports boulders down slopes can also produce erosion.

The evidence that creep and slump are very important, possibly dominant, factors in shallow canyon-head excavation does not necessarily provide any indication that creep is also important in the deeper parts of the canyons. At most of the locations where creep is demonstrated, there are steep axial slopes, commonly 20° to 30°. Creep must be far more important in these places than in the lower canyons where slopes as low as one-half degree are found. However, dives in the Saucer showed grooves and polished walls in the vicinity of 400 ft (120 m) where there is an average slope of 5°.

Additional evidence favoring creeping movement in the outer canyons does exist, but it is not well documented. The landing of the bathyscaph *Trieste I* on the channel floor of La Jolla Fan-valley punctured the mud surface of the sediment, releasing a flow of sand from beneath, as if the sand were in unstable equilibrium. Cracks in the mud cover of the same valley also suggest instability developed in the underlying sand after a half-inch layer of mud was deposited on top of it. The finding of boulders in sand and mud fill with mats of vegetation along the axis of La Jolla Fan-valley (p. 63) indicates that some type of transportation has occured that will not sort these materials as they move down the canyon.

Sliding of some type seems to have been the cause of the gullies in the rapidly deposited frontal slopes of deltas, and is equally successful as an explanation of the discontinuous valleys on fault scarps. With such an initial cause, it might seem possible that long-continued sliding or creep may have cut the canyons into their present form, perhaps with some assistance from turbidity currents. Once initiated along a plane of weakness, very little energy is required to maintain a slow downslope creep by large sedimentary masses on even very low slopes, especially if there is a possibility of increasing the pore pressures in contained sand layers.

EVIDENCE AGAINST MASS MOVEMENTS AS A MAJOR CAUSE

Despite the clear-cut evidence of erosion due to creep and slump at the canyon heads and the development of landslide valleys on submarine slopes, there appears to be evidence that other submarine erosion processes are active and that mass movement is not the only cause of the great canyons. The following points seemingly support such a mixed origin hypothesis:

(1) The submarine canyons are somewhat more dentritic in pattern than landslide valleys on land, and differ in the same respect from the valleys of the sea floor for which slump seems the most probable explanation.

(2) If the sediment mats, which form at the head of the canyons and appear to be so successful in producing erosion in that area by creep, move well down the canyons, the deposits on the canyon floor might be expected to be very much more

Fig. 145. Boulder deposit interbedded with deep-water Flysch in the Alps. Photo courtesy of A. Lombard, University of Geneva.

distorted than is indicated in cores and in most box samples. The succession of sand layers and interbedded silty clays is hard to reconcile with soil creep but may represent reworking by local currents.

(3) If mass movements were the principal cause, one would expect to find many canyons with intermediate stages of development between the typical discontinuous slope valleys, which are clearly due to slumping, and the typical dendritic canyons that extend to the base of the slopes. These have not been discovered.

Time of Canyon Cutting

Several advocates of turbidity currents as the primary cause of canyons have claimed that they were cut during the low sea level stages of the Pleistocene, when the rivers were flowing across the shelves and supplying sediments for turbidity current erosion of the slopes. No doubt in many localities much more material would have been available for canyon excavation at these times, especially off the east coast of the United States and the west coast of Europe. However, the majority of canyons are still getting a supply of sediments at their heads, so they are not limited to glacial stages for their marine erosion. Furthermore, the canyon heads that come well in across the shelves would have been dry land during the glacial stages.

As Menard (1955) has suggested, the fans outside the west coast of the United States are so large in volume that they represent far more sediment than would be produced from the cutting of the canyons alone. Also, the building of these fans at the present rate is so slow, according to available estimates, that they would require millions of years to be formed. According to Menard *et al.* (1965), the submarine fan seaward of the Rhone River Delta (Fig. 88) has proportions indicating that it has been forming since the Oligocene. As we obtain more continuous reflection profiles to show the fan thickness beyond various canyons, we may be able to evaluate these estimates more accurately.

The obvious relation of the submarine canyons off the Hawaiian Islands (p. 211-212) to the older, deeply eroded volcanoes is evidence that the canyons of the sea floor are not as recent in origin as glacial stages. This is supported by the probable post-canyon origin of the volcanic activity that formed Kalaupapa Peninsula (p. 213). This volcanism is thought to have been Pleistocene (Stearns and Macdonald, 1947, p. 33).

There is evidence that pre-Pleistocene submarine canyons have existed (Hoyt, 1959; Whitaker, 1962; Martin, 1962). To the present authors, it seems certain that canyons are forming today, and most probable that the canyons have been forming through all past ages, no matter what the agency or agencies responsible for them.

ORIGIN OF DELTA-FRONT TROUGHS AND CONGO CANYON

Troughs that cross the shelves off the huge Ganges, Indus, and Mississippi deltas are all so different from submarine canyons that they seem to require special explanation. Congo Canyon, also off a large river, may prove to be an example of a valley similar to the delta-front troughs, although there is no delta present. So far as we know, Congo Canyon has a relatively straight course with few tributaries (Fig. 101). Like the delta-front troughs, it has a gradient of approximately 10 m/km and extends all the way across a wide shelf. According to available information, the walls do not have rock. However, it may well be a V-shaped canyon and thus may differ from the delta-front troughs, at least in this one respect. It is the only submarine valley off a large river that now extends into an estuary.

While lacking evidence of turbidity current action in the Ganges and Indus troughs, we at least know that downslope displacement of foraminifera has occurred along the Mississippi Trough (Phleger, 1956). Also, cables have been broken so often at the mouth of the Congo that we can be sure that either turbidity currents or slumping is taking place at frequent intervals in this canyon. Possible upwelling along the Ganges and Indus troughs is indicated by the clearer water over the troughs and the marginal slicks.

Since these delta-front troughs and Congo Canyon show no signs of dendritic drainage and have no evidence of having been cut through rock, and because they all have long profiles with slopes at what appears to be a typical angle of repose of fine sediments on large delta fronts, it would seem reasonable to suggest that they are the result of erosion by density flows developed as sediment-charged currents flow across weak rapidly deposited sediment. This erosion is perhaps combined with some mass movements. Sediments possibly have been building up the shelf and prograding its margin while a channel was maintained at a 10 m/km gradient across the growing shelf by the slow flow of density currents. The continuous reflection profiling across the Swatch of No Ground (Fig. 125) gives some support to this idea.

The huge fans outside the delta-front troughs off the Ganges and the Mississippi and outside the Congo Canyon indicate long-continued existence of a channel across the shelves in these areas. No such accumulation could have been formed by the short periods of low sea level during the Pleistocene.

GROWING CONTINENTAL TERRACES AND VALLEY EROSION

One of the most puzzling features about submarine erosion is the newly acquired evidence that the continental terraces in general are building forward and upward, and yet submarine valleys of various types are being maintained and very likely being cut deeper. The evidence of forward growth increasing the size of the shelf has come from many recent continuous reflection profiles that show formations with dip slopes at the outer edge of many shelves (Moore and Curray, 1963a, 1963b; Curray and Moore, 1964), including those where rock is found relatively near the edge. In addition, the measurements of shear strength in sediments on slopes up to 15° has shown a general stability, suggesting that they could be building forward at even these high inclinations (Moore, 1961).

Apparently the answer to this enigma comes from both the instability of rapidly accumulating sediments, such as are being deposited in the heads of canyons and troughs that extend in close enough to receive an active supply of shore-drifted sediment, and from the ability of this sediment to erode when it fails. Here again, we are faced with the probability that some sort of valley existed with the head near shore to initiate the forming of the trough and canyon. The chances of a new canyon system originating in a relatively even slope beyond a shelf of appreciable width seem small. The absence of valleys shown in our soundings along the north slope east of Molokai, where there is no land source of sediment, in contrast to the deeply valleyed slope off the cliffed north coast of Molokai (Fig. 105), should add impetus to this idea.

CHAPTER XVII

SUMMARY
AND CONCLUSIONS

T HE ACCELERATED investigations of submarine canyons and other types of sea floor valleys have given us a wealth of new information. The interpretation of these surprising features is considerably assisted by the application of new data, such as observations from diving operations (scuba and submersibles), including instrumental measurements of currents, *in situ* tests of the properties of sediments in the fill, and the structure of sediments from large cores. However, it must be frankly admitted that any conclusions at this time can be considered only as tentative. We have presented available facts so that other scientists can use them for their own interpretation. Above everything, we hope that this work will stimulate more critical study for the future.

In most of this work we have been impressed with the fact that we are not dealing with just one type of sea valley. In addition to the common canyon type that has a V-shaped winding course, dendritic tributaries, and a steep rock-walled gorge, there are the relatively straight-walled trough-shaped valleys cut into unconsolidated sediment of the shelves off certain large deltas; winding valleys with distributaries and natural levees that cut the great sediment fans built at the base of the continental slopes; the numerous small discontinuous slope valleys with few tributaries on the submerged foreset slopes of deltas and on many submarine fault scarps; valleys that extend parallel to land structures in tectonically active areas and appear to be due to faulting; and finally, there are various types of continental shelf valleys that do not extend down the slopes. It is not always easy to classify submarine valleys into any one of these categories. Along their courses some are found to change from one type to another. However, where it is possible to classify any particular valley, it should prove far easier to offer an explanation of its origin.

Some of the sea floor valleys appear to be explained largely by fault movement (Chapt. XI). Where fault valleys on land form continuations into the sea floor, as in Sagami Bay, Japan, there can be little doubt of such an origin, but in many places it is difficult to be sure of the extent to which tectonism has participated in the production of sea valleys. We know that some canyons are cut along old faults and in some cases renewed movement along these faults may have helped form the valleys. Additionally, even if the valleys were originally formed by active faulting, erosion has no doubt been important in modifying them into their present form.

Slump or slide valleys appear to be quite common on the sea floor (Chapt. XII). They are a characteristic feature of the gentle foreset slopes of deltas where rapid sedimentation has been building the slopes forward into unstable positions. Many other small discontinuous valleys, located particularly on fault scarps, appear to owe their origin to the same type of mass movement. From available information we can conclude that the terraces usually found on the gentle concave slopes of fan-valleys are another manifestation of slumping (pp. 65, 66).

Active creep of sediments down the floors of the canyon heads, where the sands are matted together with surf grass and armed with boulders, is now well documented (Chapt. XV). This motion seems to offer the explanation for the active erosion of those inner canyons receiving a large supply of sediment. Sand flows observed in these same areas are undoubtedly a supplementary factor. Organisms attacking the wall rock must also contribute to the canyon erosion, especially in shallow water. It is still by no means clear whether these same processes are important in the outer canyons, particularly where the gradient of the floors is far less than at the headwall.

The drowning of subaerially eroded valleys appears to be a good explanation of the canyons along the west coast of Corsica and perhaps in some other areas, as at the mouth of Tokyo Bay. There is ample evidence that many coasts have stood higher in the past and have been sinking during much of the Cenozoic and even Mesozoic eras. The sinking of the Bahama Islands canyons is a good example. Submergence must have brought some subaerially eroded valleys below sea level where they would be modified by submarine processes. On the other hand, it is now evident that submarine canyons in general could not be uniquely the result of the sinking of continental margins. Despite the geographic contiguity with land valleys, most of the submarine canyons show a sharp hiatus at the coast, with the steep gradient at their headwalls completely out of line with the gentle gradients of the lower end of the adjoining land valleys. However, the somewhat dendritic pattern of the sea canyons rather suggests that these valleys may have been initiated at a time when the continental margins were higher. Otherwise, one might expect the canyons to have fewer tributaries and to be more akin to the slope gullies.

The part played by turbidity currents in the excavation of submarine canyons will have to remain somewhat of a mystery until we can learn more about the nature of these currents. The evidence of high-speed flows racing down the gentle continental slopes off the Grand Banks after the great 1929 earthquake has been shown to be very poorly documented (p. 231). That turbidity currents are ordinarily rather sluggish and probably quite incompetent in eroding rock appears to be indicated by the canyon cores from various parts of the world. The common alternating layers of fine sand and silty clay suggest that currents which preceded the implacement of the sand layers were not capable of cutting away the soft underlying sediments. However, some process has been responsible for the cutting along the steep outer slopes of fan-valleys (p. 64), and obviously some type of flow must have built the huge fans at the base of the canyons. Sand layers on the high levees along the sides of the fan-valleys demonstrate that currents have had appreciable thickness.

Another factor that we cannot evaluate accurately with presently available information is the effect of other types of currents, such as those due to internal waves, tides, winds, and differences in salinity and temperature. The observations made by our colleagues and ourselves during many dives in Cousteau's Saucer and in the bathyscaphs *Trieste I* and *II* have demonstrated that there are currents of at least 0.5 knots on rather frequent occasions along the canyon axes. These certainly can transport sand and may well be important in producing erosion. The photographic coverage of the deep ocean floor (Laughton, 1959; Shipek, 1960; Heezen and Hollister, 1964) has given further substantiation to the presence on the deep-sea floor of significant current-derived features, which are not the traditional turbidity currents. Here also we have a field wide-open for more marine studies.

The shelf valleys are more easily explained (Chapt. XIV). Virtually all of the trough-shaped valleys with basin depressions are found off glaciated land masses and seem to be explicable by glacial erosion. The shallow shelf valleys, like that off the Hudson River, seem to be slightly modified remnants of river erosion valleys, which formed during the lowered sea levels of the Pleistocene. Some of these valleys have been modified greatly by tidal erosion, as in the English Channel.

The large troughs that extend deep into the continental shelves off a few deltas contrast with the glacial troughs in having virtually continuous sloping floors and extending down the continental slopes below the shelves. These are somewhat of a mystery and still so little known as to make explanations hazardous. Perhaps they are the result of turbidity currents that are related in some way to the large amounts of sediment introduced by the rivers at the delta margin. The deep-sea channels are also an enigma. The extent to which they owe their origin to turbidity currents and the relative importance of faulting in producing valleys along which currents could circulate remain to be determined.

Finally, we wish to emphasize again that this is only an interim report and much work lies ahead before all — or even most — of the answers concerning the origin of submarine canyons and other valleys of the seafloor will be forthcoming.

1. Length of canyon measured along axis (nautical miles)
2. Depth at canyon head (feet)
3. Depth at canyon terminus (feet)
4. Character of coast inside canyon head
   A. Heads in estuary
   B. Heads off embayment
   C. Heads off straight beach or barrier
   D. Heads off relatively straight cliff
   E. Uncertain
5. Relation of canyon head to points of land
   A. On upcurrent side of point
   B. Relatively near upcurrent side of point
   C. No relation to point
6. Relation of canyon head to river valleys
   A. Probable connection
   B. No connection
   C. Uncertain
7. Source of sediments to canyon head
   A. Receives good supply
   B. Supply restricted now, greater during lowered sea level stages
   C. Little known supply of sediment because of depth
8. Gradient of axis in meters per kilometer
9. Nature of longitudinal profile
   A. Generally concave upward
   B. Generally convex upward
   C. Relatively even slope
   D. Local step-like steepening along axis

10. Maximum height of walls in feet
11. Channel curvature (see Fig. 107 of Chapt. X)
    A. Straight
    B. Slightly curving
    C. Twisting or winding
    D. Meandering
    E. One meandering bend
    F. Right-angled bends
12. Abundance of tributaries
    A. As common as typical land valleys
    B. Less common than typical land valleys
    C. Confined to canyon head
    D. No known tributaries
13. Character of transverse profile
    A. Predominantly V-shaped
    B. V-shaped inner canyon, trough-shaped outer canyon
    C. Predominantly trough-shaped
    D. Uncertain
14. Nature of canyon wall material
    A. Crystalline rock dredged
    B. Rock dredged, but all sedimentary
    C. Mud only dredged on wall
    D. Unknown
15. Nature of core sediment from axis
    A. Includes sand layers
    B. Includes sand and gravel layers
    C. Mud cores only
    D. Unknown
16. Relation to fan-valleys
    A. Has fan-valley continuation
    B. No fan-valley continuation
    C. Unknown

343

Canyon name and location	1 Canyon length	2 Depth at canyon head	3 Depth at canyon terminus	4 Coast character	5 Relation to points	6 Relation to river valleys
California						
Coronado	8.0	240	5,580	C	C	C
La Jolla	7.3	50	1,800	C	B	A
Scripps (tributary).......	1.45	60	900	D	C	A
Redondo	8.0	30	1,920	C	B	B
Dume.................	3.0	120	1,860	C	A	A
Mugu.................	8.0	40	2,400	C	B	C
Sur Partington	49.0	300	10,200	D	C	C
Carmel (tributary).......	15.0	30	6,600	A	A	A
Monterey..............	60.0	50?	9,600?	C	C	B
Delgada	55.0	90	8,400	D	C	B
Mattole	16.0	60	5,720	B	B	A
Eel	27.0	250	8,500	C	C	A
Total or Ave. (12).......	21.5	110	5,290	1A1B 7C3D	2A4B 6C	6A 3B3C
Oregon-Washington						
Columbia..............	37.0?	360	6,130?	B	B	A
Willapa	60.0	500+	7,000	B	C	A
Gray..................	30.0	500	6,440	B	C	A
Quinault	25.0	500±	5,750	C	C	A
Juan de Fuca	31.0+	800±	4,520+	B	B	C
Total or Ave. (5)	36.6	532	5,968	4B 1C	2B 3C	4A 1C
Bering Sea						
Umnak................	160.0	900	10,850	B	C	C
Bering	220.0	600±	11,160	B	C	C
Pribilof................	86.0	500±	10,700	C?	C	C
Total or Ave. (3)	155.3	667	10,903	2B1C	3C	3C
U.S. East Coast						
Corsair................	14+	360	5,400	E	C	C
Lydonia...............	16+	370	4,400+	E	C	C
Gilbert	20+	480	7,680+	E	C	C
Oceanographer	17+	600+	7,230+	E	C	C
Welker................	27+	400	6,450+	E	C	C

7	8	9	10	11	12	13	14	15	16
Sediment sources at head	Gradient in m/km	Nature of long profile	Maximum wall heights to nearest 1000 ft.	Channel curvature	Abundance of tributaries	Transverse profile character	Nature of canyon wall material	Sediment found in axial cores	Relation to fan-valleys
B	58	A	1,000	C	B	A	B	A	A
A	40	A	1,000	C	A	A	B	B	A
A	97	A	<1,000	B	C	A	B	B	B
A	39	A	1,000	C	B	C	B	A	A
A	97	A	1,000	C	B	A	A	D	C
A	49	A	<1,000	D	A	A	B	A	C
A	34	A	2,000	C	A	A	B	D	C
A	73	A	2,000	C	A	A	A	A	B
A	26.5	A+D	6,000	C or D	A	B	A	B	A
A	25	A	2,000	D	B	A	D	D	A
A	59	A	3,000	C	B	A	B	D	C
B	51	B	4,000	E	B	A	D	D	C
10A 2B	54	10A 1B1D	2,083	½B8½C 2½D1E	5A6B 1C	10A 1B1C	3A7B 2D	4A3B 5D	5A2B 5C
C	26	A	2,000	C	B	D	D	D	C
C	24	A	2,000	C	A	D	B	A	C
C	33	A	1,000	C	A	D	D	D	C
C	35	A	3,000	C	A	D	D	D	C
C	20	A	2,000	C	D	D	D	D	C
5C	27.6	5A	2,400	5C	3A1B 1D	5D	4D1B	4D1A	5C
C	10.4	A	4,000	C	A	D	D	D	C
C	8	A+D	6,000	C	A	A	B?	D	C
C	20	A	7,000	C	A	D	D	D	C
3C	12.8	2½A ½D	5,667	3C	3A	1A2D	1B2D	3D	3C
B	23	A	2,000	B	B	A	B	D	C
B	42	A	3,000	B	B	A	B	C	C
C	60	A+D	3,000	B	A	A	B	D	C
C	65	A	2,000	B	B	A	D	D	C
B	38	A+D	4,000	B	B	A	B	A	C

Canyon name and location	1 Canyon length	2 Depth at canyon head	3 Depth at canyon terminus	4 Coast character	5 Relation to points	6 Relation to river valleys
Hydrographer	27+	450+	6,600+	E	C	C
Hudson	50	300	7,000	B	C	A
Wilmington	23+	320	6,940+	E	C	C
Baltimore	28+	400	6,110+	B?	C	C
Washington	28+	360	6,740+	E	C	C
Norfolk	38	320	8,300	E	C	C
Total or Ave. (11)	26.2	395	6,623	2B9E	11C	1A 10C
Hawaiian-Molokai						
Halawai	6.0+	300±	3,540+	B	C	A
Naiwa	7.5	380	4,880	D	C	A
Waikolu	9.0	<600	6,540	B	C	A
Pelekunu	10.0	<320	6,320	B	C	A
Hawaiian-Kauai						
Hanakapiai	6.0+	280	7,480	D	C	A
Hanakoa	3.7	600±	4,820	D	C	C
Hanopu	3.6	300	5,100	D	C	C
Total or Ave. (7)	6.5	397	5,526	3B 4D	7C	5A 2C
Western Europe						
Shamrock	30+	1200±	14,400	B?	C	C
Black Mud	30+	900±	12,200	E	C	C
Audierne	27	600±	10,500	B	C	C
Cap Ferret	50+	800	11,647	C	C	C
Cap Breton	135 or 70	400±	13,100	D	C	C
Aviles	65	60±	8,000	C	B	A (old river)
Llanes	38	450	13,300	D	B	C
Nazare	93	200±	14,764	C	A	A
Lisbon	21	400	6,450	B	B	A?
Setubal	33+	350	6,880	C	C	A
Total or Ave. (10)	52.2 or 45.7	536	11,224	3B4C 2D	1A 3B5C	4A5C
Mediterranean mainland						
Grand Rhone	15+	600±	5,550	C	C	A
Marseille	20+	600±	6,840±	B	C	C
Canon de la Cassidaigne	19+	360	6,630+	B	B	A
Toulon	12+	260	6,600	A borderline	C	C
Stoechades	17+	300	4,380+	A	C	C
St. Topez	25+	60?	5,750	A borderline	C	A
Cannes	17+	100?	6,600?	C or A	C	B
Var	15	160	6,550	D delta	A	A
Nice	12	150	5,840	D	C	B

7	8	9	10	11	12	13	14	15	16
Sediment sources at head	Gradient in m/km	Nature of long profile	Maximum wall heights to nearest 1000 ft.	Channel curvature	Abundance of tributaries	Transverse profile character	Nature of canyon wall material	Sediment found in axial cores	Relation to fan-valleys
B	37	A+D	3,000	B	B	A	C	A	A
B	25	A+D	4,000	B	A	A	B	A	A
B	48	A	3,000	C	A	A	C	C	C
B	34	A+D	3,000	B	B	A	C	C	C
B	38	A+D	2,000	B	A	A	C	C	C
B	35	A+D	3,000	B	B	A	B	A	C
9B	40	7½A	2,900	10B	4A	11A	6B4C	4A4C	2A9C
2C		3½D		1C	7B		1D	3D	
B	90	C	1,000	C	D	A	D	D	C
B	100	C	1,000	B	D	A	A	A	B
B	110	A	2,000	B	B	A	A	B	A
A	100	A	1,000	C	B	A	D	D	B
B	200	B+D	1,000	B	B?	A	A	D	C
C	190	B	1,000	B	B?	A	A	A	C
B	220	B+D	2,000	B	B?	A	B	A	A
1A5B	144	2A2B	1,286	5B	5B	7A	4A1B	3A1B	2A2B
1C		2C1D		2C	2D		2D	3D	3C
C	28	C+D	3,000	B	B?	D	D	D	C
B	57	D	3,000	B	B	B	B	A	A
C	60	D	4,000	B	D	D	D	D	C
C	31	A	3,000	C	A	D	D	D	A
B	58	A	6,000	B	B	D	D	D	C
A	20 or 16	C+D	5,000 or 6,000	B	A?	B	B	D	A?
B	45	C	5,000	C	A	D	D	D	C
A	36	D	5,000	F	B	D	A?	D	C
B	48	B+D	4,000	B	B	D	B	D	C
B	33	C?	2,000	C?	B	D	B?	D	C
2A	41.6 or 41.2	2A½B	4,000	5B3C	3A	1B	1A3B	9D	2A7C
4B3C		3C3½D		1F	4B2D	8D	5D		
C	55	C?	2,000	B	C	A	D	D	C
C	52	A+D	2,000	C	A	A	D	D	C
B	55	D	3,000	C	B	A	D	D	C
B	110	D?	4,000	B	A	A	D	D	C
A	40	A	4,000	B	A	A	B?	D	C
A	38	C?	3,000	C	A	A	D	D	C
A	65	A	3,000	C	A	A	D	D	C
A	71	A	3,000	C?	A	B	D	B	A
A	79	A+D	2,000	C?	A	B	B?	B	A

Canyon name and location	1 Canyon length	2 Depth at canyon head	3 Depth at canyon terminus	4 Coast character	5 Relation to points	6 Relation to river valleys	
Cap d'Ail	14	320	6,870	B	C	C	
Nervia	16	330	6,280	C	C	A	
Taggia	12	300±	7,500	C	C	A	
Mele	31	200	6,150	C curving	C	B	
Noli	14	120	4,990	D curving	C	A?	
Polcevera	49	300	8,830	C	C	A?	
Genoa	20	260	6,260	B	C	A	
Total or Ave. (16)	17.4	276.5	6,351	3A4B 5C3D	1A1B 14C	9A 3B4C	
Mediterranean Islands							
Crete	4	<300	3,300	B?	C	A	
West Corsica							
St. Florent	25	150±	7,850	A	A	A	
Calvi	13	200±	7,800	B	C	A	
Porto	20	150±	8,200	A	C	A	
Sagone	29	150±	6,200	A	C	A	
Ajaccio	34	150±	8,200	A	C	A	
Valinco	35	150±	8,000	A	C	A	
Total or Ave. (7)	22.8	178	7,078	5A2B	1A 6C	7A	
Baja California							
San Pablo	20+	<400	8,400+	D	A	B	
Cardonal	16+	<450	7,500+	C	B	B	
Vigia	10	?	7,200	C+D	C	A or B	
San Lucas—	19	30	6,900?	A-bay	C	A	
Santa Maria	(24)		8,000				
San Jose	32	50	7,200?	C	C	A?	
Vinorama—	9	200	6,300	C	A	A	
Salado							
Los Frailes	9.5	10	5,200	A-bay	A (S. wind)	A	
Saltito	6	1200	5,100	B?	C	B	
Palmas—	13	100?	5,300	C	A	C	
Pescadero	9.3				(S. wind)		
Total or Ave. (9)	15.2	305	6,710	2A1B 4½C1½D	4A1B 4C	4½A 3½B1C	
East Honshu							
Ninomiya	4.8	400	2,600	C	C	C	
Sagami	5.0	310	3,300	C	C	C	
Enoshima	6.7	450	3,250	E	C	C	

7	8	9	10	11	12	13	14	15	16
Sediment sources at head	Gradient in m/km	Nature of long profile	Maximum wall heights to nearest 1000 ft.	Channel curvature	Abundance of tributaries	Transverse profile character	Nature of canyon wall material	Sediment found in axial cores	Relation to fan-valleys
B	78	D	1,000	B	B	B	D	D	A
B	62	D	2,000	B	B	B	D	B	A
B	100	A	2,000	C	B	A	D	D	A
B	32	A+D	1,000	C	B	B	D	D	B
A	58	A	2,000	C	B	B	D	D	B
B	29	A+D	3,000	B	B	B	D	D	C
B	50	D	2,000	B	B	C?	D	D	B
7A7B 2C	60.9	7A2C 7D	2,400	7B 9C	7A8B 1C	8A 7B1C	2B 15D	3B 13D	4A3B 8C
A	200	D	1,000	C	B	A	D	B	A
A	51	A	3,000	C	A	A	D	A	A?
B	97	A+D	3,000	C	B or A	A	D	D	A
A	67	A	4,000	C	A	A	A?	D	C
A	35	A	3,000	C	A	A	D	D	A?
A	39	A	4,000	B	A	A	D	D	B?
A	37	A+D	4,000	B	A	A	D	D	C
6A1B	75	6A 1D	3,100	2B5C	5½A 1½B	7A	1A6D	1A1B 5D	4A1B 2C
A	67	B+D	3,000	C	B	A	B	D?	C
B	73	A+D	3,000	C	A	A	B	D	C
A	115	A	3,000	B	C	B	A	B	A
A	70 56	A+D	3,000	C	A	A	A	B	A
A	41	A+D	3,000	C	A	A	A (sed.)	B	A
B	113	A	1,000	C	A	A	A	B	A
A	91	A+D	2,000	C	C	A	A	B	B
C	108	A	1,000	C?	A	A	A	D	A
A	65 or 91	A	2,000	C	A	A	A	A	A
6A2B 1C	81	6A½B 2½D	2,333	1B 8C	6A1B 2C	8A 1B	7A 2B	1A5B 3D	6A1B 2C
B	77	A	<1,000	B	C	A	B	D	C
B	100	A	<1,000	C	A	B	B	D	C
B	70	A	<1,000	B	C	A	B	B	C

Canyon name and location	1 Canyon length	2 Depth at canyon head	3 Depth at canyon terminus	4 Coast character	5 Relation to points	6 Relation to river valleys
Hayama	13	300	4,600	E	C	C
Miura	15	173		E	C	C
Misaki	14.5	330	4,600	E	C	C
Jogashima	10	330		E	C	C
Tokyo	30	300	4,900	A	C	C
Mera	20	190	5,500	B (bay)	B	C
Kamogawa	25	200	9,100	B	C	A
Total or Ave. (10)	29.25	298	4,731	1A2B 2C5E	1B 9C	1A 9C
Miscellaneous						
Great Bahama	125	4800	14,060	B	C	C
Congo	120	80	7,000	A	C	A
Ceylon Trincomalee	20+	30+	9,500+	A	A?	A
Manila	31+	300	7,800+	B	C	A
Bacarra NW Luzon	15	300	6,000+	C+D	C	A
San Antonio, Chile	20+	<150	2,700+	C?	C	A?
Total or Ave. (6)	55	943	7,843	2A2B 1½C½D	1A 5C	5A 1C

7	8	9	10	11	12	13	14	15	16
Sediment sources at head	Gradient in m/km	Nature of long profile	Maximum wall heights to nearest 1000 ft.	Channel curvature	Abundance of tributaries	Transverse profile character	Nature of canyon wall material	Sediment found in axial cores	Relation to fan-valleys
B	54	A	2,000	C	B	A	A	D	C
B	48	A	2,000	C	B	A	B	B	C
B	49	A	2,000	C	A	A	B	A	C
B	71	D	1,000	C	A	A	A	D	C
B	26	A+D	3,000	C	A	B	A	B	A
B	44	C+D	2,000	C	A	A	B	B	C
B	59	A+D	5,000	B	B	B	B	A	C
10B	60	$7A\frac{1}{2}C$	2,000	3B	5A3B	7A	3A	2A4B	1A
		$2\frac{1}{2}D$		7C	2C	3B	7B	4D	9C
C	13	A	14,000	C	A	A	C	B	A
A	96	A	4,000	B	C	A?	D	A	A
								sand	
A	79	A	4,000	F	A	A	A?	D	C
B	40	A+D	6,000	C	A	D	D	D	C
B	63	C	3,000	C	A	B?	D	D	C
A	32	A	3,000	B+C	B	D	D	D	C
3A2B	54	$4\frac{1}{2}A$	5,666	$1\frac{1}{2}B$	4A1B	3A	1A1C	1A	$4\frac{1}{2}A$
1C		$1C\frac{1}{2}D$		$3\frac{1}{2}C1F$	1C	1B2D	4D	1B4D	$1C\frac{1}{2}D$

REFERENCES

Allen, J. R. L., 1964, The Nigerian continental margin: bottom sediments, submarine morphology, and geological evolution. *Mar. Geol.,* 1 (4), 289-332.

Athearn, William D., 1963, Bathymetry of the Straits of Florida and the Bahama Islands. Pt. II, Bathymetry of the Tongue of the Ocean, Bahamas. *Bull. of Mar. Sci. of Gulf and Carib.,* 13 (3), 365-377.

Berthois, Leopold, 1962, Morphologie et géologie sous-marine. *Rev. Trav. Inst. Pêches Marit* II, 231-246.

Berthois, L. and R. Brenot, 1960, La morphologie sous-marine du Talus plateau continental entre le sud de l'Irlande et la Cap Ortegal (Espagne). *Jour. du Conseil Intl. Explor. de Mar.,* 25 (2), 111-114.

Bouma, A. H., 1964, Self-locking compass. *Mar. Geol.,* 1, 181-186.

Bouma, A. H., and F. P. Shepard, 1964, Large rectangular cores from submarine canyons and fan valleys. *Bull. Amer. Assoc. Petrol. Geol.,* 48 (2), 225-231.

Bourcart, Jacques, 1938, La marge continental. *Bull. Geol. Soc. France,* Ser. 5, v. VIII, 393-474.

——, 1950, Le socle continental de Toulon a la frontière Espagnole. *Conf. Centre Recherches et Études Oceanog.,* no. 3, 10 pp.

——, 1952, *Geographie du Fond des Mers.* Payot, Paris, 307 pp.

——, 1959, Morphologie du précontinent des Pyréneés a la Sardaigne. *Colloq. Intern. Centre Natl. Recherche Sci.,* LXXXIII, 33-50.

——, 1960, Carte topographique du fond de la Méditerranee occidentale. *Bull. Inst. Oceanogr., Monaco,* No. 1163, 3-20.

Bourcart, Jacques, François Ottmann, and Jeanne-Marie Ottmann-Richard, 1958, Premiers résultats de l'étude des carottes de la Baie des Anges, Nice. *Revue de Geographie Physique et Geol. Dynamique* (2), 1 (3), 167-173.

Bourcart, Jacques, Maurice Gennesseaux, Eloi Klimel, and Mme. Yolande le Calvez, 1960, Oceanographie. Les sédiments des vallées sous-marines au large dans le Golfe de Gênes. *Acad. Sci. (Paris) Comptes rendus,* 251, 1443-1445.

Brenot, Roger and Leopold Berthois, 1962, Bathymetrie de secteur Atlantique du Banc Porcupine (ouest de l'Irlande) au Cap Finisterre (Espagne). *Rev. Trav. Inst. Peches Marit.*, 26 (2), 219-246.

Bucher, W. H., 1940, Submarine valleys and related geologic problems of the North Atlantic. *Geol. Soc. Amer. Bull.*, 51, 489-512.

Buffington, Edwin C., 1952, Submarine "natural levees." *Jour. Geol.*, 60, 473-479.

————, 1961, Experimental turbidity currents on the sea floor. *Bull. Amer. Assoc. Petrol. Geol.*, 45 (8), 1392-1400.

————, 1964, Structural control and precision bathymetry of La Jolla submarine canyon, California. *Marine Geol.*, 1, 44-58.

Buffington, Edwin C. and David G. Moore, 1963, Geophysical evidence on the origin of gullied submarine slopes, San Clemente, California. *Jour. Geol.*, 71 (3), 356-370.

Casagrande, A., 1936, Characteristics of cohesionless soils affecting the stability of slopes and earth fills. *Jour. Boston Soc. Civil Eng.*, 23, 13.

————, 1938, Compaction tests and critical density investigations of cohesionless materials for Franklin Falls Dam. *Boston Dist., U.S. Army Corps. Eng.*

Chamberlain, T. K., 1960, Mechanics of mass sediment transport in Scripps submarine canyon, California. Ph.D. thesis, Univ. of Calif., Scripps Institution of Oceanography, 200 pp.

————, 1964, Mass transport of sediment in the heads of Scripps submarine canyon, California, in *Papers in Marine Geology* (Shepard Commem. Vol.) Macmillan, New York, pp. 42-64.

Collet, Leon W., 1925, *Les Lacs,* Paris, 320 pp.

Cooper, L. H. W. and David Vaux, 1949, Cascading over the continental slope of water from the Celtic Sea, *Mar. Biol. Assoc., U.K.*, 28, 719-750.

Coulomb, C. A., 1776, Essai sur une application des regles de maximis et minimis a quelques problemes de statique, relatifs à l'architecture; in *Mémoires de Mathematique et de Physique,* L'Academie Royale des Sci., Paris, pp. 343-382.

Crowell, J. C., 1952, Submarine canyons bordering central and southern California. *Jour. Geol.*, 60 (1), 58-83.

————, 1957, Origin of pebbly mudstones. *Bull. Geol. Soc. Amer.*, 68, 993-1009.

Curray, J. R., 1960, Sediments and history of Holocene transgression, continental shelf, northwest Gulf of Mexico, in *Recent Sediments, Northwest Gulf of Mexico,* F. P. Shepard, F. B. Phleger, and Tj. H. van Andel eds. Amer. Assoc. Petroleum Geol., pp. 221-266.

————, 1964, Shallow structure of the continental terrace, northern and central California. *Abs. Ann. Meeting Geol. Soc. Amer.*, pp. 37-38.

Curray, J. R. and D. G. Moore, 1964, Pleistocene deltaic prograda-
tion of continental terrace, Costa de Nayarit, Mexico, in *Marine
Geology of the Gulf of California — a Symposium*, Amer. Assoc. Petrol.
Geol. Mem. 3, pp. 193-215.

Daly, R. A., 1936, Origin of submarine canyons. *Amer. Jour. Sci.*, 31
(186), 401-420.

Dana, J. D., 1863, *A Manual of Geology*. Philadelphia, 798 pp.

———, 1890, Long Island Sound in the Quaternary era, with observations on the submarine Hudson River channel. *Amer. Jour. Sci.*,
ser. 3, 425-437.

Dangeard, L., 1961, A propos des phenomenes sous-marine pro-
fonds de glissement et de resedimentation. *Cahiers Oceanog.*, XIII
(2), 68-72; (31), 401-420.

———, 1962, Observations faites en "Soucoupe Plongeante" au large
de Banyuls. *Cahiers Oceanog.*, XIV (1), 19-24.

Dangeard, Louis, and Pierre Giresse, 1965, Photographie sous-
marine et geologie. *Cahiers Oceanog.*, 17 (4), 255-269.

Davidson, G., 1887, Submarine valleys on the Pacific Coast of the
United States. *Calif. Acad. Sci. Bull.*, 2, 265-268.

———, 1897, The submerged valleys of the coast of California,
U.S.A, and of Lower California, Mexico. *Calif. Acad. Sci. Proc.*,
ser. 3, 1, 73-103.

Davis, W. M., 1934, Submarine mock valleys. *Geog. Rev.*, 24, 297-308.

Day, A. A., 1959, The continental margin between Brittany and
Ireland. *Deep-Sea Res.*, 5, 249-265.

de Andrade, Carlos F., 1937. Os vales submarinos Portugueses e o
diastrofismo das Berlengas e da Estremadura (with English
summary). *Casa Portuguesa*, pp. 237-249.

Dietz, Robert S., 1953, Possible deep-sea turbidity-current channels in
the Indian Ocean. *Bull. Geol. Soc. Amer.*, 64, 375-378.

Dill, R. F., 1961, Geological features of La Jolla Canyon as revealed
by dive no. 83 of the bathyscaph TRIESTE. *Tech. mem.* no. TM-
516, U.S.N. Electronics Lab., 27 pp.

———, 1964a, Sedimentation and erosion in Scripps submarine
canyon head. In *Papers in Marine Geology* (Shepard Commem.
Vol.), Macmillan, New York, pp. 23-41.

———, 1964b, Contemporary submarine erosion in Scripps Submarine Canyon, Ph.D. Thesis, Univ. Calif., Scripps Inst. Oceanog.,
privately printed, 269 pp.

———, in press a, Submarine erosion in the head of La Jolla Canyon.
Bull. Geol. Soc. Amer.

———, in press b, Sand flows and sand falls. In *Reinholt Encyclopedia
of Earth Sciences*. R. W. Fairbridge, ed.

Dill, R. F., R. S. Dietz, and H. B. Stewart, Jr., 1954, Deep-sea channels and delta of the Monterey submarine canyon. *Bull. Geol. Soc. Amer.,* 65, 191-194.

Dill, R. F., and D. G. Moore, in press, A diver-held vane shear apparatus. *Marine Geol.*

Dill, R. F., and G. A. Shumway, 1954, Geologic use of self-contained diving apparatus. *Bull. Amer. Assoc. Petrol. Geol.,* 38 (1), 148-157.

Dott, R. H. Jr., 1963. Dymanics of subaqueous gravity depositional processes. *Bull. Amer. Assoc. Petrol. Geol.,* 47, 105-128.

Drake, C. L., M. Ewing, and G. H. Sutton, 1959, Continental margins and geosynclines: the east coast of North America north of Cape Hatteras. In *Physics and Chemistry of the Earth,* Pergamon, London, (3), 110-198.

Elmendorf, C. H., and B. C. Heezen, 1957, Oceanographic information for engineering submarine cable systems. *The Bell System Tech. Jour.,* 36 (5), 1047-1093.

Emery, K. O., 1960, *The Sea off Southern California.* John Wiley & Sons, New York, 366 pp.

——, 1965, Geology of the continental margin off eastern United States. In *Submarine Geology and Geophysics,* W. F. Whittard and R. Bradshaw, eds., Butterworths, London, pp. 1-20.

Emery, K. O., W. S. Butcher, H. R. Gould, and F. P. Shepard, 1952, Submarine geology off San Diego, California. *Jour. Geol.,* 60 (6), pp. 511-548.

Emery, K. O., and Jobst Hülsemann, 1963, Submarine canyons of southern California. Pt. I, Topography, Water and Sediments. *Allan Hancock Pacific Expeditions,* 27 (1), Univ. So. Calif. Press, Los Angeles, Calif., pp. 1-80.

Emery, K. O., and F. P. Shepard, 1945, Lithology of the sea floor off southern California. *Bull. Geol. Soc. Amer.,* 56, 431-478.

Emery, K. O., and R. D. Terry, 1956, A submarine slope of southern California. *Jour. Geol.,* 64 (3), 271-280.

Ericson, D. B., 1952, North Atlantic deep-sea sediments and submarine canyons. *Trans. N.Y. Acad. Sci.,* ser. II, 15 (2), 50-53.

Ericson, D. B., Maurice Ewing, Göesta Wollin, and B. C. Heezen, 1961, Atlantic deep-sea sediment cores. *Bull. Geol. Soc. Amer.,* 72, 193-286.

Ewing, John, Xavier Le Pichon, and Maurice Ewing, 1963, upper stratification of Hudson Apron region. *Jour. Geophys. Res.,* 68 (23), 6303-6316.

Ewing, Maurice, D. B. Ericson, and B. C. Heezen, 1958, Sediments and topography of the Gulf of Mexico. In *Habitat of Oil,* Amer. Assoc. Petrol. Geol., Tulsa, Okla., pp. 995-1053.

Fisk, H. N., and E. McFarlan, Jr., 1955, Late Quaternary deltaic deposits of the Mississippi River. In *Crust of the Earth, Geol. Soc. Amer. Spec. Paper 62,* pp. 279-302.

Francis, T. J. G., 1962, Black Mud Canyon. *Deep-Sea Res.*, 9, 457-464.

Fraser, G. D., and H. F. Barnett, 1959, Geology of the Delarof and westernmost Andreanof Islands, Aleutian Islands, Alaska. *U.S. Geol. Surv. Bull. 1028-1*, pp. 211-245.

Gates, Olcott, and William Gibson, 1956, Interpretation of the configuration of the Aleutian Ridge. *Bull. Geol. Soc. Amer.*, 67, 127-146.

Gealy, Betty Lee, 1956, Topography of the continental slope in northwest Gulf of Mexico. *Bull. Geol. Soc. Amer.*, 66, 203-227.

Gibson, William, and Haven Nichols, 1953, Configuration of the Aleutian Ridge Rat Islands—Semisopochnoi I. to west Buldir I. *Bull. Geol. Soc. Amer.*, 64, 1173-1181.

Gorsline, D. S., J. W. Vernon, and A. Shiffman, 1965, Processes of sand transport in the inner margins of the continental shelf. Abs. 39th Ann. Meeting, *Amer. Soc. Paleont. and Minerol*, New Orleans. p. 63.

Gorsline, D. S., and K. O. Emery, 1959, Turbidity-current deposits in San Pedro and Santa Monica basins off southern California. *Bull. Geol. Soc. Amer.*, 70, 279-290.

Gueze, E. C.: W. A. and T. K. Tan, 1954. The mechanical behavior of clays. In *Proc. Second Intern. Congr. Rheology,* Academic Press, New York, p. 451.

Hadley, M. L., 1964, The continental margin southwest of the English Channel. *Deep-Sea Res.*, 11, 767-779.

Hamilton, E. L., 1957, Marine geology of the southern Hawaiian Ridge. *Bull. Geol. Soc. Amer.*, 68, 1011-1026.

———, 1959, Thickness and consolidation of deep-sea sediments. *Bull. Geol. Soc. Amer.*, 70 (11), 1399-1424.

Hamilton, E. L., and H. W. Menard, 1956, Density and porosity of sea-floor surface sediments off San Diego, Calif. *Bull. Amer. Assoc. Petrol. Geol.*, 40 (4), 754-761.

Hayter, P. J. D., 1960, The Ganges and Indus Submarine Canyons. *Deep Sea Res.,* 6 (3), 184-186.

Heezen, B. C., 1956, Corrientes de turbidez del Rio Magdalena. *Bol. Soc. Geografica Colombia, Bogota,* nos. 51 and 52, pp. 135-143.

———, 1959, Note on progress in geophysics. Dynamic processes of abyssal sedimentation: erosion, transportation, and redeposition on the deep-sea floor. *Geophys. Jour. of Royal Astronom. Soc.,* 2 (2), 142-163.

Heezen, B. C., Roberta Coughlin, and W. C. Beckman, 1960, Equatorial Atlantic mid-ocean canyon. *Abs., Bull. Geol. Soc. Amer.,* 71, 1886.

Heezen, B. C., and C. L. Drake, 1964, Grand Banks slump. *Bull. Amer. Assoc. Petrol. Geol.,* 48 (2), 221-233.

Heezen, B. C., D. B. Ericson, and Maurice Ewing, 1954, Further evidence for a turbidity current following the 1929 Grands Banks earthquake. *Deep-Sea Res.*, 1, 193-202.

Heezen, B. C. and Maurice Ewing, 1952, Turbidity currents and submarine slumps, and the Grand Banks earthquake. *Amer. Jour. Sci.*, 250, 849-873.

Heezen, Bruce C., and C. Hollister, 1964, Deep-sea current evidence from abyssal sediments. *Marine Res.*, 1 (2), 141-174.

Heezen, B. C., and A. S. Laughton, 1963, Abyssal Plains. In *The Sea*, Vol. 3, M. N. Hill, ed., Interscience Pub., John Wiley & Sons, N. Y., pp. 312-364.

Heezen, B. C., R. J. Menzies, E. D. Schneider, W. M. Ewing, and C. L. Granelli, 1964, Congo submarine canyon. *Bull. Amer. Assoc. Petrol. Geol.*, 48 (7), 1126-1149.

Heezen, B. C., M. Tharp, and Maurice Ewing, 1959, The Floors of the Ocean. I, North Atlantic. *Geol. Soc. Amer. Spec. Paper 65*, 122 pp.

Heezen, B. C. and M. Tharp, 1964, physiographic diagram of the Indian Ocean. (Map) *Geol. Soc. Amer.*, New York.

Heim, Albert, 1888, Bergsturz und Menschenleben, *Vierteljahrschriften Naturforsch.*, Zurich.

Hess, H. H., 1932, Interpretation of gravity-anomalies and sounding-profiles obtained in the West Indies by the International expedition to the West Indies in 1932. *Trans. Amer. Geophys. Union*, 13th Ann. Meeting, pp. 26-32.

Hodgson, E. A., 1930, The Grand Banks earthquake. *Supp. Proc. Eastern Sect. Seis. Soc.*, pp. 72-79.

Holtedahl, Hans, 1958, Some remarks on geomorphology of continental shelves off Norway, Labrador, and southeast Alaska. *Jour. Geol.*, 66 (4), 461-471.

Holtedahl, Olaf, 1940, The submarine relief off the Norwegian coast. *Norske Videnskaps-Akad. Oslo*, 43 pp.

Hoshino, Michihei, and Takahiro Sato, 1960, On the topography and bottom sediment of Kamogawa submarine canyon, Boso Peninsula. *Quaternary Res.*, (6), 228-237.

Houtz, R. E., and H. W. Wellman, 1962, Turbidity currents at Kadavu Passage, Fiji. *Geol. Mag.*, 99 (1), 57-62.

Hoyt, W. V., 1959, Erosional channel in the Middle Wilcox near Yoakum, Lavaca County, Texas. *Trans. Gulf Coast Assn. Geol. Soc.*, 9, 41-50.

Hubert, John F., 1964, Textural evidence for deposition of many western North Atlantic deep-sea sands by ocean-bottom currents. *Jour. Geol.*, 72 (6), 757-785.

Hull, Edward, 1912, *The Sub-Oceanic Physiography of the North Atlantic Ocean*, Edward Stanford, London, 41 pp.

Hurley, Robert J., 1960, The geomorphology of abyssal plains in the northeast Pacific Ocean. Mimeo. Rept., Scripps Inst. Oceanog., ref. 60-7, 105 pp.

————, 1963, Analysis of bathymetric data from the search for U.S.S. THRESHER. *Program 76th Ann. Meeting, Geol. Soc. Amer.*, pp. 85a-86a.

Hurley, R. J., and F. P. Shepard, 1964, Submarine canyons in the Bahamas. *Abs. 77th Ann. Meeting, Geol. Soc. Amer.*, p. 99.

Inman, D. L., 1950, Submarine topography and sedimentation in the vicinity of Mugu submarine canyon, California. *Beach Erosion Board, Corps of Engrs. Tech. Memo No. 19*, 45 pp.

————, 1953, Areal and seasonal variations in beach and nearshore sediments at La Jolla, California, *Beach Erosion Board, Corps of Engrs. Tech. Memo. No. 39*, ii, 82 pp.

————, 1963, in Shepard, F. P. *Submarine Geology*, 2nd Edit., Harper & Row, New York, pp. 138-140.

Inman, D. L. and T. K. Chamberlain, 1960, Littoral sand budget along the southern California coast. *Rept. 21st Intl. Geol. Cong.*, Copenhagen, Vol., abs., pp. 245-246.

Inman, D. L., and Earl Murray, 1961, Mechanics of sedimentation. *ONR Progr. Rept.* Jan. 1—June 30, pp. 11-13.

Jennings, C. W. and R. G. Strand, 1965, Geol. map of California. Santa Cruz sheet. Div. of Mines, State of Calif.

Johnson, D. W., 1925, *New England—Acadian Shoreline.* John Wiley and Sons, New York, 608 pp.

————, 1939, *The Origin of Submarine Canyons.* Columbia Univ. Press, New York, 126 pp.

Kaplin, P. A., 1961, Diver studies of the heads of submarine canyons. *Okeanologiya,* 1 (6), 1034-1038.

Keith, Arthur, 1930, The Grand Banks earthquake. *Proc. Seisomol. Soc. Amer.* Eastern Sec., Suppl. 5 pp.

Kiersch, George A., 1965, Vaiont reservoir disaster. *Geotimes,* 9 (9), 9-12.

Kiilerich, A., 1958, The Ganges Submarine Canyon. *Andhra Univ. Mem. Oceanog.* ser. 62 (11), 29-32.

Kindle, E. M., 1931, Sea-bottom samples from the Cabot Strait earthquake zone. *Bull. Geol. Soc. Amer.*, 42, 557-574.

Kjellman, W., 1955, Mechanics of large Swedish landslips. *Geotechnique,* 5, 74-78.

Kuenen, Ph. H., 1937, Experiments in connection with Daly's hypothesis on the formation of submarine canyons. *Leidsche Geologische Mededeelingen,* VIII, 316-351.

————, 1950, *Marine Geology.* John Wiley and Sons, New York, 568 pp.

————, 1953, Origin and classification of submarine canyons. *Bull. Geol. Soc. Amer.*, 64, 1295-1314.

Kuenen, Ph.H. and C. I. Migliorini, 1950, Turbidity currents as a cause of graded bedding. *Jour. Geol.*, 58, 91-127.

Lambe, T. W., 1958, The structure of compacted clay, *Jour. Soil Mechanics and Foundation Div., Amer. Soc. Civil Engineers,* 85 (SM2), 55.

Laughton, A. S., 1959, Photography of the ocean floor. *Endeavour,* 18 (72), 178-185.

Laughton, A. S., 1960, An interplain deep-sea channel system. *Deep-Sea Research,* 7 (2), 75-88.

Lawson, Andrew, 1893, The Geology of Carmelo Bay. *Univ. Calif., Dept. Geol., Bull.* 1, 1-59.

Le Conte, Joseph, 1891, Tertiary and post Tertiary changes of the Atlantic and Pacific coasts. *Bull. Geol. Soc. Amer.,* 2, 323-328.

Leonards, G. A., 1962, *Foundation Engineering.* McGraw-Hill, New York, 1136 pp.

Limbaugh, Conrad and F. P. Shepard, 1957, Submarine canyons. In *Marine Ecology,* Joel Hedgepeth, ed., *Geol. Soc. Amer. Mem. 67,* 1, 633-639.

Lindenkohl, A., 1885, Geology of the sea-bottom in the approaches to New York Bay. *Amer. Jour. Sci.,* ser. 3, 29, 475-480.

Lisitzin, A. P. and A. V. Zhivago, 1960, Marine geological work of the Soviet Antarctic Expedition, 1955-1957. *Deep-Sea Research,* 6 (2), 77-87.

Ludwick, J. C., 1950, Deep water sands off San Diego. Unpublished Ph.D. thesis, Univ. of Calif., Los Angeles, 55 pp.

Ma, Ting Ying H., 1947, Submarine valleys around the southern part of Taiwan and their geological significance. *Bull. Oceanog. Inst. Taiwan,* 2, 1-12.

Martin, B. D., 1963, Rosedale Channel — Evidence for Late Miocene submarine erosion in the Great Valley of California. *Bull. Amer. Asso. Petrol. Geol.,* 47 (3), 441-456.

————, 1964, Geology of Monterey Canyon. Unpublished Ph.D. Thesis, Univ. of So. Calif., Los Angeles.

Mathews, W. H., and F. P. Shepard, 1962, Sedimentation of the Fraser River Delta, British Columbia. *Bull. Amer. Assoc. Petrol. Geol.,* 46, 1416-1437.

Matthes, F. E., 1907, Quoted by A. C. Lawson in the California Earthquake of 1906, State earthquake investigation commission rept., *Carnegie Inst. of Washington, pub. 87,* I (1), 54-58.

Menard, H. W. Jr., 1955, Deep-sea channels, topography and sedimentation. *Bull. Amer. Assoc. Petrol. Geol.,* 39 (2), 236-255.

————, 1960, Possible pre-Pleistocene deep-sea fans off central California. *Bull. Geol. Soc. Amer.,* 71, 1271-1278.

————, 1964, *Marine Geology of the Pacific.* McGraw-Hill, New York, 271 pp.

Menard, H. W., E. C. Allison, and J. W. Durham, 1962, A drowned Miocene terrace in the Hawaiian Islands. *Science,* 138, 896-897.

Menard, H. W., and J. C. Ludwick, 1951, Applications of hydraulics to the study of marine turbidity currents. *Soc. Econ. Paleont. and Mineralog., Spec. Pub. No. 2,* 2-13.

Menard, H. W., S. M. Smith, and R. M. Pratt, 1965, The Rhone deep-sea fan. In *Submarine Geology and Geophysics,* W. F. Whittard and R. Bradshaw, eds., Butterworths, London, pp. 271-285.

Middleton, G. V., in press, Small-scale models of turbidity currents and the criterion for auto-suspension.

Milne, John, 1897, Sub-oceanic changes. *Geo. Jour.,* 10 (2), 129-146, 259-289.

Moore, D. G., 1956, Vane shear strength, porosity and permeability relationship of some sieved cohesionless sands. *XX Cong. Geol. Internat. Resum. de los Trabajos Presentados Mexico,* pp. 266-267.

————, 1960, Acoustic-reflection studies of the continental shelf and slope off southern California. *Bull. Geol. Soc. Amer.,* 71, 1121-1136.

————, 1961, Submarine slumps. *Jour. Sed. Petrol.,* 31 (3), 343-357.

————, 1965, The erosional channel wall in La Jolla sea-fan valley seen from bathyscaph TRIESTE II. *Bull. Geol. Soc. Amer.,* 76, 385-392.

Moore, D. G., and J. R. Curray, 1963a, Structural framework of the continental terrace, Northwest Gulf of Mexico. *Jour. Geophys. Res.,* 68, 1725-47.

————, 1963b, Sedimentary framework of continental terrace off Norfolk, Virginia and Newport, Rhode Is. *Bull. Amer. Assoc. Petrol. Geol.,* 47, 2051-2054.

Moore, D. G., and George Shumway, 1959, Sediment thickness and physical properties: Pigeon Point Shelf, California. *Jour. Geophys. Res.,* 64 (3), 367-374.

Morgan, J. P., and W. G. McIntire, 1956, Quaternary geology of the Bengal Basin. *Coastal Studies Inst., Louisiana State Univ., Tech. Rept. No. 9,* 56 pp.

Moriarty, J. R., 1964, The use of oceanography in the solution of problems in a submarine archaeological site. In *Papers in Marine Geology* (Shepard Commem. Vol.) R. L. Miller, ed. The Macmillan Company, New York, pp. 511-522.

Murray, G. E., 1960, Geologic framework of Gulf coastal province of United States. In *Recent Sediments, Northwest Gulf of Mexico,* F. P. Shepard, F. B. Phleger, and Tj. H. van Andel, edits., Amer. Assoc. Petrol. Geol., Tulsa, Oklahoma. pp. 5-33.

Nasu, Noriyuki, 1964, The provenance of the coarse sediments on the continental shelves and the trench slopes off the Japanese Pacific Coast. In *Papers in Marine Geology* (Shepard Commem. Vol.) R. L. Miller, ed., The Macmillan Company, New York, pp. 65-101.

Natland, M. L., and Ph. H. Kuenen, 1951, Sedimentary history of the Ventura Basin, California, and the action of turbidity currents. *Soc. Econ. Paleontol. & Mineralog. Spec. Publ. No. 2,* pp. 76-107.

Nesteroff, W. D., 1958, Recherches sur les sediments marins actuels de la region d'Antibes. Ph.D. thesis, Univ. of Paris, 347 pp.

Niino, Hiroshi, 1952, The bottom character of the banks and submarine valleys on and around the continental shelf of the Japanese Islands. *Jour. Tokyo Univ. Fisheries,* 38 (3), 391-410.

North, W. H., 1960, Fabulous Cape San Lucas. *Skin Diver Mag.,* May, pp. 24-26, 52.

Nota, D. J. G., and D. H. Loring, 1964, Recent depositional conditions in the St. Lawrence River and Gulf—a reconnaissance survey. *Mar. Geol.,* 2, 198-235.

Peck, R. B., W. E. Hanson, and T. H. Thornburn, 1953, *Foundation Engineering.* John Wiley and Sons, New York, 410 pp.

Peckham, V. O., and J. H. McLean, 1961, Biological exploration at the head of Carmel submarine canyon. *Ann. Rept. Amer. Malacolog. Union,* p. 43.

Pérès, J. M., J. Piccard, and M. Ruivo, 1957, Resultats de la Campagne de Recherches du Bathyscaphe F.N.R.S. III. *Bull. Inst. Oceanog. Monaco,* 1,092, 1-29.

Perry, R. B., and Haven Nichols, 1965, Bathymetry of Adak Canyon, Aleutian Arc, Alaska. *Geol. Soc. Amer. Bull.,* 76, 365-370.

Phipps, C. V. G., 1963, Topography & sedimentation of the continental shelf and slope between Sydney & Montague Island—N.S.W. *Austr. Oil and Gas Jour.,* Dec.

Phleger, F. B., 1942, Foraminifera of submarine cores from the continental slope, Pt. 2 *Bull. Geol. Soc. Amer.,* 53, 1073-1098.

———, 1956, Foraminiferal faunas in cores offshore from the Mississippi Delta, *Deep-Sea Res.,* 3 (Suppl.), 45-57.

Poland, J. F., A. A. Garrett, and A. Sinnott, 1948, Geology, hydrology, and chemical character of the ground waters in the Torrance-Santa Monica area, Los Angeles County, California. *U.S. Geol. Surv., Ground Water Branch,* 475 pp, (duplicated).

Powers, H. A., R. R. Coats, and W. H. Nelson, 1960, Geology and submarine physiography of Amchitka Island, Alaska. *U.S. Geol. Surv. Bull. 1028-P,* pp. 521-554.

Reineck, H.-E., 1963, Der Kastengreifer. *Natur und Museum,* 93 (2), 65-68.

Revelle, R. R., and F. P. Shepard, 1939, Sediments off the California coast. In *Recent Marine Sediments*, P. D. Trask, ed., Amer. Assoc. Petrol. Geol., Tulsa, Oklahoma, pp. 245-282.

Richards, A. F., 1961, Investigations of deep-sea sediment cores, I. Shear strength, bearing capacity, and consolidation. *U.S. Navy Hydrogr. Office Tech. Rept. No. 63,* 70 pp.

————, 1962, Investigations of deep-sea sediment cores, II. Mass physical properties. *U.S. Navy Hydrogr. Office Tech. Rept. No. 63,* 143 pp.

Richards, A. F., and G. H. Keller, 1962, Water content variability in a silty clay core from off Nova Scotia. *Limnol. and Oceanog.,* 7 (3), 426-427.

Richards, H. G., and J. L. Ruhle, 1955, Mollusks from a sediment core from the Hudson Submarine Canyon. *Proc. Penn. Acad. Sci.,* 29, 186-190.

Ritter, W. E., 1902, A summer of dredging on the coast of California. *Science,* n.s., 15, 55-65.

Roberson, M. I., 1964, Continuous seismic profiler survey of Oceanographer, Gilbert, and Lydonia Submarine Canyons, Georges Bank. *Jour. Geophys. Res.,* 69 (22), 4779-4789.

Rosfelder, André, 1954, Carte Provisoire au 1/500.000^{me} de la Marge Continentale Algerienne. *Bull. Geol. de l'Algerie,* n.s., 5, 57-106.

Royse, C. F., Jr., 1964, Sediments of Willapa Submarine Canyon. *Univ. of Washington Tech. Rept. no. 111,* 62 pp.

Schalk, Marshall, 1964, Submarine topography off Eleuthera Island, Bahamas. *Bull. Geol. Soc. Amer.,* 57, 1228.

Schoeffler, J., 1965, Le Gouf de Cap Breton, de l'Eocene inférieur à nos jours. In *Submarine Geology and Geophysics,* W. F. Whittard and R. Bradshaw, eds., Butterworths, London, pp. 265-270.

Scruton, P. C., 1960, Deltaic building and the delta sequence. In *Recent Sediments, Northwest Gulf of Mexico,* F. P. Shepard, F. B. Phleger, and Tj. H. van Andel, eds. Amer. Assoc. Petrol. Geol., pp. 82-107.

Seed, H. B., J. K. Mitchell, and C. K. Chan, 1960, The strength of compacted cohesive soils, Research Conf. Shear Strength of Cohesive Soils, *Proc. Amer. Soc. Civil Engineers,* pp. 877-964.

Shepard, F. P., 1934, Canyons off the New England Coast. *Amer. Jour. Sci.,* 27, 24-36.

————, 1937a, "Salt" domes related to Mississippi Submarine Trough. *Bull. Geol. Soc. Amer.,* 48, 1349-1362.

————, 1937b, Investigation of submarine topography during the past year. *Trans. Amer. Geophys. Union,* pp. 226-228.

————, 1948, *Submarine Geology.* Harper & Bros., New York, 338 pp.

————, 1949, Terriestrial topography of submarine canyons revealed by diving. *Bull. Geol. Soc. Amer.,* 60, 1597-1616.

———, 1951, Mass movements in submarine canyon heads. *Trans. Amer. Geophys. Union,* 32 (3), 405-418.

———, 1954, High-velocity turbidity currents, a discussion. *Proc. Roy. Soc.,* A, 222, 323-326.

———, 1955, Delta-front valleys bordering the Mississippi distributaries. *Bull. Geol. Soc. Amer.,* 66 (12), 1489-1498.

———, 1957, Northward continuation of the San Andreas Fault. *Bull. Seismol. Soc. Amer.,* 37 (3), 263-266.

———, 1961, Deep sea sands. *21st Intl. Geol. Congr. Repts.* pt. 23, pp. 26-42.

———, 1963, *Submarine Geology,* 2nd ed., Harper & Row, New York, 557 pp.

———, 1964, Sea-floor valleys of Gulf of California. In *Marine Geology of the Gulf of California—A Symposium,* Amer. Assoc. Petrol. Geol., Mem. 3, pp. 157-192.

———, 1965, Submarine canyons explored by Cousteau's Diving Saucer. In *Submarine Geology and Geophysics,* W. F. Whittard and R. Bradshaw, eds., Butterworths, London, pp. 303-311.

Shepard, F. P., and C. N. Beard, 1938, Submarine canyons: distribution and longitudinal profiles. *Geograph. Rev.,* 28 (3), 439-451.

Shepard, F. P., and G. V. Cohee, 1936, Continental shelf sediments off the Mid-Atlantic States. *Bull. Geol. Soc. Amer.,* 47, 441-458.

Shepard, F. P., J. R. Curray, D. L. Inman, E. A. Murray, E. L. Winterer, and R. F. Dill, 1964, Submarine geology by diving saucer. *Science,* 145, (3636), 1042-1046.

Shepard, F. P., and Gerhard Einsele, 1962, Sedimentation in San Diego Trough and contributing submarine canyons. *Sedimentology,* 1 (2), 81-133.

Shepard, F. P., and K. O. Emery, 1941, Submarine topography off the California Coast: Canyons and tectonic interpretation. *Geol. Soc. Amer. Spec. Paper No. 31,* 171 pp.

———, 1946, Submarine photography off the California Coast. *Jour. Geol.,* 44 (5), 306-321.

Shepard, F. P., and G. A. Macdonald, 1938, Sediments of Santa Monica Bay, California. *Bull. Amer. Assoc. Petrol. Geol.,* 22, 201-216.

Shepard, F. P., Hiroshi Niino, and T. K. Chamberlain, 1964, Submarine canyons and Sagami Trough, east-central Honshu, Japan. *Bull. Geol. Soc. Amer.,* 75, 1117-1130.

Shepard, F. P., R. R. Revelle, and R. S. Dietz, 1939, Ocean-bottom currents off the California Coast. *Science,* 89 (2317), 488-489.

Shipek, C. J., 1960, Photographic study of some deep-sea floor environments in the Eastern Pacific. *Bull. Geol. Soc. Amer.,* 71, 1067-1074.

Smith, E. H., F. M. Soule, and O. Mosby, 1937, MARION and GENERAL GREENE expeditions to Davis Strait and Labrador Sea under the direction of the U.S. Coast Guard, 1928-1931-1933-1934-1935. *U.S. Coast Guard Bull.*, 19, 1-259.

Smith, P. A., 1937, The submarine topography of Bogoslof. *Geograph. Rev.* 27 (4), 630-636.

Smith, W. S. R., 1902, The submarine valleys of the California coast. *Science*, XV (382), 670-672.

Spencer, J. W., 1895, Reconstruction of the Antillean continent. *Bull. Geol. Soc. Amer.* 6, 103-140.

————, 1898, On the continental elevation of the glacial epoch. *Geol. Mag.*, 4 (5), 32-38.

————, 1903, Submarine valleys off the American coast and in the North Atlantic. *Bull. Geol. Soc. Amer.*, 14, 207-226.

Sprigg, Reg. C., 1947, Submarine canyons of the New Guinea and South Australian Coasts. *Trans. Roy. Soc. S. Austr.*, 71 (2, Dec.), 296-310.

————, 1963, New structural discoveries off Australia's southern coast. *Australasian Oil and Gas Jour.* (Sept.), 9 (12), 32-33, 36, 40, 42.

Stearns, H. T., and G. A. Macdonald, 1947, Geology and ground water resources of the Island of Molokai, Hawaii. *Hawaii Div. of Hydrog. Bull.*, 11, 113 pp.

Stetson, H. C., 1936, Geology and paleontology of the Georges Bank Canyons, I. Geology. *Bull. Geol. Soc. Amer.*, 47, 339-366.

————, 1937, Current measurements in Georges Bank Canyons. *Trans. Amer. Geophys. Union*, pp. 216-219.

————, 1949, The sediments and stratigraphy of the East Coast continental margin. *Papers in Phys. Oceanog. and Meteorol.*, Mass. Inst. Tech. and Woods Hole Oceanog. Inst., 11 (2), 60 pp.

Stewart, H. B., Jr., R. S. Dietz, and F. P. Shepard, 1964, Submarine valleys off the Ganges Delta. *Abs., Ann. Meeting Geol. Soc. Amer.*, pp. 195-196.

Stewart, H. B., Jr., F. P. Shepard, and R. S. Dietz, 1964, Submarine canyons off Eastern Ceylon. *Abs., Ann. Meeting, Geol. Soc. Amer., p.* 197.

Stokes, W. L., and D. J. Varnes, 1955, Glossary of selected geologic terms with special reference to their use in engineering. *Proc. Colorado Sci. Soc.*, v. 16, 165 pp.

Stride, A. H., 1963, Current-swept sea floors near the southern half of Great Britain. *Quart. J. Geol. Soc.* London, 119, 175-199.

Suess, Edouard, 1900, *La Face de la Terre*, 3 vols., A. Colin, Paris.

Sundborg, Åke, 1956, The river Klarälven, a study of fluvial processes. *Meddelanden Frau Uppsala Univ. Geografiska Inst.*, no. 115, pp. 128-316.

Sverdrup, H. U., M. W. Johnson, and R. H. Fleming, 1942, *The Oceans, Their Physics, Chemistry, and General Biology*. Prentice-Hall, Englewood Cliffs, N.J., 1087 pp.

Taylor, D. W., 1948, *Fundamentals of Soil Mechanics.* John Wiley & Sons, New York, 200 pp.

Terada, R., 1928, On the geophysical significance of the Kwanto earthquake. *Tokyo Imp. Acad. Proc.,* 4, 45-55.

Terzaghi, K., 1943, *Theoretical Soil Mechanics.* John Wiley & Sons, New York, 510 pp.

———, 1950, Mechanism of landslides. In *Application of Geology to Engineering Practice,* (Berkey Vol.), Geol. Soc. Amer., pp. 83-123.

———, 1953, Discussion. *Proc. Third Intl. Conf. Soil Mechanics and Found. Engr.,* 3, 158.

———, 1956, Varieties of submarine slope failures. *Proc. 8th Texas Conf. on Soil Mech. and Found. Engr., Spec. Publ. 29,* Bur. Engr. Res., Univ. Texas, Austin, Tex., 41 pp.

Terzaghi, Karl, 1962, Discussion. *Bull. Amer. Assoc. Petrol. Geol.,* 46, 1438-1443.

Terzaghi, K., and R. B. Peck, 1948, *Soil Mechanics in Engineering Practice.* John Wiley & Sons, New York, 566 pp.

Uchupi, Elazar, 1965, Maps showing relation of land and submarine topography, Nova Scotia to Florida. *U.S. Geol. Surv., Misc. Geol. Investig.,* Map 1-451.

Veatch, A. C., and P. A. Smith, 1939, Atlantic submarine valleys off the United States and the Congo submarine valley. *Geol. Soc. Amer. Spec. Paper 7,* 101 pp.

von Rad, U., F. P. Shepard, A. M. Rostelder, and R. F. Dill, 1965, Origin of deepwater sands off La Jolla, California. *Abs. Geol. Soc. Amer. Ann. Meeting,* Kansas City, Mo., p. 177.

Wegener, Alfred, 1924, *The Origin of Continents and Oceans.* Eng. translation from German 3rd edit., E. P. Dutton & Co., New York, 212 pp.

Whitaker, J. H. McD., 1962, The geology of the area around Leintwardine, Herefordshire. *Quart. Jour. Geol. Soc. of London,* 118, 319-351.

Wilde, Pat, 1964, Sand-sized sediment from the Delgada and Monterey deep-sea fans. *Abs. Ann. Meeting Geol. Soc. Amer.,* pp. 224-225.

———, 1965, Estimates of bottom current velocities from grain size measurements for sediments from the Monterey deep-sea fan. *Trans. Mar. Tech. Soc. — Amer. Soc. Limnol. and Oceanog.,* 2, 718-727.

Wimberley, C. S., 1955, Marine sediments north of Scripps Submarine Canyon, La Jolla, California. *Jour. Sed. Petrology,* 25 (1), 24-37.

Winterer, E. L., and D. L. Durham, 1962, Geology of southeastern Ventura Basin, Los Angeles County, California. *U.S. Geol. Surv. Prof. Paper 334H,* pp. 275-366.

Woodford A. O., 1951, Stream gradients and Monterey Sea Valley. *Bull. Geol. Soc. Amer.*, 62, 799-852.

Yamsaki, Naomasa, 1926, Physiographical studies of the great earthquake of the Kwanto District, 1923. *Jour. Faculty Sci.*, Univ. of Tokyo, sec II, II (2), 77-119.

INDEX

Bold face type indicates reference to an illustration on that page number.

Printed in the U.S.A.